1983

Basic Factoring Formulas:

$$au + av = a(u + v)$$
$$u^2 - v^2 = (u - v)(u + v)$$
$$u^3 - v^3 = (u - v)(u^2 + uv + v^2)$$
$$u^3 + v^3 = (u + v)(u^2 - uv + v^2)$$

Properties of Radicals:

$$\sqrt[n]{a} = a^{1/n}$$
$$\sqrt[n]{a^m} = (\sqrt[n]{a})^m$$
$$\sqrt[n]{a^n} = a \quad (a > 0)$$
$$\sqrt[m]{\sqrt[n]{a}} = \sqrt[mn]{a}$$
$$\sqrt[pn]{a^{pm}} = \sqrt[n]{a^m}$$
$$\sqrt[n]{a} \, \sqrt[n]{b} = \sqrt[n]{ab}$$
$$\frac{\sqrt[n]{a}}{\sqrt[n]{b}} = \sqrt[n]{\frac{a}{b}}$$

Quadratic Formula:

$$x = \frac{-b \pm \sqrt{b^2 - 4ac}}{2a}$$

Properties of Absolute Value:

$$|x| = \begin{cases} x \text{ if } x \geq 0 \\ -x \text{ if } x < 0 \end{cases}$$
$$\sqrt{a^2} = |a|$$

$$|-a| = |a|$$
$$|ab| = |a| \, |b|$$
$$\left|\frac{a}{b}\right| = \frac{|a|}{|b|} \quad (b \neq 0)$$
$$|p| = a \text{ iff } (p = a \text{ or } p = -a)$$
When $a \geq 0$, $|p| < a$ iff $(-a < p < a)$
When $a \geq 0$, $|p| > a$ iff $(p > a \text{ or } p < -a)$

Distance Formula:

$$\sqrt{(x_2 - x_1)^2 + (y_2 - y_1)^2}$$

Properties of Logarithms:

$$y = \log_b x \text{ iff } x = b^y$$
$$\log_b(xy) = \log_b x + \log_b y$$
$$\log_b\left(\frac{x}{y}\right) = \log_b x - \log_b y$$
$$\log_b(x^k) = k \log_b x$$
$$b^{\log_b x} = x$$
$$\log_a x = \frac{\log_b x}{\log_b a}$$

Binomial Theorem:

$$(a + b)^n = a^n + \frac{n}{1!} a^{n-1}b + \frac{n(n-1)}{2!} a^{n-2}b^2$$
$$+ \frac{n(n-1)(n-2)}{3!} a^{n-3}b^3 + \cdots$$

COLLEGE ALGEBRA

Under the Editorship of **Calvin A. Lathan**

COLLEGE ALGEBRA

William G. Ambrose

West Texas State University

Macmillan Publishing Co., Inc.
New York

Collier Macmillan Publishers
London

Printed in the United States of America

Macmillan Publishing Co., Inc.
866 Third Avenue, New York, New York 10022

Collier Macmillan Canada, Ltd.

Library of Congress Cataloging in Publication Data

Ambrose, William G.
  College algebra.

  Includes index.
  1. Algebra. I. Title.
QA154.2.A4   512.9   75-24145
ISBN 0-02-302520-4

Printing: 1 2 3 4 5 6 7 8   Year: 6 7 8 9 0 1 2

preface

When writing this book, my main objectives were (a) to write a textbook that the student could read and understand, and (b) to *stress problem solving* as a means of obtaining an understanding of the topics that traditionally comprise college algebra courses. To accomplish these goals, I have done the following:

1. Worked out many examples in detail to emphasize both the theoretical and the computational aspects of the topics covered in the text.

2. Following many of the examples (particularly those in the earlier chapters), I have given other problems, similar in nature to the examples, as exercises for the student to work so that he can be sure that he understands the concepts discussed in the examples.

3. Given an extensive selection of problems at the end of each section so that the student can solidify his understanding of the concepts considered in that section.

4. Provided chapter review problems at the end of each chapter so that the student can further solidify his understanding of the topics considered in that chapter.

For the great majority of colleges, this textbook includes more material than can be covered in a one-semester course that meets a total of three classroom hours per week. This extra material was included for two reasons: to permit the instructor to choose only topics that are relevant to his students; and to provide enough material so that a second course in college algebra can be offered by those colleges that wish to.

The problems at the end of each section are arranged so that the student can obtain a balanced coverage of the material in that section by working every third problem. For the convenience of the instructor and the student, the answers to problems 1, 4, 7, 10, . . . and 2, 5, 8, 11, . . . are given immediately after the problem set. The answers to problems 3, 6, 9, 12, ... are given in a separate answer book, which is available to the instructor upon request.

Canyon, Texas   W. G. A.

contents

3 **equations and inequalities in one variable**   78

4 **relations**   121

5 **functions**   168

6 **exponential and logarithmic functions**   201

7   systems of equations and inequalities   238

8   matrices and determinants   265

9   theory of equations   295

1

introductory topics

1.1 Real Numbers

Since numbers and their properties are of fundamental importance in the study of algebra, we begin with a discussion of various kinds of numbers.

Natural Numbers and Integers

The first kind of numbers with which you became acquainted were the **counting numbers** (also known as the **natural numbers**) 1, 2, 3, ... Next you were introduced to the number 0 and the negatives, $-1, -2, -3, \ldots$, of the natural numbers. The natural numbers and their negatives, together with the number zero, are known as the **integers.** An integer is said to be an **even integer** if it can be expressed in the form $2k$, where k is an integer. An integer is said to be an **odd integer** if it can be expressed in the form $2k + 1$, where k is an integer. Note that every integer is either even or odd.

EXAMPLE 1

The integers -6, 0 and 10 are examples of even integers, since

$$-6 = 2(-3),$$
$$0 = 2(0),$$

and

$$10 = 2(5).$$

On the other hand, the integers -13, 1, and 11 are examples of odd integers, since

$$-13 = 2(-7) + 1,$$
$$1 = 2(0) + 1,$$

and

$$11 = 2(5) + 1.$$

If a, b, and c are integers with $a \cdot b = c$, then a (and also b) is said to be a **factor** (or **divisor**) of c, and c is said to be a **multiple** of a (and also of b).

EXAMPLE 2

Since $2 \cdot 3 = 6$, 2 and 3 are factors (divisors) of 6, and 6 is a multiple of 2 and of 3.

EXERCISE 1

List all factors of 6.

Answer   The factors of 6 are 1, -1, 2, -2, 3, -3, 6, and -6, since $6 = (6)(1) = (-6)(-1) = (3)(2) = (-3)(-2)$.

EXERCISE 2

Is -9 a multiple of 3?

Answer   Yes, since $3(-3) = -9$.

A natural number greater than 1 is said to be a **prime number** if it has no natural numbers as divisors except itself and 1. A natural number greater than 1 is said to be a **composite number** if it is not a prime number.

EXAMPLE 3

The natural number 2 is a prime number, since 2 (itself) and 1 are the only divisors of 2 that are natural numbers. Other prime numbers are $3, 5, 7, 11, 13, 17, 19$, and so on. The natural number 6 is a composite number, since 6 and 1 are not the only divisors of 6 that are natural numbers. Other such divisors are 2 and 3. Some other composite numbers are $4, 8, 9, 10, 12, 14, 15, 16, 18$, and so on.

Every composite number can be expressed as the product of primes in a way that is *unique* except for the order of the factors. For example,

$$12 = 4 \cdot 3 = (2 \cdot 2) \cdot 3 = 2 \cdot 2 \cdot 3$$

and

$$12 = 6 \cdot 2 = (2 \cdot 3) \cdot 2 = 2 \cdot 3 \cdot 2.$$

In each case, the factors are the same. However, the order of the factors is different.

Two integers are said to be **relatively prime** if they have no prime factors in common.

EXAMPLE 4

The prime factors of 10 are 2, 5, and 10, and the prime factors of 21 are 3, 7, and 21. Thus 10 and 21 are relatively prime, since none of the prime factors of 10 and of 21 are the same.

EXERCISE 3

Are 10 and 35 relatively prime?

Answer No. They have a common prime factor, namely 5.

Rational Numbers and Irrational Numbers

A **rational number** is a number that can be expressed in the form p/q, where p and q are integers and $q \neq 0$. For example, $\frac{3}{5}, -\frac{2}{7}$, and 2 are rational numbers. Note that 2 is a rational number, since $2 = \frac{2}{1}$.

By using ordinary division, each rational number can be expressed as a **periodic decimal** (i.e., a decimal in which a block of one or more digits in the decimal repeats itself during the division process). Examples are:

$$\tfrac{4}{5} = .8000\ldots = .8\overline{0},$$
$$\tfrac{1}{3} = .333\ldots = .\overline{3},$$
$$\tfrac{2}{11} = .181818\ldots = .\overline{18}.$$

In each of the previous examples, the bar above the decimal is used to indicate the block of numbers that repeats itself.

It is also true that each periodic decimal can be expressed as the quotient of two integers. That is, each periodic decimal represents a rational number.

EXAMPLE 5

Express $3.\overline{24}$ as the quotient of two integers.

Solution   Let $x = 3.2424\ldots$. Then $100x = 324.2424\ldots$. Subtracting the sides of the first equation from the corresponding sides of the second equation, we get

$$100x = 324.2424\ldots$$
$$\underline{x = 3.2424\ldots} \quad \text{(subtract)}$$
$$99x = 321$$

from which it follows that

$$x = \frac{321}{99} = \frac{107}{33}.$$ ∎

EXERCISE 4

Express each of the numbers (a) $2.\overline{171}$ and (b) $4.3\overline{95}$ as the quotient of two integers.

Answer   (a) $\frac{2169}{999}$ (b) $\frac{4352}{990}$

Since each rational number can be represented as a periodic decimal, and vice versa, it follows that each decimal that is not periodic must represent some kind of number other than a rational number. We call this new kind of number an irrational number. Thus an **irrational number** is a number whose decimal representation is not periodic. For example, the number .1010010001 ..., which is formed by adding one additional zero between each two successive 1's, is an irrational number, since it is not a periodic decimal. Other examples of irrational numbers are π, $\sqrt{2}$, and $\sqrt{3}$. To prove that π is irrational requires more mathematics than is available to us in this course. However, we shall show in Section 1.3 that each of the numbers $\sqrt{2}$ and $\sqrt{3}$ is an irrational number. Additional examples of irrational numbers are $\pi/5$, $2 - \sqrt{2}$, $\sqrt[3]{2}$, $\sqrt[5]{3}$, and $\sqrt{5} + \sqrt{3}$.

Each irrational number can be approximated to any desired degree of accuracy by some rational number. For example, the rational number 3.14159 is a five-decimal approximation of the irrational number π. Four-decimal approximations of $\sqrt{2}$ and $\sqrt{3}$ are 1.4142 and 1.7321, respectively.

Real Numbers

The rational numbers together with the irrational numbers are called the **real numbers**. That is, a real number is any number that has a decimal representation. Even though there are other kinds of numbers, when we speak of numbers in this book we shall mean real numbers unless otherwise specified.

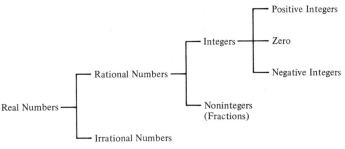

Figure 1.1

The various kinds of (real) numbers considered in the previous discussion and their relationships to one another are summarized in Figure 1.1.

Problems 1.1

1. Which of the numbers -4, $\frac{2}{3}$, 0, $\pi/2$, $\sqrt[3]{2}$, 7, $\sqrt{5}$, -1, $.02$, and $.\overline{02}$ are natural numbers?
2. Which of the numbers in problem 1 are integers?
3. Which of the numbers in problem 1 are rational numbers?
4. Which of the numbers in problem 1 are irrational numbers?
5. Explain why 50 is an even integer.
6. Explain why -37 is an odd integer.
7. List the factors of 12 that are natural numbers.
8. List the factors of 99 that are natural numbers.
9. List five multiples of 7.
10. List five multiples of 5.
11. List the prime numbers between 20 and 30.
12. List the prime numbers between 30 and 40.
13. Express 98 as the product of primes.
14. Express 323 as the product of primes.
15. Are 77 and 117 relatively prime? Explain.
16. Are 35 and 99 relatively prime? Explain.
17. Every rational number can be expressed as a ____?____ decimal.
18. Every irrational number can be expressed as a ____?____ decimal.

In problems 19–24, determine the decimal expansion of the given rational number.

19. $\frac{2}{7}$　　　　　　　　　　20. $\frac{4}{9}$　　　　　　　　　　21. $\frac{6}{13}$
22. $\frac{23}{99}$　　　　　　　　　23. $\frac{4}{37}$　　　　　　　　　24. $\frac{23}{7}$

In problems 25–36, express the given decimal as the quotient of two integers.

25. $.444\ldots$　　　　　　　26. $.3838\ldots$　　　　　　27. $.5353\ldots$
28. $1.369369\ldots$　　　　29. $2.765765\ldots$　　　30. $1.88\ldots$
31. $.\overline{35}$　　　　　　　　　32. $.\overline{7}$　　　　　　　　　33. $.\overline{123}$

34. $.021\overline{21}$ **35.** $1.3\overline{7}$ **36.** $2.7\overline{3}$

37. The rational number $\frac{22}{7}$ is frequently used as an approximation of the irrational number π. To how many decimal places are the decimal expansions of $\frac{22}{7}$ and π the same? Obtain a rational number that represents π correct to four decimal places.

38. Express $.239\overline{9}$ as the quotient of two integers. Express $.240\overline{0}$ as the quotient of two integers. Can a rational number have two different decimal expansions?

Answers 1.1

1. 7	**2.** $-4, 0, 7, -1$	**4.** $\frac{\pi}{2}, \sqrt[3]{2}, \sqrt{5}$	**5.** 2(25)
7. 1, 2, 3, 4, 6, 12	**8.** 1, 3, 9, 11, 33, 99	**10.** $-5, 0, 5,$ 10, 15	**11.** 23, 29
13. $2 \cdot 7 \cdot 7$	**14.** $17 \cdot 19$	**16.** yes	**17.** periodic
19. $.\overline{285714}$	**20.** $.\overline{4}$	**22.** $.\overline{23}$	**23.** $.1\overline{08}$
25. $\frac{4}{9}$	**26.** $\frac{38}{99}$	**28.** $\frac{152}{111}$	**29.** $\frac{307}{111}$
31. $\frac{35}{99}$	**32.** $\frac{7}{9}$	**34.** $\frac{7}{330}$	**35.** $\frac{62}{45}$
37. $2, \frac{31413}{9999}$		**38.** yes	

1.2 Sets

The main objective of this section is to present an introduction to sets, set terminology, and set symbolism. Our primary interest in set terminology and symbolism is as a means of abbreviating and clarifying various concepts that appear in later sections of this book. The idea of a set is such a basic idea in mathematics that we will not attempt to give a formal definition of a set. However, a **set** should be thought of intuitively as a collection of objects. Each object in this collection of objects is called an **element** of the set. A set must be *well defined*. That is, there must be some criterion for deciding whether a particular object *is* or *is not* an element of the set. The following are examples of sets:

> The set of all letters in the word "TARANTULA."
> The set of all points of a given line.
> The set of all persons in your class.

Capital letters, $A, B, C, \ldots$, are generally used to represent sets, while lowercase letters, $a, b, c, \ldots$, are used to represent the elements of sets. If the object a belongs to the set A, we write "$a \in A$" to mean that "a is an element of the set A." Similarly, we write "$a \notin A$" to mean that "a is *not* an element of the set A." Thus, if A is the set of all countries in Europe, we write

$$\text{France} \in A \quad \text{and} \quad \text{Canada} \notin A.$$

Sets are usually described by one of two methods. In either method, the set description is included inside braces { }. A set is said to be described by the **roster method** if each of the elements of the set is actually listed inside the braces. For example, the set consisting of the last four letters of the English alphabet is denoted by

$$\{w, x, y, z\}.$$

Another example of a set described by the roster method is the set

$$\{\text{New Mexico, Oklahoma, Arkansas, Louisiana}\},$$

whose elements are the names of those states which share a border in common with Texas.

A set is said to be described by the **rule method** if a common property that describes the elements of the set, and only the elements of the set, is enclosed inside the braces. In such situations, the set is generally expressed in the form

$$\{x \mid x \text{ has property } P\},$$

which is read "the set of all objects x such that x has the property P." For example, the set $\{1, 2, 3, 4, 5\}$ can be described as

$$\{x \mid x \text{ is a counting number less than } 6\}.$$

As another example, the set {California, Colorado, Connecticut} can be described as

$$\{x \mid x \text{ is a state of the United States whose name begins with C}\}.$$

As a matter of future convenience, we shall reserve the capital letters N, I, Q, and R to represent certain special sets of numbers. These sets can now be described in set notation by the rule method as follows:

$$N = \{x \mid x \text{ is a natural number}\},$$
$$I = \{x \mid x \text{ is an integer}\},$$
$$Q = \{x \mid x \text{ is a rational number}\},$$
$$R = \{x \mid x \text{ is a real number}\}.$$

The letter x used in describing a set by the rule method is an example of a variable. In general, a symbol, such as x, which represents an unspecified element of a given set, is called a **variable.** On the other hand, a **constant** is a symbol, such as 2 or π, which is used to represent exactly one object.

Two sets of special interest are the empty set and the universal set. The **empty set** (sometimes called the **null set**), denoted by $\varnothing$, is defined as the set that contains no elements. As an example, the set of all men who are over 10 feet tall is the empty set. Can you think of another set that is the empty set? In many instances, it is convenient to decide upon a totality of objects that are to be considered as elements of sets in a particular discussion. In such cases we define the **universal set,** denoted by U, as the set that contains all the objects that are to be considered as elements of sets. The choice of the universal set depends upon the particular problem being discussed.

Related Sets

The set A is said to be a **subset** of the set B, denoted by $A \subseteq B$, if and only if each element of A is also an element of B. If A is not a subset of B, we write $A \nsubseteq B$.

EXAMPLE 1

(a) $\{2, 7\} \subseteq \{2, 5, 7, 9\}$ (b) $\{2, 7\} \subseteq \{2, 7\}$
(c) $\varnothing \subseteq \{2, 7\}$ (d) $\{2, 7\} \nsubseteq \{2, 3, 6, 8\}$

Observe that the empty set is a subset of every set. Also observe that every set is a subset of itself.

If $C = \{2, 3, 7\}$, then $\{2\} \subseteq C$ and $2 \in C$. It is incorrect to write $2 \subseteq C$, since 2 is not a set. It is also incorrect to write $\{2\} \in C$, since $\{2\}$ is a set rather than an element.

EXERCISE 1

If $B = \{0, 1, \pi\}$, which of the following are true?
(a) $\varnothing \subseteq B$ (b) $0 \subseteq B$ (c) $\pi \in B$
(d) $2 \notin B$ (e) $\{2, \pi\} \subseteq B$ (f) $\{\pi\} \nsubseteq B$

Answer   (a), (c), and (d) are true.

Two sets A and B are **equal** to one another, denoted by $A = B$, if and only if $A \subseteq B$ and $B \subseteq A$. That is, two sets are equal if and only if they have exactly the same elements.

EXAMPLE 2

The sets $\{a, b, c\}$ and $\{c, a, b\}$ are equal, since each set is a subset of the other set.

EXERCISE 2

Are the sets $\{t, e, n, t\}$ and $\{n, e, t\}$ equal?

Answer Yes. Each is a subset of the other. Note that listing an element more than once inside the braces does *not* add additional elements to the set.

Two sets are **disjoint** if and only if they have no elements in common.

EXAMPLE 3

The sets $\{x, y, z\}$ and $\{p, q\}$ are disjoint, since they have no elements in common.

EXERCISE 3

Are the sets $\{0, 1, 2\}$ and $\varnothing$ disjoint?

Answer Yes. There is no element that belongs to both sets.

A **one-to-one correspondence** exists between the sets A and B if and only if it is possible to pair the elements of the two sets in such a way that each element of A is associated with exactly one element of B and each element of B is associated with exactly one element of A. Note that a one-to-one correspondence exists between any two sets that have the same number of elements.

EXAMPLE 4

A one-to-one correspondence exists between the sets $\{a, b, c\}$ and $\{x, y, z\}$ since it is possible to associate each element of $\{a, b, c\}$ with a unique element of $\{x, y, z\}$, and vice versa. One way of doing this is demonstrated as follows:

$$\{a, b, c\}$$
$$\updownarrow \;\; \times$$
$$\{x, y, z\}.$$

EXERCISE 4

Establish a one-to-one correspondence between the set N of natural numbers and the set E of even natural numbers.

Answer The number $n \in N$ can be paired with the number $2n \in E$, and vice versa.

If U is a universal set and $A \subseteq U$, then the **complement** of the set A (with respect to U), written A', is defined as

$$A' = \{x \mid x \in U \text{ and } x \notin A\}.$$

EXAMPLE 5

If $U = \{0, 1, 2, 3, 4\}$ and $A = \{1, 3, 4\}$, then $A' = \{0, 2\}$.

EXAMPLE 6

If $U = R = \{x|x \text{ is a real number}\}$ and $Q = \{x|x \text{ is a rational number}\}$, then $Q' = \{x|x \text{ is an irrational number}\}$.

The **union** of two sets A and B, written $A \cup B$, is defined as

$$A \cup B = \{x|x \in A \text{ or } x \in B\}.$$

In mathematics, the word "or" is used to mean *one or the other*, or *both*.

EXAMPLE 7

If $A = \{0, 1\}$ and $B = \{3, 5\}$, then $A \cup B = \{0, 1, 3, 5\}$.

EXAMPLE 8

If $A = \{0, 1, 2\}$ and $B = \{2, 3, 4\}$, then $A \cup B = \{0, 1, 2, 3, 4\}$.

EXAMPLE 9

If $E = \{x|x \text{ is an even integer}\}$ and $O = \{x|x \text{ is an odd integer}\}$, then $E \cup O = I = \{x|x \text{ is an integer}\}$.

The **intersection** of two sets A and B, written $A \cap B$, is defined as

$$A \cap B = \{x|x \in A \text{ and } x \in B\}.$$

EXAMPLE 10

If $A = \{0, 1, 2\}$ and $B = \{2, 3, 4\}$, then $A \cap B = \{2\}$.

EXAMPLE 11

If $A = \{0, 1, 7\}$ and $B = \{1, 7, 9\}$, then $A \cap B = \{1, 7\}$.

EXAMPLE 12

If $E = \{x|x \text{ is an even integer}\}$ and $O = \{x|x \text{ is an odd integer}\}$, then $E \cap O = \varnothing$.

The **difference** of two sets A and B, written $A - B$, is defined as

$$A - B = \{x|x \in A \text{ and } x \notin B\}.$$

EXAMPLE 13

If $A = \{0, 1, 2\}$ and $B = \{2, 3, 4\}$, then $A - B = \{0, 1\}$ and $B - A = \{3, 4\}$.

EXERCISE 5

If $A = \{2, 3, 4\}$, $B = \{0, 2, 4\}$, $C = \{1, 4, 5\}$, and $U = \{0, 1, 2, 3, 4, 5, 6\}$, determine each of the following.

(a) $A \cap B$ (b) $A \cup C$ (c) C'
(d) $A - C$ (e) $C - B$ (f) $A \cap B'$

Answer   (a) $\{2, 4\}$ (b) $\{1, 2, 3, 4, 5\}$ (c) $\{0, 2, 3, 6\}$ (d) $\{2, 3\}$ (e) $\{1, 5\}$
(f) $\{3\}$

Problems 1.2

1. Explain what is meant by a well defined set.
2. Explain what is meant by the empty set.
3. Explain what is meant by a universal set.
4. Explain why the empty set is a subset of every set.
5. Explain why every set is a subset of itself.
6. List all the subsets of $\{0, 1, 2\}$.
7. Does $\varnothing = \{0\}$? Explain.
8. Does $\{d, a, d\} = \{a, d\}$? Explain.
9. Give an example of two sets that are not disjoint.
10. Explain why $\varnothing$ is disjoint with every set.
11. Does a one-to-one correspondence exist between the set $\{1, 2, 3\}$ and the set $\{a, b, c, d\}$? Explain.
12. Does a one-to-one correspondence exist between the set $\{0, 1, 2, 3, . . .\}$ and the set $\{1, 2, 3, 4, . . .\}$? Explain.
13. If $A = \{0, 4\}$, determine which of the following are true.
    (a) $4 \in A$ (b) $\varnothing \subseteq A$ (c) $4 = \{4\}$
    (d) $\varnothing \in A$ (e) $4 \subseteq A$ (f) $4 \in \{4\}$
14. If $A = \{b, r, e, a, d\}$ and $B = \{b, a, d\}$, determine which of the following are true.
    (a) $A \in B$ (b) $a \subseteq A$ (c) $\varnothing \in B$
    (d) $A \subseteq B$ (e) $b \in B$ (f) $B \subseteq A$
15. If $x \in A$, $y \in B$, $A \subseteq C$, and $B \subseteq C$, determine which of the following must be true.
    (a) $x \in C$ (b) $x \in B$ (c) $y \in C$
    (d) There is an element of C that is also an element of both A and B.
    (e) There is an elenent of C that is also an element of A but not of B.
    (f) There is an element of C that is neither an element of A nor of B.

In problems 16–21, describe the given set by the rule method.

16. $\{1, 3, 5, 7, 9, . . .\}$ 17. $\{1, 4, 9, 16, 25, . . .\}$
18. $\{2, 4, 8, 16, 32, . . .\}$ 19. $\{a, e, i, o, u\}$
20. $\{$Mercury, Venus, Earth, Mars, Jupiter, Saturn$\}$
21. $\{$California, Oregon, Washington, Hawaii, Alaska$\}$

In problems 22–27, describe the given set by the roster method.

22. $\{x|x$ is a month that has exactly 30 days$\}$
23. $\{x|x$ is a state whose name begins with the letter I$\}$
24. $\{x|x$ is one of the five largest states in population$\}$
25. $\{x|x$ is a continent whose name begins with the letter A$\}$
26. $\{x|x$ is a month that has 28 or 29 days$\}$
27. $\{x|x$ is a course in which you made an A last semester$\}$

In problems 28–36, describe the given set by the roster method if $U = \{1, 2, 3, 4, 5, 6, 7\}$, $A = \{1, 2, 3, 4\}$, $B = \{2, 4, 6\}$, and $C = \{2, 5, 6, 7\}$.

28. $A \cap B$ 29. $A \cup C$ 30. $A \cap B'$
31. $A' \cup C'$ 32. $C - A'$ 33. $A - B'$
34. $A \cap (B - C)$ 35. $A' - (B \cap C)$ 36. $(A - B) \cup (A - C)$

   Answers 1.2

13. (a) T (b) T (c) F (d) F (e) F (f) T
14. (a) F (b) F (c) F (d) F (e) T (f) T
16. $\{x|x$ is a positive odd integer$\}$
17. $\{x|x$ is the square of a natural number$\}$
19. $\{x|x$ is a vowel in the English alphabet$\}$
20. $\{x|x$ is one of the six known planets closest to our sun$\}$
22. $\{$April, June, September, November$\}$ 23. $\{$Idaho, Illinois, Indiana, Iowa$\}$
25. $\{$Africa, Asia, Australia, Antarctica$\}$
26. Be careful! Can you name a month that does *not* have 28 days?
28. $\{2, 4\}$ 29. $\{1, 2, 3, 4, 5, 6, 7\}$ 31. $\{1, 3, 4, 5, 6, 7\}$
32. $\{2\}$ 34. $\{4\}$ 35. $\{5, 7\}$

1.3 Deductive Reasoning

Proving "If . . . , then . . ." Theorems

   Recall that many mathematical theorems are statements of the form "If H, then C," where H and C are simple statements. Such a statement is called an **implication**. Statement H is called the **hypothesis** of the implication, and statement C is called the **conclusion** of the implication. The following are examples of implications:

   If $x + 2 = 5$, then $x = 3$.

   If x is an even integer, then x^2 is an even integer.

   Implications frequently occur as simple statements. For example, the simple statement "The sum of two odd integers is an even integer" has the same meaning as the implication "If x and y are odd integers, then $x + y$ is an even integer."

In proving a theorem of the form "If H, then C," we must show that C is true when H is true. That is, we must show that the conclusion C is a logical consequence of the given hypothesis H. To do this, we use a process known as **deductive reasoning.** In deductive reasoning, we start with the hypothesis H as a given fact. We then use facts such as axioms, definitions, or previously established theorems to obtain a true statement from the hypothesis. Applying the same procedure to the latter statement, we obtain a chain of true statements whose final statement is the conclusion C of the theorem.

EXAMPLE 1

Prove that the sum of two odd integers is an even integer (i.e., if x and y are odd integers, prove that $x + y$ is an even integer).

Proof As our hypothesis, we are given that x and y are odd integers. Hence

$$x = 2k_1 + 1 \qquad \text{and} \qquad y = 2k_2 + 1,$$

where k_1 and k_2 are integers. Therefore,

$$\begin{aligned} x + y &= (2k_1 + 1) + (2k_2 + 1) \\ &= 2k_1 + 2k_2 + 2 \\ &= 2(k_1 + k_2 + 1) \\ &= 2k_3, \end{aligned}$$

where $k_3 = k_1 + k_2 + 1$ is an integer. In the previous string of equalities we used several well-known properties of numbers which we discuss in detail in the next section. In the last step we used the fact that the sum of two or more integers is an integer. Assuming these facts, we have shown that $x + y$ is an even integer since $x + y = 2k_3$, where k_3 is an integer. ∎

In general, the proof of an implication depends upon earlier theorems which we have already established. The proofs of these theorems, in turn, depend upon other theorems. Such a chain cannot continue backward indefinitely. Eventually there must be a theorem whose proof cannot depend on earlier theorems. Thus the proof of this first theorem must depend upon one or more unproved statements, which are called **axioms.** In a similar manner, each definition depends upon terms that were defined earlier. Thus there must be some **undefined terms** to start with.

Proof by Contradiction

It is sometimes easier to prove an implication by using an *indirect proof* (also called a *proof by contradiction*). We again start with the hypothesis *H* as a given fact and show that the conclusion *C* is true when *H* is true. However, in a proof by contradiction, we show that *C* is true by showing that it is *not false*. To do this, we *assume that C is false* and then we show that this assumption leads to a contradiction of some known fact or the given hypothesis. Since contradictions are impossible in logical thought processes, it follows that the assumption that *C* is false is incorrect. This, in turn, means that *C* must be true.

EXAMPLE 2

Prove that $\sqrt{2}$ is not a rational number.

Proof We wish to show that $\sqrt{2}$ is not rational. Thus we *assume that $\sqrt{2}$ is rational* (i.e., we assume that the desired conclusion is false). We must now show that this assumption leads to a contradiction. If $\sqrt{2}$ is rational, then $\sqrt{2}$ can be expressed in the form p/q, where p and q are relatively prime integers with $q \neq 0$. Since

$$\sqrt{2} = \frac{p}{q},$$

it follows that

$$2 = \frac{p^2}{q^2}$$

and

$$2q^2 = p^2.$$

Since $p^2 = 2q^2$, it follows that p^2 is even and hence p is even (see problem 13). Since p is even, $p = 2r$, where r is an integer. Thus $p^2 = (2r)^2 = 4r^2$, and hence

$$2q^2 = p^2 = 4r^2$$

and

$$q^2 = 2r^2.$$

Since $q^2 = 2r^2$, q^2 is even and hence q is even. Since p and q are both even, we have obtained a contradiction to the fact that p and q are relatively prime.

Thus the *italicized* assumption must be incorrect, and therefore it follows that $\sqrt{2}$ is not rational. ∎

Proving ". . . if and only if . . ." Theorems

The statement "If C, then H" is called the **converse** of the implication "If H, then C." For example, the converse of "If today is Sunday, then tomorrow is Monday" is "If tomorrow is Monday, then today is Sunday."

Even though an implication is true, its converse *may* or *may not* be true. That is, the truth of an implication does *not* guarantee the truth of its converse. For example, the converse of the valid implication "If x and y are odd integers, then $x + y$ is an even integer" is the false statement "If $x + y$ is an even integer, then x and y are odd integers." On the other hand, the converse of the valid implication "If $x = 2$, then $4x = 8$" is the true statement "If $4x = 8$, then $x = 2$."

Many mathematical theorems are statements of the form "If H, then C, and conversely." Another statement that has the same meaning is "H if and only if C." In proving a theorem of the form "If H, then C, and conversely" or of the form "H if and only if C," we must prove both the implication "If H, then C" and its converse "If C, then H." For example, to prove the theorem

$$\text{``}\frac{a}{b}=\frac{c}{d} \quad \text{if and only if} \quad ad=bc(b,\ d \neq 0),\text{''}$$

we must prove both the implication

$$\text{``If } \frac{a}{b}=\frac{c}{d}(b,\ d \neq 0), \quad \text{then } ad=bc\text{''}$$

and its converse

$$\text{``If } ad=bc(b,\ d \neq 0), \quad \text{then } \frac{a}{b}=\frac{c}{d}.\text{''}$$

Problems 1.3

In problems 1–3, rewrite the given simple statement in "If . . . , then . . ." form.

1. The sum of two even integers is an even integer.
2. The square of an odd integer is an odd integer.
3. The product of two rational numbers is a rational number.
4. To prove the theorem "The product of two real numbers is zero if and only if

at least one of the numbers is zero," we must prove both the implication ____?____ and its converse ____?____.

5. To prove the theorem "A triangle is equiangular if and only if it is equilateral," we must prove both the implication ____?____ and its converse ____?____.

6. To prove the theorem "Equal arcs of a circle subtend equal chords, and conversely," we must prove both the implication ____?____ and its converse ____?____.

In problems 7–18, whenever necessary use the fact that the sum (or product) of two or more integers is an integer.

7. Prove *directly* that the sum of two even integers is an even integer.

8. Prove *directly* that the product of two odd integers is an odd integer.

9. If an integer is a multiple of the integer a, prove *directly* that the square of the integer is also a multiple of a.

10. Prove *directly* that the square of an odd integer is an odd integer.

11. Prove *directly* that the cube of an even integer is an even integer.

12. Prove *directly* that the sum of two rational numbers is a rational number.

13. If $x \in I$ and x^2 is an even integer, prove *indirectly* that x is an even integer.

14. If $x \in I$ and x^2 is an odd integer, prove *indirectly* that x is an odd integer.

15. Prove *indirectly* that the sum of a rational number and an irrational number is an irrational number.

16. Prove *indirectly* that the product of a nonzero rational number and an irrational number is an irrational number.

17. Given that π is an irrational number, prove *indirectly* that $1/\pi$ is an irrational number.

18. Prove *indirectly* that $\sqrt{3}$ is not a rational number. (*Hint:* Follow a line of reasoning similar to that used in Example 2.)

Answers 1.3

1. If x and y are even integers, then $x + y$ is an even integer.

2. If x is an odd integer, then x^2 is an odd integer.

4. If $a,b \in R$ with $ab = 0$, then $a = 0$ or $b = 0$. If $a,b \in R$ with $a = 0$ or $b = 0$, then $ab = 0$.

5. If a triangle is equiangular, then it is equilateral. If a triangle is equilateral, then it is equiangular.

1.4 The Field of Real Numbers

A **number system** consists of a set of objects (the numbers) and a set of facts (axioms) that characterize the properties of the numbers in the system with respect to certain operations and relations. In particular, the **real number system** consists of the set of real numbers and a collection of axioms that characterize the properties of the real numbers with respect to certain operations (such as $+$ and $\cdot$) and relations (such as $=$, $>$, and $<$). In the remainder of this chapter, we shall examine these axioms and certain properties that follow from them.

The Equality Relation

In mathematics, the *equality sign*, $=$, is used between two expressions to show that the two expressions are names for the same thing. In particular, if $a,b \in R$, then $a = b$ means that the symbols a and b each represent the same number. For example, since $\frac{1}{3}$ and $.\overline{3}$ are different names for the same rational number, we write $\frac{1}{3} = .\overline{3}$. A mathematical statement, such as $x^2 - x - 2 = 0$, which involves the equality relation is called an **equation.**

For any set S, we shall assume that the equality relation satisfies the following axioms.

The Axioms of Equality For $a,b,c \in S$:

E1 $a = a$. *Reflexive Axiom for $=$*
E2 If $a = b$, then $b = a$. *Symmetric Axiom for $=$*
E3 If $a = b$ and $b = c$, then $a = c$. *Transitive Axiom for $=$*
E4 If $a = b$, then a can be substituted for b *Substitution Axiom for $=$*
and b can be substituted for a in any
mathematical statement that involves a
and b.

EXAMPLE 1

Assume that all variables represent real numbers.
(a) If $6 = a$, then $a = 6$ by the symmetric axiom for equality.
(b) If $a = 7$ and $a + 2 = b$, then $7 + 2 = b$ by the substitution axiom for equality.
(c) If $a = 3$ and $3 = x + y$, then $a = x + y$ by the transitive axiom for equality.

EXERCISE 1

If each variable represents a real number, state the axiom of equality that justifies each of the following statements.
(a) If $x + z = x + z$ and $x = y$, then $x + z = y + z$.
(b) If $x = -5$, then $-5 = x$.
(c) If $x + y = z$ and $z = a + 3$, then $x + y = a + 3$.

Answer (a) E4 (b) E2 (c) E3

The Field of Real Numbers

In addition to the real numbers themselves, many of the axioms that characterize certain properties of real numbers involve one or both of the two basic operations of *addition* (+) and *multiplication* (·). If $a,b \in R$, we write $a + b$ to indicate addition and $a \cdot b$, $a \times b$, or ab to indicate multiplication. The numbers $a + b$ and ab are called the *sum* and *product* of a and b, respectively.

We now examine a collection of axioms, known as the **field axioms,** which are used to justify many of the properties of real numbers involving the operations of addition and multiplication.

The Field Axioms   For $a,b,c \in R$:

F1 $a + b \in R$.   *Closure Axiom for* +

F2 $ab \in R$.   *Closure Axiom for* ·

F3 $(a + b) + c = a + (b + c)$.   *Associative Axiom for* +

F4 $(ab)c = a(bc)$.   *Associative Axiom for* ·

F5 $a + b = b + a$.   *Commutative Axiom for* +

F6 $ab = ba$.   *Commutative Axiom for* ·

F7 $a(b + c) = ab + ac$.   *Distributive Axiom*

F8 There exists a unique real number,   *Identity Axiom for* +
    namely 0, called the **additive identity,**
    such that $a + 0 = 0 + a = a$.

F9 There exists a unique real number,   *Identity Axiom for* ·
    namely 1, called the **multiplicative
    identity,** such that $a \cdot 1 = 1 \cdot a = a$.

F10 There exists a unique real number $-a$,   *Inverse Axiom for* +
     called the **additive inverse** (or **negative**)
     of a, such that $a + (-a) = (-a) + a = 0$.

F11 If $a \neq 0$, there exists a unique real   *Inverse Axiom for* ·
     number $1/a$, called the **multiplicative
     inverse** (or **reciprocal**) of a, such that
     $a \cdot (1/a) = (1/a) \cdot a = 1$.

The *closure axioms,* F1 and F2, state that the sum (or product) of any two real numbers is a real number. The *associative axioms,* F3 and F4, state that the sum (or product) of three numbers is the same regardless of the way in which we group the numbers for addition (or multiplication). The *commutative axioms,* F5 and F6, state that the sum (or product) of two numbers is the same regardless of the order in which the addition (or multiplication) is performed. The *distributive axiom,* F7, states that the product obtained by multiplying a given number by the sum of two other numbers is the same as the sum of the products obtained by multiplying the given number by each of the other two numbers. The *identity axioms*, F8 and F9, imply the existence of certain unique real numbers, namely 0 and 1, which play special roles with respect to the operations of addition and multiplication, respectively. The *inverse axioms*, F10 and F11, also imply the existence of certain special real numbers.

EXAMPLE 2

Assume that all variables represent real numbers.
(a) $x + 3 \in R$ by the closure axiom for addition.
(b) $(2x)y = 2(xy)$ by the associative axiom for multiplication.
(c) $x + 5 = 5 + x$ by the commutative axiom for addition.
(d) $3(x + 2) = 3x + 3 \cdot 2$ by the distributive axiom.
(e) $x + 0 = x$ by the identity axiom for addition.

EXERCISE 2

If each variable represents a real number, state the field axiom that justifies each of the following statements.
(a) $7y \in R$ (b) $x(y + z) = xy + xz$
(c) $x + (-x) = 0$ (d) $(x + 3) + 5 = x + (3 + 5)$

Answer (a) F2 (b) F7 (c) F10 (d) F3

In general, a set S is called a **field** under the operations of addition and multiplication if axioms F1 to F11 are satisfied by the elements of S. Thus the set of real numbers R is a field, since the real numbers satisfy axioms F1 to F11.

Before ending this section we define what is meant by the sum (or product) of three or more numbers.

Definition 1.1 If $a, b, c, d, \ldots \in R$, then

$$a + b + c = a + (b + c),$$
$$a + b + c + d = a + (b + c + d), \text{ etc.} \tag{1-1}$$

Similarly,

$$a \cdot b \cdot c = a \cdot (b \cdot c),$$
$$a \cdot b \cdot c \cdot d = a \cdot (b \cdot c \cdot d), \text{ etc.} \tag{1-2}$$

Problems 1.4

In problems 1–9, use one or more axioms of equality to justify the given statement. Assume that each variable represents a real number and that each sum or product of two or more real numbers is also a real number.

1. $x+2=x+2$.
2. If $x+1=y$, then $y=x+1$.
3. If $x=yz$ and $yz=y+3$, then $x=y+3$.
4. If $a=3$ and $a+2=b$, then $3+2=b$.
5. If $ac=ac$ and $a=b$, then $ac=bc$.
6. If $a=b+2$ and $c=a+3$, then $c=(b+2)+3$.
7. If $x=y$, then $x+z=y+z$.
8. If $x=y+5$ and $y=2$, then $x=7$.
9. If $x+3=y$ and $x=2$, then $y=5$.

In problems 10–21, use a field axiom to justify the given statement.

10. $(3+4)+5=3+(4+5)$.
11. $0+6=6$.
12. $3\cdot(\frac{1}{3})=(\frac{1}{3})\cdot 3$.
13. $7+8=8+7$.
14. $9\cdot(\frac{1}{9})=1$.
15. $3(2+5)=3\cdot 2+3\cdot 5$.
16. $(\frac{4}{3})\cdot 1=\frac{4}{3}$.
17. $(2\cdot 3)\cdot 4=2\cdot(3\cdot 4)$.
18. $(-2)+(-(-2))=0$.
19. $2(5+8)=2\cdot 5+2\cdot 8$
20. If $x \in R$, then $x+7 \in R$.
21. If $x \in R$, then $3x \in R$.

In problems 22–27, use the field axioms to justify the steps in the given proof. Assume that each variable represents a real number.

22. Prove: $x(yz)=(zx)y$.

$$x(yz)$$
$$=x(zy) \quad \underline{\quad ? \quad}$$
$$=(xz)y \quad \underline{\quad ? \quad}$$
$$=(zx)y \quad \underline{\quad ? \quad}$$

23. Prove: $z(x+y)=xz+yz$.

$$z(x+y)$$
$$=zx+zy \quad \underline{\quad ? \quad}$$
$$=xz+yz \quad \underline{\quad ? \quad}$$

24. Prove: $(x+y)+z=(x+z)+y$.

$$(x+y)+z$$
$$=(y+x)+z \quad \underline{\quad ? \quad}$$
$$=y+(x+z) \quad \underline{\quad ? \quad}$$
$$=(x+z)+y \quad \underline{\quad ? \quad}$$

25. Prove: $(-x)+(y+x)=y$.

$$(-x)+(y+x)$$
$$=(-x)+(x+y) \quad \underline{\quad ? \quad}$$
$$=((-x)+x)+y \quad \underline{\quad ? \quad}$$
$$=0+y \quad \underline{\quad ? \quad}$$
$$=y \quad \underline{\quad ? \quad}$$

26. Prove: $w(x+y+z)=wx+wy+wz$.

$$w(x+y+z)$$

$$=w[x+(y+z)] \quad \text{Definition 1.1}$$

$$=wx+w(y+z) \quad \underline{\quad ? \quad}$$

$$=wx+(wy+wz) \quad \underline{\quad ? \quad}$$
$$=wx+wy+wz \quad \text{Definition 1.1}$$

27. Prove: if $y \neq 0$, $[(1/y)\cdot x]y=x$.

$$\left(\frac{1}{y}\cdot x\right)y$$

$$=\left(x\cdot\frac{1}{y}\right)y \quad \underline{\quad ? \quad}$$

$$=x\left(\frac{1}{y}\cdot y\right) \quad \underline{\quad ? \quad}$$

$$=x(1) \quad \underline{\quad ? \quad}$$
$$=x \quad \underline{\quad ? \quad}$$

In problems 28–36, use the axioms of equality, the field axioms, and Definition 1.1 to prove the given statement. Assume that each variable represents a real number.

28. $(x+y)+z=(z+x)+y$.

29. $1 \cdot (x+y)+0=y+x$.

30. $(y+x)+(-y)=x$.

31. If $x \neq 0$, $x[y \cdot (1/x)]=y$.

32. $(x+3) \cdot 2+(x+3)y=(y+2)(x+3)$.

33. $(x+y)z=xz+yz$.

34. $(x+y)+(x+z)=(x+x)+(y+z)$

35. $x+2x+3x=6x$.

36. $(x+1)(x+2)=x \cdot x+3x+2$.

37. Is the set N of natural numbers a field under the operations of addition and multiplication? If not, explain which field axioms fail to be true for N.

38. Answer problem 37 for the set I of integers.

39. Answer problem 37 for the set Q of rational numbers.

Answers 1.4

1. E1	**2.** E2	**4.** E4	**5.** E4
7. E1, E4	**8.** E4, E4	**10.** F3	**11.** F8
13. F5	**14.** F11	**16.** F9	**17.** F4
19. F7	**20.** F1	**22.** F6, F4, F6	**23.** F7, F6
25. F5, F3, F10, F8	**26.** F7, F7	**37.** No; axioms F8, F10, and F11 fail.	
38. No; axiom F11 fails.			

1.5 Properties of Real Numbers

Using deductive reasoning, the field axioms can be combined with the axioms of equality to derive other important properties of real numbers.

Theorem 1.1   If $a,b,c \in R$, then

$$a=b \quad \text{if and only if} \quad a+c=b+c.$$

Proof   Remember that the proof of an "if and only if" theorem requires two parts.

Proof of: if $a=b$, then $a+c=b+c$ As a hypothesis, we are given that $a,b,c \in R$ with $a=b$. Since $a,c \in R$, it follows by the closure axiom of addition that $a+c \in R$. Thus the reflexive law of equality yields

$$a+c=a+c.$$

Then using the substitution axiom of equality to substitute b for a (since $a=b$) in the right side of the previous equation, we obtain

$$a+c=b+c.$$

Proof of: if $a + c = b + c$, then $a = b$ Since c is a real number, $-c$ is also a real number according to the inverse axiom for addition. Since $a + c = b + c$, it follows by the first part of this theorem that

$$(a+c)+(-c)=(b+c)+(-c).$$

Applying the associative axiom of addition to both sides of the previous equation, we get

$$a+[c+(-c)]=b+[c+(-c)].$$

Then applying the inverse axiom of addition, we have

$$a+0=b+0.$$

Finally, we obtain the desired conclusion,

$$a=b,$$

by applying the identity axiom of addition. ∎

You should note that in each of the last three steps in the previous proof, it was necessary to apply axiom E4 to each side of the equation when substituting equals for equals. Since we shall be substituting in this way quite frequently in proofs, we shall accept such substitutions without mentioning them every time.

Theorem 1.2 If $a,b,c \in R$ with $c \neq 0$, then

$$a=b \quad \text{if and only if} \quad ac=bc.$$

Proof The proof, which is similar to that of Theorem 1.1, is left as a problem. ∎

The following theorem involves two fundamental properties of the number 0.

Theorem 1.3 If $a,b \in R$, then
(a) $a \cdot 0 = 0$.
(b) $ab = 0$ if and only if $a = 0$ or $b = 0$ (or both).

Proof of (a)

$$0+1=1 \qquad \text{by axiom F8}$$
$$(0+1)a=1 \cdot a \qquad \text{by Theorem 1.2}$$

$$a(0+1)=a\cdot 1 \qquad \text{by axiom F6}$$
$$a\cdot 0+a\cdot 1=a\cdot 1 \qquad \text{by axiom F7}$$
$$a\cdot 0+a\cdot 1=0+a\cdot 1 \qquad \text{by axiom F8}$$
$$a\cdot 0=0 \qquad \text{by Theorem 1.1.}$$

Proof of (b)

Proof of: if $ab=0$, then $a=0$ or $b=0$ We consider two cases.
Case 1. If $a=0$, then the conclusion of the theorem is established.
Case 2. If $a \neq 0$, we must show that $b=0$. Since $a \neq 0$, $1/a \in R$ according to axiom F11. Thus

$$ab=0 \qquad \text{by hypothesis}$$
$$\frac{1}{a}(ab)=\frac{1}{a}\cdot 0 \qquad \text{by Theorem 1.2}$$
$$\left(\frac{1}{a}\cdot a\right)b=\frac{1}{a}\cdot 0 \qquad \text{by axiom F4}$$
$$1\cdot b=\frac{1}{a}\cdot 0 \qquad \text{by axiom F11}$$
$$b=\frac{1}{a}\cdot 0 \qquad \text{by axiom F9}$$
$$b=0 \qquad \text{by Theorem 1.3(a).}$$

Proof of: if $a=0$ or $b=0$, then $ab=0$ The proof of this follows immediately from Theorem 1.3(a).   ∎
Several familiar rules involving signs are summarized in the following theorem.

Theorem 1.4   If $a,b \in R$, then
(a) $-(-a)=a$.
(b) $(-a)b=-(ab)$.
(c) $(-a)(-b)=ab$.
(d) $-(a+b)=(-a)+(-b)$.

Proof   The proof of each part follows from the field axioms and the earlier parts of the theorem. See problems 28–31 for skeleton proofs of the various parts of the theorem.   ∎
Before discussing any more theorems, we define the operations of subtraction and division.

Definition 1.2   The operation of **subtraction** is defined in terms of addition as follows:

$$a-b=a+(-b).$$

That is, in order to subtract b from a, we add the negative of b to a. We call the number $a - b$, the *difference* of a and b. Note that the minus symbol $(-)$ has been used in two distinct ways in Definition 1.2. It has been used to indicate the operation of subtraction in $a - b$. and to represent the negative of b in $-b$.

Definition 1.3 The operation of **division** is defined in terms of multiplication as follows:

$$a \div b = \frac{a}{b} = a \cdot \frac{1}{b} \qquad \text{when } b \neq 0.$$

That is, in order to divide a by b, we multiply a by the reciprocal of b when $b \neq 0$. We call the number $a \div b$ (or a/b), the *quotient* of a divided by b. The symbol a/b is called a **fraction.** We call a the **numerator** of the fraction a/b, and b is called the **denominator.** It is important to note that *division by zero is left undefined.* In other words,

$$\frac{a}{0} \text{ has no meaning.}$$

The following theorem gives an equality test for fractions.

Theorem 1.5 If $a,b,c,d \in R$ with $b,d \neq 0$, then

$$\frac{a}{b} = \frac{c}{d} \quad \text{if and only if} \quad ad = bc.$$

Proof The proof follows directly from the field axioms and Theorem 1.2. In the first part of the proof, multiply both sides of $a/b = c/d$ by bd, and then apply the field axioms to get the conclusion $ad = bc$. In the second part of the proof, multiply both sides of $ad = bc$ by $(1/b) \cdot (1/d)$, and then apply the field axioms to get the conclusion $a/b = c/d$. ∎

The next theorem justifies the fact that the value of a fraction remains unchanged when the numerator and the denominator of a fraction are multiplied or divided by the same nonzero number.

Theorem 1.6 If $a,b,c \in R$ with $b,c \neq 0$, then

$$\frac{a}{b} = \frac{ac}{bc}.$$

Proof Using the associative and commutative axioms of multiplication, we have

$$a(bc) = (bc)a = b(ca) = b(ac).$$

Then since $a(bc) = b(ac)$ with $b,c \neq 0$, it follows by Theorem 1.5 that

$$\frac{a}{b} = \frac{ac}{bc}. \qquad \blacksquare$$

Other important properties of fractions are given in the following theorem.

Theorem 1.7 If $a,b,c,d \in R$, then

(a) $\dfrac{a}{d} + \dfrac{c}{d} = \dfrac{a+c}{d} \ (d \neq 0)$.

(b) $\dfrac{a}{d} - \dfrac{c}{d} = \dfrac{a-c}{d} \ (d \neq 0)$.

(c) $\dfrac{1}{b} \cdot \dfrac{1}{d} = \dfrac{1}{bd} \ (b,d \neq 0)$.

(d) $\dfrac{a}{b} \cdot \dfrac{c}{d} = \dfrac{ac}{bd} \ (b,d \neq 0)$.

(e) $\dfrac{1}{c/d} = \dfrac{d}{c} \ (c,d \neq 0)$.

(f) $\dfrac{a/b}{c/d} = \dfrac{ad}{bc} \ (b,c,d \neq 0)$.

Proof of (a) Using the definition of division and the field axioms, we have

$$\frac{a}{d} + \frac{c}{d} = a \cdot \frac{1}{d} + c \cdot \frac{1}{d} = \frac{1}{d} \cdot a + \frac{1}{d} \cdot c = \frac{1}{d} \cdot (a+c) = (a+c) \cdot \frac{1}{d} = \frac{a+c}{d}.$$

The proof of (b) is similar to that of (a). See problems 32–35 for skeleton proofs of parts (c) to (f). $\qquad \blacksquare$

The final theorem summarizes the familiar sign rules for fractions.

Theorem 1.8 If $a,b \in R$ with $b \neq 0$,
(a) $-a/-b = a/b$.
(b) $-a/b = a/-b = -(a/b)$.

Proof of (a) Using Theorem 1.4(b) and the commutative axiom, we have

$$(-a)b = -(ab) = -(ba) = (-b)a.$$

Now applying Theorem 1.5 to the equation $(-a)b = (-b)a$, we get

$$\frac{-a}{-b} = \frac{a}{b}$$

The proof of (b), which is similar to that of (a), is left as a problem. ∎

Problems 1.5

In problems 1–18, use the theorems of this section to justify the given statement. Assume that each variable represents a real number.

1. If $x = 2$, then $x + 4 = 2 + 4$.
2. If $x + 3 = y + 3$, then $x = y$.
3. If $ax = bx$ and $x \neq 0$, then $a = b$.
4. If $xy = 0$, then $x = 0$ or $y = 0$.
5. $7 \cdot 0 = 0$.
6. If $(x + 1)(x - 3) = 0$, then $x + 1 = 0$ or $x - 3 = 0$.
7. $-(-\frac{1}{2}) = \frac{1}{2}$.
8. $(-3)x = -3x$.
9. $(-2)(-x) = 2x$.
10. $-(x + 2) = (-x) + (-2)$.
11. If $\frac{3}{5} = x/2$, then $3 \cdot 2 = 5x$.
12. If $x \neq 0$, $\frac{3}{5} = 3x/5x$.
13. $\dfrac{x}{5} + \dfrac{3y}{5} = \dfrac{x + 3y}{5}$.
14. $\dfrac{x}{2} - \dfrac{3}{2} = \dfrac{x - 3}{2}$.
15. If $z \neq 0$, $\dfrac{x}{2} \cdot \dfrac{y}{z} = \dfrac{xy}{2z}$.
16. If $x,y \neq 0$, $\dfrac{2/x}{3/y} = \dfrac{2y}{x \cdot 3}$.
17. $\dfrac{-y}{-3} = \dfrac{y}{3}$.
18. $\dfrac{-x}{3} = -\dfrac{x}{3}$.

19. If $a = b$ and $c = d$, prove that $a + c = b + d$. (*Hint:* Use Theorem 1.1 and axiom E4.)
20. Prove Theorem 1.2.
21. If $a + b = a$, prove that $b = 0$. (*Remark:* This proves that the additive identity is unique.)
22. If $ab = a$, prove that $b = 1$. (*Remark:* This proves that the multiplicative identity is unique.)
23. If $a + b = 0$, prove that $b = -a$. (*Remark:* This proves that the additive inverse of a given number is unique.)
24. If $ab = 1$ with $a \neq 0$, prove that $b = 1/a$. (*Remark:* This proves that the multiplicative inverse of a given nonzero number is unique.)
25. Prove that $abc = 0$ if and only if $a = 0$, $b = 0$, or $c = 0$.
26. Prove that $x + a = b$ if and only if $x = b - a$.
27. If $a \neq 0$, prove that $ax = b$ if and only if $x = b/a$.

In problems 28–35, complete the proof of the given theorem by giving reasons for each step.

28. Prove Theorem 1.4(a).
29. Prove Theorem 1.4(b).

$$a + (-a) = 0$$
$$[a + (-a)] + [-(-a)] = 0 + [-(-a)]$$
$$a + [(-a) + (-(-a))] = 0 + [-(-a)]$$
$$a + 0 = 0 + [-(-a)]$$
$$a = -(-a)$$
$$-(-a) = a$$

$$(-a) + a = 0$$
$$((-a) + a)b = 0 \cdot b$$
$$((-a) + a)b = 0$$
$$b((-a) + a) = 0$$
$$b(-a) + ba = 0$$
$$(-a)b + ab = 0$$
$$[(-a)b + ab] + (-ab) = 0 + (-ab)$$
$$(-a)b + [ab + (-ab)] = 0 + (-ab)$$
$$(-a)b + 0 = 0 + (-ab)$$
$$(-a)b = -ab$$

30. Prove Theorem 1.4(c).

$$\begin{aligned}
(-a)(-b) &= -[a(-b)] \\
&= -[(-b)a] \\
&= -[-ba] \\
&= ba \\
&= ab
\end{aligned}$$

31. Prove Theorem 1.4(d).

$$\begin{aligned}
-(a + b) &= -[1(a + b)] \\
&= (-1)(a + b) \\
&= (-1)a + (-1)b \\
&= [-(1 \cdot a)] + [-(1 \cdot b)] \\
&= -a + (-b)
\end{aligned}$$

32. Prove Theorem 1.7(c).

$$\frac{1}{b} = \frac{1 \cdot d}{b \cdot d}$$
$$\frac{1}{b} = \frac{d}{bd}$$
$$\frac{1}{b} \cdot \frac{1}{d} = \frac{d}{bd} \cdot \frac{1}{d}$$
$$= \left(d \cdot \frac{1}{bd}\right) \cdot \frac{1}{d}$$
$$= \frac{1}{d}\left(d \cdot \frac{1}{bd}\right)$$
$$= \left(\frac{1}{d} \cdot d\right) \cdot \frac{1}{bd}$$
$$= 1 \cdot \frac{1}{bd}$$
$$= \frac{1}{bd}$$

33. Prove Theorem 1.7(d).

$$\frac{a}{b} \cdot \frac{c}{d} = \left(a \cdot \frac{1}{b}\right)\left(c \cdot \frac{1}{d}\right)$$
$$= \left(\frac{1}{b} \cdot a\right)\left(c \cdot \frac{1}{d}\right)$$
$$= \left[\left(\frac{1}{b} \cdot a\right)c\right] \cdot \frac{1}{d}$$
$$= \left[\frac{1}{b}(ac)\right] \cdot \frac{1}{d}$$
$$= \left[(ac)\frac{1}{b}\right] \cdot \frac{1}{d}$$
$$= (ac)\left(\frac{1}{b} \cdot \frac{1}{d}\right)$$
$$= (ac)\frac{1}{bd}$$
$$= \frac{ac}{bd}$$

34. Prove Theorem 1.7(e).

$$1 \cdot c = \left(d \cdot \frac{1}{d}\right)c$$
$$= d\left(\frac{1}{d} \cdot c\right)$$
$$= d\left(c \cdot \frac{1}{d}\right)$$
$$= d\left(\frac{c}{d}\right)$$
$$= \left(\frac{c}{d}\right)d$$
$$\frac{1}{c/d} = \frac{d}{c}$$

35. Prove Theorem 1.7(f).

$$\frac{a/b}{c/d} = \frac{a}{b} \cdot \frac{1}{c/d}$$
$$= \frac{a}{b} \cdot \frac{d}{c}$$
$$= \frac{ad}{bc}$$

36. Prove Theorem 1.8(b). [*Hint:* First show that $-a/b = a/-b$ by replacing b with $-b$ in Theorem 1.8(a). Then show that $-a/b = -(a/b)$ by using Definition 1.3 and Theorem 1.4(b).]

Answers 1.5

1. Theorem 1.1   2. Theorem 1.1   4. Theorem 1.3(b)   5. Theorem 1.3(a)
7. Theorem 1.4(a)   8. Theorem 1.4(b) 10. Theorem 1.4(d) 11. Theorem 1.5
13. Theorem 1.7(a) 14. Theorem 1.7(b) 16. Theorem 1.7(f)   17. Theorem 1.8(a)
28. F10, Theorem 1.1, F3, F10, F8, E2
29. F10, Theorem 1.2, Theorem 1.3(a), F6, F7, F6, Theorem 1.1, F3, F10, F8
31. F9, Theorem 1.4(b), F7, Theorem 1.4(b), F9
32. Theorem 1.6, F9, Theorem 1.2, Definition 1.3, F6, F4, F11, F9
34. F11, F4, F6, Definition 1.3, F6, Theorem 1.5
35. Definition 1.3, Theorem 1.7(e), Theorem 1.7(d)

1.6 The Real Number Line, and the Order and Completeness Axioms

The Real Number Line

It is possible to represent the real numbers graphically as the points of a geometric line in such a way that corresponding to each point P of the line there is associated a unique real number x, and vice versa. This one-to-one correspondence between the real numbers and the points of a geometric line is established as follows. Choose a direction on the line as positive (toward the right in Figure 1.2) and indicate this positive direction by an arrowhead. Select an arbitrary point O, called the **origin,** of the line and associate it with the number 0. Select another point P_1 of the line in the positive direction from the origin and associate this point with the number 1. The length of the line segment $\overline{OP_1}$ from O to P_1 is known as the **unit length.** Now starting at P_1, we measure off line segments $\overline{P_1P_2}$, $\overline{P_2P_3}$, $\overline{P_3P_4}$, ... of unit length in the positive direction from P_1. The numbers 2, 3, 4, ... are then associated uniquely with the points P_2, P_3, P_4, ..., respectively, of the line. In a similar manner, we measure off line segments of unit length in the negative direction from the origin, and then we associate the numbers -1,

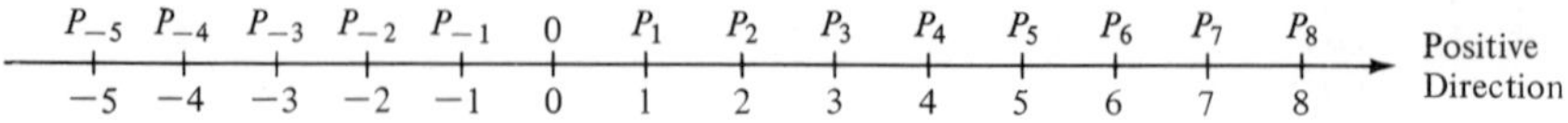

Figure 1.2

$-2, -3, \ldots$ with the endpoints of these segments. Thus we have established a one-to-one correspondence (see Figure 1.2) between the set of integers and certain equally spaced points of the geometric line.

To determine the point of the line associated with the rational number p/q, where $p, q \in N$, we proceed as follows. Divide each of the line segments $\overline{OP_1}$, $\overline{P_1P_2}$, $\overline{P_2P_3}$, and so on, into q segments of equal length by geometric construction. Starting at the origin and measuring off p such segments in the positive direction, we locate the point of the line that we associate with the rational number p/q. In the same way, the point of the line that we associate with the rational number $-p/q$ can be located by starting at the origin and measuring off p segments in the negative direction.

EXAMPLE 1

Locate the rational numbers $\frac{7}{3}$ and $-\frac{4}{3}$ on the real number line.

Solution We begin by dividing each line segment whose endpoints are integers into three equal parts (since $q = 3$). Then we locate $\frac{7}{3}$ by measuring off seven such segments (since $p = 7$) in the positive direction. Similarly, we locate $-\frac{4}{3}$ by measuring off four such segments (since $p = 4$) in the negative direction. See Figure 1.3.

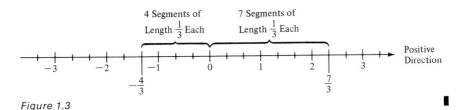

Figure 1.3

It is not as easy to locate the point of the line that is associated with an arbitrary irrational number. However, we can geometrically determine the point of the line associated with certain irrational numbers. For example, the point of the line associated with $\sqrt{2}$ can be found by constructing a line segment of unit length perpendicular to the line (see Figure 1.4) and forming the right triangle OAB whose hypotenuse has length $\sqrt{1^2 + 1^2} = \sqrt{2}$. The arc of the circle with center at O and radius $\sqrt{2}$ in Figure 1.4 will then meet the line at the point of the line that is associated with $\sqrt{2}$.

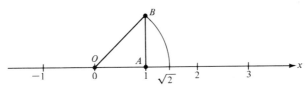

Figure 1.4

Although we cannot geometrically locate the points of the line that are associated with all irrational numbers, we can approximate the location of each irrational number by using a decimal approximation for the number. For instance, the point corresponding to π can be approximated by using some of the digits in its decimal representation $3.14159\ldots$.

The one-to-one correspondence discussed above between the set of real numbers and the set of points of a geometric line is called a **coordinate system** for the line. A line that has such a coordinate system is called a **real number line** (or a **coordinate line**). The number x that is associated with the point P is called the **coordinate** of P. We use the symbol $P(x)$ to represent the point of the line whose coordinate is x. We shall often find it convenient to speak of the point x when we actually mean the point P whose coordinate is x. That is, as a matter of convenience we shall frequently use the terms *real number* and *point* interchangeably. However, you should realize that a point is not a number and that a number is not a point. The point of the line merely represents the number. Several points together with their coordinates are shown in Figure 1.5.

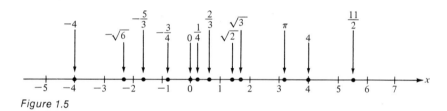

Figure 1.5

The Order Axioms

In Section 1.4, we discussed the fact that the real numbers satisfied the field axioms. In this section we shall see that the real numbers also satisfy three additional axioms, which are known as the **order axioms.** It is these three axioms which allow us to compare real numbers. That is, the order axioms will permit us to arrange the real numbers in order from smaller to larger. In general, any field that has this property is called an **ordered field.** Hence we shall see that the set of real numbers R is an ordered field.

If we denote the set of positive real numbers as R^+, the order axioms are as follows:

The Order Axioms

O1 If $a \in R$, exactly one of the following   *Trichotomy Axiom*
is true: a is positive, $a=0$, or $-a$
is positive.

O2 If $a,b \in R^+$, then $a + b \in R^+$.   *Closure Axiom of + for R^+*
O3 If $a,b \in R^+$, then $a \cdot b \in R^+$.   *Closure Axiom of $\cdot$ for R^+*

Since *$-a$ is negative whenever a is positive*, the *trichotomy axiom* states that each real number is either positive, zero, or negative. In words, the *closure axioms for R^+* state that the sum and product of any two real numbers is positive.

With the order axioms in mind, we can now order the real numbers as follows.

Definition 1.4 If $a,b \in R$, then *a* **is greater than** *b* (written $a > b$) if and only if $a - b$ is positive. We say that *a* **is less than** *b* (written $a < b$) if and only if $b > a$.

The symbols $>$ and $<$ are known as *inequality signs*. Any mathematical statement, such as $x > 3$ or $3x < 6$, which contains an inequality sign is called an **inequality.**

In the following example, we see how Definition 1.4 confirms our intuitive understanding of "greater than" and "less than."

EXAMPLE 2

(a) $5 > 3$, since $5 - 3 = 2$ is positive.
(b) $3 < 5$, since $5 > 3$.
(c) $3 > -2$ (and hence $-2 < 3$), since $3 - (-2) = 5$ is positive.
(d) Since $7 - 2 = 5$ is positive, $7 > 2$ (and hence $2 < 7$).
(e) Since $0 - (-3) = 3$ is positive, $0 > -3$ (and hence $-3 < 0$).

Note that Definition 1.4 implies that *$c > 0$ if and only if c is positive,* since $c > 0$ means that $c - 0 = c$ is positive, and vice versa. Similarly, it follows that *$c < 0$ if and only if c is negative.*

Having made the meaning of order clear, we shall now derive some important order properties of real numbers.

Theorem 1.9 If $a,b \in R$, exactly one of the following is true:

$$a > b, \quad a = b, \quad \text{or} \quad a < b.$$

Proof Applying the trichotomy axiom to the real number $a - b$, we have

$$a - b \text{ is positive}, \quad a - b = 0, \quad \text{or} \quad -(a - b) \text{ is positive.}$$

Hence

$$a - b > 0, \quad a = b, \quad \text{or} \quad -(a - b) > 0,$$

which in turn means that

$$a-b>0, \quad a=b, \quad \text{or} \quad 0<-(a-b)=b-a. \tag{1-3}$$

If $a - b > 0$, then $(a - b) - 0 = a - b$ is positive and hence $a > b$. Similarly, $0 < b - a$ means that $a < b$. Combining the two previous facts with (1–3), we find that

$$a>b, \quad a=b, \quad \text{or} \quad a<b. \qquad\blacksquare$$

In the next theorem, we summarize several important order properties of real numbers that will be needed for solving inequalities in Chapter 3.

Theorem 1.10   If $a,b,c \in R$,
(a) If $a > b$ and $b > c$, then $a > c$.
(b) If $a > b$, then $a + c > b + c$.
(c) If $a > b$ and c is positive, then $ac > bc$.
(d) If $a > b$ and c is negative, then $ac < bc$.

Proof   The proof of (a), which follows from Definition 1.4 and axiom O2, is left as a problem.

Proof of (b)   Since $a > b$, $a - b$ is positive. Since it follows from the field axioms and the definition of subtraction that $a - b = (a + c) - (b + c)$, $(a+c)-(b+c)$ is positive and hence $a+c>b+c$ by Definition 1.4.

Proof of (c)   Since $a > b$, $a - b$ is positive by Definition 1.4. Since c is positive, it then follows from axiom O3 that $(a - b)c$ is positive. Since $(a - b)c = ac - bc$, $ac - bc$ is positive and hence $ac > bc$ according to Definition 1.4.
     The proof of (d), which is similar to that of (c), is left as a problem. $\blacksquare$
     Note that in the problems (see problems 9–12) you will be asked to show that Theorem 1.10 can be modified to apply to inequalities of the form $a < b$.
     The following theorem will also be needed to solve inequalities in Chapter 3.

Theorem 1.11   If $a,b \in R$,
(a) $ab > 0$ if and only if ($a > 0$ and $b > 0$) or ($a < 0$ and $b < 0$).
(b) $ab < 0$ if and only if ($a > 0$ and $b < 0$) or ($a < 0$ and $b > 0$).

Proof of (a)

Proof of: if $(a > 0$ and $b > 0)$ or if $(a < 0$ and $b < 0)$, then $ab > 0$ First we note that if $a > 0$ and $b > 0$, then $ab > 0$ by axiom O3. On the other hand, if $a < 0$ and $b < 0$, then $0 > a$ and $0 > b$ by Definition 1.4. Hence it also follows by Definition 1.4 that $0 - a = -a$ is positive and $0 - b = -b$ is positive. Thus axiom O3 implies that $(-a)(-b)$ is positive. Then since $(-a)(-b) = ab$ by Theorem 1.4(c), ab is positive and therefore $ab > 0$.

Proof of: if $ab > 0$, then $(a > 0$ and $b > 0)$ or $(a < 0$ and $b < 0)$ Since $ab > 0$, it follows by Theorem 1.9 that $ab \neq 0$. Hence it follows from Theorem 1.3(b) that $a \neq 0$ and $b \neq 0$. Thus $(a > 0$ or $a < 0)$ and $(b > 0$ or $b < 0)$ according to Theorem 1.9. This leads to the following four possibilities:

(1) $a > 0$ and $b > 0$.
(2) $a > 0$ and $b < 0$.
(3) $a < 0$ and $b > 0$.
(4) $a < 0$ and $b < 0$.

Examining these possibilities one at a time as we did in the first part of the proof, we find that (1) and (4) each satisfy the hypothesis that $ab > 0$, while (2) and (3) each contradict the fact that $ab > 0$. Thus $ab > 0$ if and only if $(a > 0$ and $b > 0)$ or $(a < 0$ and $b < 0)$.

The proof of (b), which is similar to that of (a), is left as a problem. ∎

In mathematics we often encounter mathematical statements of the form $a \geq b$ or of the form $a \leq b$. The *inequality symbols* $\geq$ and $\leq$ are defined as follows.

Definition 1.5   If $a,b \in R$, then $a \geq b$ (read "a is greater than or equal to b") if and only if $a > b$ or $a = b$. We say that $a \leq b$ (read "a is less than or equal to b") if and only if $a < b$ or $a = b$.

The results of Theorems 1.10 and 1.11 can easily be extended to inequalities of the form $a \geq b$ or of the form $a \leq b$.

As a matter of convenience, the double inequality $a < x < b$ is used to represent the fact that $a < x$ *and* $x < b$. That is, $a < x < b$ means that x satisfies both the inequality $a < x$ *and* the inequality $x < b$ simultaneously. Similar comments can be made for other double inequalities, such as $-2 < x \leq 1$ and $3 \geq x \geq 0$.

The Completeness Axiom

In addition to the field axioms and the order axioms, one additional axiom must be considered if we wish to completely characterize the real numbers. It is this new axiom which guarantees that a one-to-one correspondence exists between the set of real numbers and the points of a real number line.

Before formally stating this final axiom, we must first consider some preliminary terminology.

Definition 1.6   Let S be a nonempty subset of the set of real numbers. A number M is said to be an **upper bound** of S if $x \leq M$ for every $x \in S$. A number m is said to be a **lower bound** of S if $m \leq x$ for every $x \in S$.

EXAMPLE 3

The number 7 is an upper bound of the set $S = \{x | 0 < x \leq 5\}$, since $x \leq 7$ for every $x \in S$. Other upper bounds are 5, 100, and 1000. Each of the numbers $0, -3, -10$, and -100 is a lower bound for the same set S.

Note that an upper bound for a set S is *not* unique. In fact, if M is an upper bound of S, then any number that is greater than M is also an upper bound of S. Similar comments can be made concerning lower bounds.

EXERCISE 1

Which of the numbers $-5, -3, -\frac{2}{3}, \frac{7}{3}, \pi$, and 10 are upper bounds (and which are lower bounds) of the set $S = \{x | -1 \leq x < 2\}$?

Answer $\frac{7}{3}, \pi$, and 10 are upper bounds; -5 and -3 are lower bounds.

In Example 3, each of the numbers 5, 7, 100, and 1000 was seen to be an upper bound of the set $S = \{x | 0 < x \leq 5\}$. However, the number 5 seems to be the smallest possible upper bound of S. Similarly, the number 0 appears to be the largest possible lower bound of S. We formalize these ideas in the following definition.

Definition 1.7   Let S be a nonempty subset of the set of real numbers. If M is an upper bound of S and if any other upper bound M' of S satisfies the inequality $M \leq M'$, then M is said to be the **least upper bound** of S. If m is a lower bound of S and if any other lower bound m' of S satisfies the inequality $m' \leq m$, then m is said to be the **greatest lower bound** of S.

EXAMPLE 4

The number 5 is the least upper bound of $S = \{x | 0 < x \leq 5\}$, since every other upper bound M' of S satisfies $5 \leq M'$. The number 0 is the greatest lower bound of $S = \{x | 0 < x \leq 5\}$, since every other lower bound m' of S satisfies $m' \leq 0$.

EXAMPLE 5

The set N of natural numbers has no least upper bound (in fact, it has no upper bound). However, the number 1 is its greatest lower bound.

EXAMPLE 6

The least upper bound of $S = \{x|x$ is a nonnegative rational number with $x^2 < 2\}$ is $\sqrt{2}$, and its greatest lower bound is 0.

Note that Example 6 shows that even though a subset of the rationals has a least upper bound, this least upper bound is *not* necessarily a rational number. However, when considering a subset of the real numbers that has a least upper bound, it seems reasonable to expect this least upper bound to be a real number. We formalize this conjecture in the following axiom.

The Completeness Axiom   If a nonempty subset S of R has an upper bound in R, then S has a least upper bound in R. Similarly, if a nonempty subset S of R has a lower bound in R, then S has a greatest lower bound in R.

An ordered field that satisfies the completeness axiom is called a **complete ordered field.** Thus the set of real numbers is a complete ordered field. On the other hand, the set of rational numbers is an ordered field (i.e., the rationals satisfy the field axioms and the order axioms), but we have seen in Example 6 that it is not a complete ordered field.

Problems 1.6

In problems 1–6, use the theorems of this section to justify the given statement. Assume that each variable represents a real number.

1. If $x > 2$, then $x + 3 > 2 + 3$.
2. If $x > -4$, then $-2x < 8$.
3. If $x > z$ and $z > 2$, then $x > 2$.
4. Either $y > 3$, $y = 3$, or $y < 3$.
5. If $x > -7$, then $2x > -14$.
6. If $x > 3$, then $-3x < -9$.

7. Prove Theorem 1.10(a).
8. Prove Theorem 1.10(d).
9. If $a < b$ and $b < c$, prove that $a < c$.
10. If $a < b$, prove that $a + c < b + c$.
11. If $a < b$ and c is positive, prove that $ac < bc$.
12. If $a < b$ and c is negative, prove that $ac > bc$.
13. If a and b are positive with $a > b$, prove that $a^2 > b^2$.
14. If $a \neq 0$, prove that $a^2 > 0$.
15. If $a > b$ and $c > d$, prove that $a + c > b + d$.
16. Give an example which shows that the following implication is false: if $a > b$ and $c > d$, then $a - c > b - d$.
17. If a, b, c, and d are positive numbers with $a > b$ and $c > d$, prove that $ac > bd$.
18. Prove Theorem 1.11(b).

In problems 19–30, determine, when they exist, the least upper bound and the greatest lower bound of the given set.

19. $\{x|1 < x < 3\}$

20. $\{x|-1 \leq x < 4\}$

21. $\{x|x \geq 1\}$

22. $\{x|x < -2\}$

23. $\{1, 7, -2, 5\}$

24. $\{x|x \in I\}$

25. $\{x|x^2 < 3\}$

26. $\{x|x > 0 \text{ and } x^2 < 3\}$

27. $\{x|x > 0, x \in Q, \text{ and } x^2 < 3\}$

28. $\{x|x = (n-1)/n, \text{ where } n \in N\}$

29. $\{x|x = 1/n, \text{ where } n \in N\}$

30. $\{x|-\frac{3}{2} < x < 10 \text{ and } x \in I\}$

In problems 31–36, give an example of a subset of S of R that satisfies the given conditions.

31. S has neither an upper bound nor a lower bound.

32. S has an upper bound but no lower bound.

33. S does not contain its least upper bound.

34. S contains its least upper bound and has no lower bound.

35. S contains both its least upper bound and its greatest lower bound.

36. S contains neither its least upper bound nor its greatest lower bound.

Answers 1.6

1. Theorem 1.10(b)

2. Theorem 1.10(d)

4. Theorem 1.9

5. Theorem 1.10(c)

19. $M = 3, m = 1$

20. $M = 4, m = -1$

22. $M = -2$

23. $M = 7, m = -2$

25. $M = \sqrt{3}, m = -\sqrt{3}$

26. $M = \sqrt{3}, m = 0$

28. $M = 1, m = 0$

29. $M = 1, m = 0$

chapter 1 review problems

1. Describe $\{2, 3, 5, 7, 11, 13, 17\}$ by the rule method.

2. Describe $\{x|x$ is a positive multiple of 7 which is less than 45$\}$ by the roster method.

3. If $U = \{0, 1, 2, 3, 4, 5, 6\}$, $A = \{0, 2, 4, 6\}$, and $B = \{0, 1, 5, 6\}$, describe the following sets by the roster method:

(a) $A \cup B'$ (b) $A \cap (B \cup A')$ (c) $(A - B) \cap (A' - B)$

4. Which of the numbers $-3, -\frac{2}{3}, 0, .17, .\overline{17}, \pi/3, \frac{6}{5}, \sqrt{9}, \sqrt{10}$, and 7 are

(a) natural numbers?   (b) integers?   (c) rational numbers?

(d) irrational numbers?

5. Explain the difference between a rational number and an irrational number.

6. State the axioms of equality.

7. Use the axioms of equality to justify the following statements:

(a) If $a = b + c$ and $2 = b + c$, then $a = 2$.

(b) If $a + 3 = 2b$ and $a = 1$, then $2b = 4$.

8. State the field axioms.
9. Use the field axioms to prove that $(1/a)(ba) = b$ if $a \neq 0$.
10. Give reasons (axioms, definitions, or theorems) for each step in the following skeleton proofs:

(a)

$x - a = b$	Given
$x + (-a) = b$	?
$[x + (-a)] + a = b + a$	?
$x + [(-a) + a] = b + a$	?
$x + 0 = b + a$	?
$x = b + a$	?
$x = a + b$	?

(b)

$b, c \neq 0$	Given
$ab = ab$	?
$ab = (ab) \cdot 1$	?
$ab = (ab) \cdot \left(\dfrac{1}{c} \cdot c \right)$	?
$ab = \left[(ab)\dfrac{1}{c} \right] \cdot c$	?
$ab = \left[a\left(b \cdot \dfrac{1}{c} \right) \right] \cdot c$	?
$ab = \left[\left(b \cdot \dfrac{1}{c} \right) \cdot a \right] c$	?
$ab = \left(b \cdot \dfrac{1}{c} \right)(ac)$	?
$ab = \left(\dfrac{b}{c} \right)(ac)$	?
$\dfrac{a}{b/c} = \dfrac{ac}{b}$	?

11. Prove that $(a + 1)(b + 1) = ab + b + a + 1$.
12. Prove that

$$\frac{a}{b} + \frac{c}{d} = \frac{ad + bc}{bd} \qquad \text{if } b, d \neq 0.$$

13. State the order axioms.
14. If $a > b$ and $c > d$, prove that $a + c > b + d$.
15. Determine the least upper bound and the greatest lower bound (if they exist) for the following sets:
    (a) $\{x \mid 1 \leq x < 8\}$ (b) $\{x \mid x \in I \text{ and } x > \frac{1}{2}\}$
16. Explain what the completeness axiom guarantees in terms of the real number line.

answers

1. $\{x \mid x \text{ is a prime number less than } 18\}$ 2. $\{7, 14, 21, 28, 35, 42\}$
3. (a) $\{0, 2, 3, 4, 6\}$ (b) $\{0, 6\}$ (c) $\varnothing$
4. (a) $\sqrt{9} = 3, 7$ (b) $-3, 0, \sqrt{9}, 7$ (c) $-3, -\frac{3}{5}, 0, .17, .\overline{17}, \frac{6}{5}, \sqrt{9}, 7$
   (d) $\pi/3, \sqrt{10}$
7. (a) E2, E3   (b) E4, E4, E2   9. F6, F4, F11, F9

10. (a) Definition 1.2, Theorem 1.1, F3, F10, F8, F5   (b) E1, F9, F11, F4, F4, F6, F4, Definition 1.3, Theorem 1.5
11. F7, F6, F7, F9, F3, Definition 1.1, Definition 1.1
12. Theorem 1.3(c), Definition 1.3, F6, F7, F6, Definition 1.3
14. Theorem 1.10(b), Theorem 1.10(b), Theorem 1.10(a)
15. (a) $M = 8$, $m = 1$ (b) $m = 1$
16. The one-to-one correspondence between the real numbers and the points of the real number line.

2

operations on algebraic expressions

2.1 Natural Numbers As Exponents

In a product of numbers, each number is said to be a **factor** of the product. If all the factors of a product are the same, the product is called a **power** of the common factor.

Definition 2.1 If $n \in N$ and $a \in R$, then the **nth power of a,** denoted by a^n, is defined as

$$a^n = \underbrace{a \cdot a \cdot a \cdot \ldots \cdot a.}_{n \text{ factors of } a}$$

The real number a is called the **base** of the power, and the natural number n is called the **exponent** of the base.

EXAMPLE 1
(a) $3^4 = 3 \cdot 3 \cdot 3 \cdot 3 = 81$.
(b) $(-2)^3 = (-2)(-2)(-2) = -8$.
(c) $(\frac{2}{5})^3 = \frac{2}{5} \cdot \frac{2}{5} \cdot \frac{2}{5} = \frac{8}{125}$.

EXERCISE 1
Evaluate.
(a) $(\frac{1}{2})^5$　　(b) $(-3)^4$

Answer (a) $\frac{1}{32}$　　(b) 81

Using Definition 2.1, we obtain the following **laws of exponents.**

Theorem 2.1   If $a,b \in R$ and $m,n \in N$, then
(a) $a^m a^n = a^{m+n}$.
(b) $(a^m)^n = a^{mn}$.
(c) $(ab)^m = a^m \cdot b^m$.

Proof of (a)

$$a^m \cdot a^n = \underbrace{(a \cdot a \cdot a \cdot \ldots \cdot a)}_{m \text{ factors of } a} \underbrace{(a \cdot a \cdot a \cdot \ldots \cdot a)}_{n \text{ factors of } a}$$

$$= \underbrace{a \cdot a \cdot a \cdot \ldots \cdot a}_{m+n \text{ factors of } a} = a^{m+n}.$$

Since the proofs of (b) and (c) are similar, they are left as problems.∎

EXAMPLE 2
(a) $x^2 \cdot x^{10} = x^{2+10} = x^{12}$.
(b) $(2^4)^7 = 2^{4 \cdot 7} = 2^{28}$.
(c) $(x^2 y)^3 = (x^2)^3 (y)^3 = x^{2 \cdot 3} y^{1 \cdot 3} = x^6 y^3$.

EXERCISE 2
Use the laws of exponents to simplify the following.
(a) $y^4 y^3$ (b) $(x^3)^5$ (c) $(2y^2)^3$

Answer   (a) y^7 (b) x^{15} (c) $8y^6$

Using Definition 2.1 and previous results, we obtain the following additional **laws of exponents.**

Theorem 2.2   If $a,b \in R$ and $m,n \in N$, then
(a) $a^m/a^n = a^{m-n}$ if $m > n$ and $a \neq 0$.
(b) $a^m/a^n = 1/a^{n-m}$ if $m < n$ and $a \neq 0$.
(c) $a^m/a^n = 1$ if $m = n$ and $a \neq 0$.
(d) $(a/b)^m = a^m/b^m$ if $b \neq 0$.

Proof of (a)   Using Definition 1.3, Theorem 2.1(a), and the field axioms, we have

$$\frac{a^m}{a^n} = a^m \cdot \frac{1}{a^n} = (a^{m-n} \cdot a^n) \cdot \frac{1}{a^n} = a^{m-n} \cdot \left(a^n \cdot \frac{1}{a^n}\right) = a^{m-n} \cdot 1 = a^{m-n}.$$

Since the proofs of (b), (c), and (d) are similar, they are left as problems. ∎

EXAMPLE 3

(a) $3^5/3^2 = 3^{5-2} = 3^3$.

(b) $x^2/x^6 = 1/x^{6-2} = 1/x^4$.

(c) $a^3/a^3 = 1$.

(d) $(\frac{2}{3})^3 = 2^3/3^3 = \frac{8}{27}$.

EXERCISE 3

Use the laws of exponents to simplify the following.

(a) x^8/x^3 (b) $y^3/2y^5$ (c) $x^3(2/x)^3$

Answer   (a) x^5 (b) $1/2y^2$ (c) 8

Problems 2.1

In problems 1–24, simplify the given expressions by using the laws of exponents to combine all powers having a common base.

1. x^4x^5 **2.** y^3y^{10} **3.** $z^4z^2z^8$

4. $(y^6)^4$ **5.** $(x^3)^3$ **6.** $(z^5)^2$

7. $(xy^2)^4$ **8.** $(x^2z)^5$ **9.** $(y^3z)^4$

10. $x^3(xy^5)^2$ **11.** $(xy^2)^2(xy)^3$ **12.** $(x^3y^2)(xy^2)^3$

13. x^5/x^2 **14.** x^3/x^7 **15.** x^9/x^{12}

16. $(x^2/y)^5$ **17.** $(2x/y^2)^3$ **18.** $(x^3/3y^2)^4$

19. $\dfrac{(2x^3y)^2}{x^6y^4}$ **20.** $\dfrac{(3xy^2)^3}{-6(xy^4)^2}$ **21.** $\dfrac{-2x^3y^4}{8(x^4y)^3}$

22. $(-3x^3y)^2\left(\dfrac{xy^2}{y^4}\right)^3$ **23.** $\left(\dfrac{x^3y}{xy^3}\right)^2\left(\dfrac{y}{x^3}\right)^4$ **24.** $\dfrac{1}{(2x^3y)^4}\left(\dfrac{4y^3}{x^2y}\right)^3$

25. Prove Theorem 2.1(b).   **26.** Prove Theorem 2.1(c).

27. Prove Theorem 2.2(b).   **28.** Prove Theorem 2.2(c).

29. Prove Theorem 2.2(d).

Answers 2.1

1. x^9 **2.** y^{13} **4.** y^{24} **5.** x^9

7. x^4y^8 **8.** $x^{10}z^5$ **10.** x^5y^{10} **11.** x^5y^7

13. x^3 **14.** $1/x^4$ **16.** x^{10}/y^5 **17.** $8x^3/y^6$

19. $4/y^2$ **20.** $-9x/2y^2$ **22.** $9x^9/y^4$ **23.** $1/x^8$

2.2 Basic Operations on Polynomials

An **algebraic expression** is a constant, a variable, or any combination of constants and variables formed by a finite number of additions, subtractions, multiplications, divisions, or extraction of roots. For instance,

$$7, \quad x^3, \quad x^3 - 2x^2 + \pi, \quad \frac{x-1}{x+2}, \quad \text{and} \quad 2x+3$$

are algebraic expressions. Whenever a given algebraic expression is written as the sum of other algebraic expressions, each of the algebraic expressions forming the given algebraic expression is called a **term** of the given algebraic expression. For example, the terms of the algebraic expression $(x/y) - 3x + x + 7$ are x/y, $-3x$, x, and 7.

EXERCISE 1

List the terms of the given algebraic expressions.
(a) $x^3 + 3x^2 - 7x - 3$ (b) $\sqrt{x} + (x-1) - 3xy$

Answer   (a) x^3, $3x^2$, $-7x$, -3 (b) $\sqrt{x}$, $x-1$, $-3xy$

An algebraic expression consisting of a constant, a variable, or the product of two or more nonzero constants and variables is called a **monomial.** Examples are

$$7, \quad x^3, \quad \tfrac{2}{3}x^2y^7, \quad \text{and} \quad -3x^4y^3z.$$

The **degree** of a monomial that is not a constant is defined as the sum of the exponents of the variables in the monomial. Thus the degree of x is 1, the degree of $5x^2y$ is 3, and the degree of $-3x^3yz^9$ is 13. The *degree* of any nonzero constant monomial is defined to be 0. Hence the degree for each of the constant monomials 7, -5, and $\tfrac{2}{3}$ is 0. The constant monomial 0 is said to have *no degree*.

EXERCISE 2

Give the degree for each of the given monomials.
(a) $2x^3y^5$ (b) y^6 (c) -10 (d) 0

Answer   (a) 8   (b) 6   (c) 0   (d) no degree

In a product, any factor is called the **coefficient** of the rest of the product. For instance, in the monomial $2xy$, 2 is the coefficient of xy, x is the coefficient of $2y$, and y is the coefficient of $2x$. In a monomial, the constant or product of constants is called the **numerical coefficient** of the monomial. For example, -3 is the numerical coefficient of $-3xy$, and 6 is the numerical coefficient of $(2x)(3y)$. Note that 1 is understood to be the numerical coefficient of terms such as x, x^2, xy, and so on. When the variable factors of two terms are exactly the same, the terms are said to be **like terms.** Hence $3x^3$ and $-7x^3$ are like terms, whereas $5x$ and $5x^2$ are not like terms.

Polynomials

A **polynomial** is an algebraic expression in which each term of the algebraic expression is a monomial. For instance,

$$7, \quad x^3y - xy^3, \quad \text{and} \quad x^3 - 3x^2 + x - 7$$

are polynomials. A polynomial that is the sum of two or of three monomials is called a **binomial** or a **trinomial**, respectively. For example, the polynomial $3xy - 7$ is a binomial, while the polynomial $x^2 - x + 7$ is a trinomial.

A polynomial involving one or more variables is called a polynomial in those variables. For instance, $x^3 - 3x^2 + x - 7$ is a polynomial in x, and $2x^5y + 3xy - 7y^2$ is a polynomial in x and y. The **degree** of a polynomial is the degree of the term of the polynomial that has the largest degree. For instance, the degree of $2x^5y + 3xy - 7y^2$ is 6, since the term with the largest degree, namely $2x^5y$, has a degree of 6. As other examples, the degree of $x^3 - 3x^2 + x - 7$ is 3, the degree of $3xy + 5$ is 2, and the degree of the polynomial 7 is 0. Note that the zero polynomial, 0, has no degree since the monomial, 0, has no degree.

When all the numerical coefficients of a polynomial belong to a set S, the polynomial is called a **polynomial over S.** For instance, $2x^3 + 5x^2 - 7$ is a polynomial over I, and $x^4 - \sqrt{2}\, x^3 + \pi$ is a polynomial over R. When the variables in a polynomial over S are known to represent only real numbers, the polynomial is called a **real polynomial over S.** A real polynomial over the set R of real numbers is generally called a *real polynomial*, for short.

EXERCISE 3

(a) Which of the algebraic expressions $x^3y + 3$, $(x - 1)/(x + 1)$, $7x$, and $x^3 - \sqrt{x} + 1$ are polynomials?
(b) The polynomial $x^3 - xz + 3z^4$ is a polynomial in what variables? What is its degree?
(c) Is $x^4 - 3x^3 - 2x + 7$ a polynomial over N? over I? over R?

Answer (a) $x^3y + 3$, $7x$ (b) x and z, 4 (c) no, yes, yes

Polynomials are frequently denoted by symbols such as $P(x)$, $Q(y)$, and $R(x, y)$, where the letters in parentheses designate the variables in the polynomial. For instance, we might write

$$P(x) = 3x^4 - 2x + 7,$$
$$Q(y) = 3y^3 + 2y^2 + y - \pi,$$

and

$$R(x, y) = 3x^2y - 3xy^2 + y^3.$$

Addition and Subtraction of Polynomials

Since the variables in a real polynomial represent real numbers, the properties of real numbers that we discussed in Chapter 1 are also valid for real polynomials.

Thus to add polynomials, we begin by using the associative and commutative axioms of addition to group like terms together. Then we combine like terms by using the distributive axiom.

EXAMPLE 1

Add $x^4 - 2x^3 + 3x - 1$ and $5x^3 - 2x^2 + 7x - 6$.

Solution

$$(x^4 - 2x^3 + 3x - 1) + (5x^3 - 2x^2 + 7x - 6)$$
$$= (x^4) + (-2x^3 + 5x^3) + (-2x^2) + (3x + 7x) + (-1 - 6)$$
$$= x^4 + 3x^3 - 2x^2 + 10x - 7. \qquad\blacksquare$$

By placing like terms under one another, we can add the polynomials in Example 1 more conveniently as follows:

$$\begin{array}{l} x^4 - 2x^3 \qquad\;\; + \;\; 3x - 1 \\ \underline{\qquad 5x^3 - 2x^2 + \;\; 7x - 6} \\ x^4 + 3x^3 - 2x^2 + 10x - 7 \end{array} \longleftarrow \text{adding like terms.}$$

To subtract polynomials, we begin by using the definition of subtraction to convert the problem to an addition problem, and then we add the polynomials in the manner indicated above.

EXAMPLE 2

Subtract $3x^3 - 2x + 7$ from $x^4 - 3x^3 + 5x^2 - 1$.

Solution

$$(x^4 - 3x^3 + 5x^2 - 1) - (3x^3 - 2x + 7)$$
$$= (x^4 - 3x^3 + 5x^2 - 1) + (-3x^3 + 2x - 7)$$
$$= (x^4) + (-3x^3 - 3x^3) + (5x^2) + (2x) + (-1 - 7)$$
$$= x^4 - 6x^3 + 5x^2 + 2x - 8. \qquad\blacksquare$$

Again by placing like terms under one another, we can subtract the polynomials in Example 2 as follows:

$$x^4 - 3x^3 + 5x^2 \qquad - 1$$
$$\underline{\quad\quad 3x^3 \qquad - 2x + 7\quad}$$
$$x^4 - 6x^3 + 5x^2 + 2x - 8 \longleftarrow \text{subtracting like terms.}$$

EXERCISE 4

Perform the indicated operations.
(a) $(x^4 + x^2 - 3x - 7) + (3x^4 + x^3 - x^2 + 5x)$
(b) $(x^3y + 3x^2y^2 - y^4) - (2x^2y^2 - 2xy^3 - 3y^4)$

Answer (a) $4x^4 + x^3 + 2x - 7$ (b) $x^3y + x^2y^2 + 2xy^3 + 2y^4$

Multiplication of Polynomials

To multiply polynomials, we begin by using repeated applications of the
distributive axiom. Next we simplify the resulting terms by using the laws
of exponents, then we group like terms together by using the associative and
commutative axioms, and finally we combine like terms by again using the
distributive axiom.

EXAMPLE 3
Multiply $x^2 - 2xy - y^2$ by $x + 2y$.

Solution

$$(x^2 - 2xy - y^2)(x + 2y)$$
$$= (x^2 - 2xy - y^2)(x) + (x^2 - 2xy - y^2)(2y)$$
$$= (x^3 - 2x^2y - xy^2) + (2x^2y - 4xy^2 - 2y^3)$$
$$= x^3 - 5xy^2 - 2y^3. \qquad\qquad\qquad\blacksquare$$

A more convenient way of multiplying the polynomials in Example 3
is demonstrated as follows:

$$x^2 - 2xy - y^2$$
$$\underline{x + 2y\quad\quad\quad\quad\quad}$$
$$x^3 - 2x^2y - \ xy^2 \qquad \longleftarrow \text{product of } x \text{ and } x^2 - 2xy - y^2$$
$$\underline{\quad + 2x^2y - 4xy^2 - 2y^3 \ \longleftarrow \text{product of } 2y \text{ and } x^2 - 2xy - y^2}$$
$$x^3 \qquad\quad - 5xy^2 - 2y^3 \ \longleftarrow \text{sum of the previous two products.}$$

When we are multiplying polynomials which contain only one variable, it will make the multiplication more orderly if, before we multiply, we rearrange the terms of the polynomials so that their exponents decrease from term to term. For example, $-3x^2 + x^4 - 7 + 2x$ would be rewritten as $x^4 - 3x^2 + 2x - 7$.

EXAMPLE 4

Multiply $x^2 - 3 - x^3$ by $x - 2x^2$.

Solution   First we rearrange the terms of the polynomials so that the exponents decrease from term to term. Then we have

$$
\begin{array}{l}
\quad -x^3 + x^2 - 3 \\
\quad -2x^2 + x \\
\hline
2x^5 - 2x^4 \qquad\quad + 6x^2 \\
\quad\quad - x^4 + x^3 \qquad\quad - 3x \\
\hline
2x^5 - 3x^4 + x^3 + 6x^2 - 3x.
\end{array}
$$

EXERCISE 5

Multiply $(x^2 - x + 1)(3x - x^2 + 5)$.

Answer $-x^4 + 4x^3 + x^2 - 2x + 5$

Division of Polynomials

To divide a polynomial *by a monomial,* we use parts (a) and (b) of Theorem 1.7.

EXAMPLE 5

Divide $2x^5y + x^4y^4 - 1$ by x^2y^3.

Solution   Using Theorem 1.7 and the laws of exponents, we get

$$
\frac{2x^5y + x^4y^4 - 1}{x^2y^3} = \frac{2x^5y}{x^2y^3} + \frac{x^4y^4}{x^2y^3} - \frac{1}{x^2y^3} = \frac{2x^3}{y^2} + x^2y - \frac{1}{x^2y^3}.
$$

EXERCISE 6

Divide $3x^3 - x^2 + 5$ by x^2.

Answer $3x - 1 + (5/x^2)$

In the remainder of our discussion about division of polynomials, we shall restrict ourselves to polynomials which contain only one variable. To divide a polynomial $P(x)$ (called the *dividend*) by another polynomial $D(x)$ (called the *divisor*), we use the following steps, which are known as the **long-division algorithm:**

1. Arrange the dividend $P(x)$ and the divisor $D(x)$ so that the exponents decrease from term to term.
2. The first term of the *quotient* $Q(x)$ is obtained by dividing the first term of the dividend $P(x)$ by the first term of the divisor $D(x)$.
3. Multiply the divisor $D(x)$ by the first term of the quotient $Q(x)$ and subtract this product from the dividend $P(x)$.
4. Consider the difference obtained as a new dividend and repeat the procedure of the last two steps until the degree of the *remainder* $R(x)$ is less than the degree of the divisor $D(x)$.

In general, when a polynomial $P(x)$ is divided by another polynomial $D(x)$ using the long-division algorithm, we have

$$\frac{P(x)}{D(x)} = Q(x) + \frac{R(x)}{D(x)},$$

where $Q(x)$ is the quotient and $R(x)$ is the remainder. Multiplying the previous equation by $D(x)$, we obtain the equation

$$P(x) = Q(x) \cdot D(x) + R(x), \tag{2-1}$$

which can be used to check the answer obtained in the division algorithm.

EXAMPLE 6
Divide $3x^3 - x + 70$ by $x + 3$.

Solution Using the long-division algorithm, we get

$$
\begin{array}{r}
3x^2 - 9x + 26 \qquad \text{(quotient)} \\
(\text{divisor}) \quad x+3 \, \overline{\smash{\big)}\, 3x^3 \quad - \quad x + 70 \quad \text{(dividend)}} \\
\underline{3x^3 + 9x^2 \qquad\qquad} \\
-9x^2 - \quad x + 70 \\
\underline{-9x^2 - 27x \qquad} \\
26x + 70 \\
\underline{26x + 78} \\
-8 \quad \text{(remainder)}
\end{array}
$$

Using Eq. (2–1) as a check, we have $Q(x) \cdot D(x) + R(x) = (3x^2 - 9x + 26)$ $(x + 3) + (-8) = 3x^3 - x + 70 = N(x)$.   ∎

EXERCISE 7

Divide $3x^3 + 7x^2 - x + 1$ by $x^2 - 3x + 1$.

Answer $3x + 16 + \dfrac{44x - 15}{x^2 - 3x + 1}$

Problems 2.2

In problems 1–30, perform the indicated operations.

1. $(2x - y - 3z) + (3x + y - 5z)$
2. $(2x^2 - 3xy + 5y^2) + (3x^2y + 5xy - 7x^2)$
3. $(3x^2 - xy + 5y^2) + (2x^2 + 7xy - 6y^2)$
4. $(5y^2 - 2xy + 7x^2) - (2x^2y - 3xy + 5x^2)$
5. $(2xy + 5xz - 6yz) - (7xz - 3xy - 2yz)$
6. $(xy - 3xz - yz) - (3yz - 2xz - 5xy)$
7. $(5x^3 - 2x + 1) + (x^2 - x + 4) - (7x^3 - 2x)$
8. $(x^4 - 3x^3 + 1) - (x^3 - x^2) - (x^2 + 2x - 2)$
9. $(3x^3 + x^2 - 7) - (x^2 - x + 5) - (3x + 1)$
10. $(x^4 - 2x^2) - [x^3 - x + 1 - (x^2 - 2x + 5)]$
11. $(3x^3 - 2x + 1) - [x^2 - 2x - (2x^3 - x^2 - 3)]$
12. $(x^3 - x^4 + x) - [x^2 - (3x^4 - 2) + 3x - 1]$
13. $(x^2 - xy + 2y^2)(x - 2y)$
14. $(x^2 + xy - 3y^2)(2x + y)$
15. $(x^2 - y^2)(x + y)$
16. $(x^2 - x + 1)(2x - 1)$
17. $(x^3 - x^2 + 1)(3x - 1)$
18. $(x^2 - x)(x^2 - 2x + 4)$
19. $(1 - 2x + x^2)(x^2 + 1 + 2x)$
20. $(5 - 2x + x^2)(2x^2 + 1 - 3x)$
21. $(x + 2x^2 - 3)(x^2 - 1 + 3x)$

22. $\dfrac{2x^3y - 3xy^4}{x^3y^2}$

23. $\dfrac{3x^3 - a^2x^2 + 5a}{ax}$

24. $\dfrac{3x^3y - 2x^2y^2 - 5xy^3}{x^2y^2}$

25. $\dfrac{x^3 - 5x^2 + 17}{x - 4}$

26. $\dfrac{2x^3 - x^2 - x + 5}{x - 2}$

27. $\dfrac{2x^3 - 3x + 20}{x + 3}$

28. $\dfrac{3x^4 - 5x^2 + 2x + 1}{x^2 + x - 2}$

29. $\dfrac{2x^3 - 5x + 25}{x^2 - 2x + 5}$

30. $\dfrac{2x^3 + x^2 + 3}{2x^2 - x + 3}$

Answers 2.2

1. $5x - 8z$

2. $3x^2y + 2xy + 5y^2 - 5x^2$

4. $5y^2 + xy + 2x^2 - 2x^2y$

5. $5xy - 2xz - 4yz$

7. $-2x^3 + x^2 - x + 5$

8. $x^4 - 4x^3 - 2x + 3$

10. $x^4 - x^3 - x^2 - x + 4$

11. $5x^3 - 2x^2 - 2$

13. $x^3 - 3x^2y + 4xy^2 - 4y^3$

14. $2x^3 + 3x^2y - 5xy^2 - 3y^3$

16. $2x^3 - 3x^2 + 3x - 1$

17. $3x^4 - 4x^3 + x^2 + 3x - 1$

19. $x^4 - 2x^2 + 1$

20. $2x^4 - 7x^3 + 17x^2 - 17x + 5$

22. $\dfrac{2}{y} - \dfrac{3y^2}{x^2}$

23. $\dfrac{3x^2}{a} - ax + \dfrac{5}{x}$

25. $x^2 - x - 4 + \dfrac{1}{x-4}$

26. $2x^2 + 3x + 5 + \dfrac{15}{x-2}$

28. $3x^2 - 3x + 4 + \dfrac{-8x+9}{x^2+x-2}$

29. $2x + 4 + \dfrac{-7x+5}{x^2-2x+5}$

2.3 Factoring Special Polynomials

The factoring of polynomials can be thought of as the reverse process of determining the product of two or more polynomials. That is, *to factor a polynomial* means to express the given polynomial as the product of two or more other polynomials, each of which is called a **factor** of the given polynomial. For instance, $x + 1$ and $x - 1$ are factors of $x^2 - 1$, since $x^2 - 1 = (x + 1)(x - 1)$.

If a polynomial is factored in such a way that the numerical coefficients of the terms in the factors are each elements of the same set S and if each of the factors cannot be factored further by choosing numerical coefficients from S, we say that the polynomial is *completely factored over S*. As examples, $x^2 - 1 = (x + 1)(x - 1)$ is completely factored over I, and $x^2 - 2 = (x + \sqrt{2})(x - \sqrt{2})$ is completely factored over the set of real numbers. Note that $x^2 - 2$ cannot be factored further in terms of integer coefficients. That is, $x^2 - 2$ is completely factored over I to begin with. In general, when a polynomial over I cannot be factored further in terms of integer coefficients, we say the polynomial is *prime over I*. Thus $x^2 - 2$ is prime over I.

Removing Common Factors

If each of the terms of a polynomial has a particular factor in common, we begin by using the distributive axiom to factor out this common factor.

EXAMPLE 1

Factor $8x^3y^2 + 4x^2y - 2x$ completely over I.

Solution In this case, $2x$ is a factor of each term. Using the distributive axiom to remove this common factor, we have

$$8x^3y^2 + 4x^2y - 2x = 2x(4x^2y^2 + 2xy - 1).$$ ∎

EXAMPLE 2

Factor $y(x - 1) + 2(x - 1)$ completely over I.

Solution Removing the common factor $(x - 1)$, we get

$$y(x - 1) + 2(x - 1) = (x - 1)(y + 2).$$ ∎

EXERCISE 1

Factor completely over I.
(a) $10x + 15$ (b) $x^2yz - 2xy$

Answer (a) $5(2x + 3)$ (b) $xy(xz - 2)$

Factoring by Formula

By carrying out the indicated multiplications, we can show that

$$u^2 - v^2 = (u - v)(u + v), \tag{2-2}$$
$$u^3 + v^3 = (u + v)(u^2 - uv + v^2), \tag{2-3}$$

and

$$u^3 - v^3 = (u - v)(u^2 + uv + v^2). \tag{2-4}$$

Consequently, polynomials of the form $u^2 - v^2$ (*the difference of two squares*), $u^3 + v^3$ (*the sum of two cubes*), and $u^3 - v^3$ (*the difference of two cubes*) can be factored by using Eqs. (2-2), (2-3), and (2-4), respectively. In each of these equations, u and v can be replaced with any algebraic expression.

EXAMPLE 3

Factor $8x^3 + 27y^6$ completely over I.

Solution   Using Eq. (2–3) with $u = 2x$ and $v = 3y^2$, we have

$$8x^3 + 27y^6 = (2x)^3 + (3y^2)^3$$
$$= (2x + 3y^2)(4x^2 - 6xy^2 + 9y^4).$$ ∎

EXAMPLE 4

Factor $(x + 1)^2 - (x - 4)^2$ completely over I.

Solution   Using Eq. (2–2) with $u = x + 1$ and $v = x - 4$, we have

$$(x + 1)^2 - (x - 4)^2 = [(x + 1) - (x - 4)][(x + 1) + (x - 4)]$$
$$= 5(2x - 3).$$ ∎

EXAMPLE 5

Factor $3x^4 - 81x$ completely over I.

Solution   Removing the common factor $3x$, we get

$$3x^4 - 81x = 3x(x^3 - 27).$$

Then using Eq. (2–4) with $u = x$ and $v = 3$, we can factor $x^3 - 27$ to obtain

$$3x^4 - 81x = 3x(x - 3)(x^2 + 3x + 9).$$ ∎

EXERCISE 2

Factor completely over I.
(a) $x^3 - x$ (b) $8x^6 - 1$ (c) $x^3 + a^3y^6$

Answer   (a) $x(x - 1)(x + 1)$ (b) $(2x^2 - 1)(4x^4 + 2x^2 + 1)$
(c) $(x + ay^2)(x^2 - axy^2 + a^2y^4)$

Factoring the Trinomial $pu^2 + qu + r$ by Inspection

The trinomial $pu^2 + qu + r$, where $p,q,r \in I$ and u is any algebraic expression, can sometimes be factored over I by using the following fact. Since $(au + b)(cu + d) = acu^2 + (ad + bc)u + bd$, it follows that

$$pu^2 + qu + r = (au + b)(cu + d) \quad \text{if and only if} \quad p = ac,$$
$$q = ad + bc, \text{ and } r = bd. \tag{2–5}$$

Note that when $p > 0$, a and c can always be chosen as positive numbers, since $(-au - b)(-cu - d) = (au + b)(cu + d)$.

EXAMPLE 6

Factor $x^2 + 2x - 3$ completely over I.

Solution According to Eq. (2–5), to express $x^2 + 2x - 3$ in the form $(ax + b)(cx + d)$, we must find integers a, b, c, and d such that

$$1 = ac, \quad -3 = bd, \quad \text{and} \quad 2 = ad + bc.$$

The possibilities for a and c, and for b and d, are listed in the following tables:

a	1
c	1

b	1	-1	3	-3
d	-3	3	-1	1

Trying each possibility for a and c with each possibility for b and d, we find that

$$x^2 + 2x - 3 = (x - 1)(x + 3).$$ ∎

EXAMPLE 7

Factor $3x^2 - 8x + 4$ completely over I.

Solution According to Eq. (2–5), to express $3x^2 - 8x + 4$ in the form $(ax + b)(cx + d)$, we must find integers a, b, c, and d such that

$$3 = ac, \quad 4 = bd, \quad \text{and} \quad -8 = ad + bc.$$

The possibilities for a and c, and for b and d, are listed in the following tables:

a	1	3
c	3	1

b	1	-1	2	-2	4	-4
d	4	-4	2	-2	1	-1

Trying each possibility for a and c with each possibility for b and d, we find that

$$3x^2 - 8x + 4 = (x - 2)(3x - 2).$$ ∎

EXERCISE 3

Factor completely over I.
(a) $x^2 - 2x - 15$ (b) $2x^2 + 5x - 3$ (c) $x^2 + 2x + 2$

Answer   (a) $(x - 5)(x + 3)$ (b) $(2x - 1)(x + 3)$ (c) prime over I

Factoring by Grouping

The terms of polynomials can sometimes be grouped in such a way that one of the previous methods can then be applied.

EXAMPLE 8

Factor $2x^3 - 3x^2 - 2x + 3$.

Solution   Grouping the first two terms together and the last two terms together, and then factoring the common factor out of each group, we get

$$2x^3 - 3x^2 - 2x + 3 = (2x^3 - 3x^2) - (2x - 3)$$
$$= x^2(2x - 3) + (-1)(2x - 3)$$
$$= (x^2 - 1)(2x - 3)$$
$$= (x - 1)(x + 1)(2x - 3).$$

EXAMPLE 9

Factor $x^2 + 4xy + 4y^2 - 64$.   ∎

Solution   Grouping the first three terms together, we have

$$x^2 + 4xy + 4y^2 - 64 = (x^2 + 4xy + 4y^2) - 64$$
$$= (x + 2y)^2 - (8)^2$$
$$= (x + 2y - 8)(x + 2y + 8).$$ ∎

EXERCISE 4

Factor completely over I.
(a) $2ax^2 + 5ax - 2bx - 5b$ (b) $x^2 + 2x + 1 - y^2$

Answer   (a) $(ax - b)(2x + 5)$ (b) $(x - y + 1)(x + y + 1)$

Problems 2.3

In problems 1–6, factor the given polynomial completely over I by removing the common factor.

1. $3x + 24$ **2.** $y^2 - 4y$ **3.** $x^4 - x^2 - 2x$
4. $x^2y^3z^4 - 2x^4y^2z^2$ **5.** $y(2x + 3) + 2z(2x + 3)$ **6.** $x^2y(x - 2) - 2x(x - 2)$

In problems 7–18, factor the given polynomial completely over I by formula.

7. $25x^2 - 9$ 8. $27x^3 + b^3$ 9. $x^3y^3 - 27$

10. $x^3y^6 + 64$ 11. $1 - 64b^3$ 12. $x^4 - 8xy^3$

13. $2x^6 - 16y^3$ 14. $x^6 - 1$ 15. $x^8 - 16$

16. $3(4x - y)^3 - 81(x + y)^3$ 17. $(3x + 2)^2 - (2x - 3)^2$ 18. $(x^2 - y)^3 + 8$

In problems 19–36, factor the given trinomial completely over I by inspection.

19. $x^2 + x - 6$ 20. $x^2 - 4x - 5$

21. $x^3 - 14x^2 + 49x$ 22. $3x^2 - x - 4$

23. $2x^2 - 3x - 9$ 24. $4x^2 + 5x - 6$

25. $6x^2 + x - 2$ 26. $8x^2 + 10x - 3$

27. $4x^2 - 16x + 15$ 28. $x^2 + 6x + 10$

29. $2x^2 + 5x + 6$ 30. $3x^2 + 3x + 4$

31. $x^4 + 10x^2 + 25$ 32. $x^4 - 15x^2 - 16$

33. $x^4 - 13x^2 + 36$ 34. $(x - y)^2 + 3(x - y) - 4$

35. $2(x + 2y)^2 - 7(x + 2y) + 6$ 36. $3(2x - y)^2 - 4(2x - y) - 4$

In problems 37–48, factor the given polynomial completely over I by grouping.

37. $xy + bx - ay - ab$ 38. $2xy - 3y - 2xz + 3z$ 39. $3xy - 6bx + ay - 2ab$

40. $2x^3 - x^2 - 18x + 9$ 41. $4x^3 - 12x^2 + 9x - 27$ 42. $4y^3 - 12y^2 - y + 3$

43. $x^2 - y^2 + 4y - 4$ 44. $25x^2 - 4y^2 + 24y - 36$ 45. $y^2 + 6y + 9 - 4z^2$

46. $y^2 + py + 3p - 9$ 47. $x^2 - 2xy + 4y - 4$ 48. $x^2 + 2xz - y^2 - 2yz$

In problems 49–51, begin by first expressing the given polynomial in the form $(x^2 + ?)^2 - (?)^2$. For instance, $x^4 + 4 = (x^4 + 4x^2 + 4) - (4x^2) = (x^2 + 2)^2 - (2x)^2$. Then factor the resulting expression.

49. $x^4 + 64$ 50. $x^4 - 3x^2 + 9$ 51. $x^4 + x^2 + 25$

Answers 2.3

1. $3(x + 8)$ 2. $y(y - 4)$

4. $x^2y^2z^2(yz^2 - 2x^2)$ 5. $(y + 2z)(2x + 3)$

7. $(5x - 3)(5x + 3)$ 8. $(3x + b)(9x^2 - 3bx + b^2)$

10. $(xy^2 + 4)(x^2y^4 - 4xy^2 + 16)$ 11. $(1 - 4b)(1 + 4b + 16b^2)$

13. $2(x^2 - 2y)(x^4 + 2x^2y + 4y^2)$ 14. $(x - 1)(x + 1)(x^2 + x + 1)(x^2 - x + 1)$

16. $3(x - 4y)(37x^2 + 19xy + 7y^2)$ 17. $(x + 5)(5x - 1)$

19. $(x + 3)(x - 2)$ 20. $(x - 5)(x + 1)$

22. $(x + 1)(3x - 4)$ 23. $(x - 3)(2x + 3)$

25. $(2x - 1)(3x + 2)$ 26. $(2x + 3)(4x - 1)$

28. prime over I 29. prime over I

31. $(x^2 + 5)(x^2 + 5)$ 32. $(x - 4)(x + 4)(x^2 + 1)$

34. $(x - y + 4)(x - y - 1)$ 35. $(2x + 4y - 3)(x + 2y - 2)$

37. $(x - a)(y + b)$ 38. $(2x - 3)(y - z)$

40. $(x-3)(x+3)(2x-1)$ **41.** $(x-3)(4x^2+9)$
43. $(x-y+2)(x+y-2)$ **44.** $(5x-2y+6)(5x+2y-6)$
46. $(y-3+p)(y+3)$ **47.** $(x-2)(x+2-2y)$
49. $(x^2+4x+8)(x^2-4x+8)$ **50.** $(x^2-3x+3)(x^2+3x+3)$

2.4 Basic Operations on Rational Expressions

A **rational expression** is defined as the quotient of two polynomials. For example,

$$\frac{1}{xy}, \quad \frac{x^2yz^3}{2x+3z}, \quad \text{and} \quad \frac{x^2-2x-3}{x^3-27}$$

are rational expressions. Since rational expressions are quotients containing real numbers and variables that represent real numbers, the properties of real numbers concerning quotients discussed in Chapter 1 are also valid for rational expressions.

You will recall that *division by zero is undefined.* Hence it is understood that each variable in a rational expression represents any real number except those which make the denominator zero. For example, in the rational expression $z/x(y-1)$, it is understood that $x \neq 0$ and $y \neq 1$. Similarly, it is understood that $x \neq 1$ and $x \neq -1$ in the rational expression $(x-1)(x+2)/(x-1)(x+1)$.

Equivalent Rational Expressions

Converting Theorems 1.5, 1.6, and 1.8 into rational-expression notation, we have the following theorem concerning the equivalence of rational expressions.

Theorem 2.3   If P, Q, R, and S are polynomials, then
(a) $P/Q = R/S$ if and only if $PS = QR$.
(b) $P/Q = PS/QS$.
(c) $-P/-Q = P/Q$
(d) $-P/Q = P/-Q = -(P/Q)$.
for those values of the variables for which $Q, S \neq 0$.

A rational expression is said to be in **lowest terms** if the numerator and the denominator have no factors in common when they are completely factored. For example,

$$\frac{x(x-2)}{(x-1)(x+1)} \quad \text{is in lowest terms,}$$

whereas

$$\frac{x^2y}{xy^2} \quad \text{is } \textit{not} \text{ in lowest terms.}$$

Note that Theorem 2.3(b) allows us to reduce any rational expression to lowest terms by canceling each *nonzero* common factor that appears in both the numerator and the denominator of the rational expression. It also permits us to multiply both the numerator and the denominator of a rational expression by the same *nonzero* factor.

EXAMPLE 1
Reduce x^2y/xy^2 to lowest terms.

Solution   Using Theorem 2.3(b), we have

$$\frac{x^2y}{xy^2} = \frac{x(xy)}{y(xy)} = \frac{x}{y}. \qquad \blacksquare$$

EXAMPLE 2
Reduce

$$\frac{2x^2 - 3x + 1}{2x^2 + 3x - 2}$$

to lowest terms.

Solution   Factoring the numerator and denominator of the given rational expression, and then using Theorem 2.3(b), we get

$$\frac{2x^2 - 3x + 1}{2x^2 + 3x - 2} = \frac{(2x-1)(x-1)}{(2x-1)(x+2)} = \frac{x-1}{x+2}. \qquad \blacksquare$$

EXERCISE 1

Reduce to lowest terms.

(a) $\dfrac{x^2yz}{xy^2z}$ (b) $\dfrac{x^2-5x+6}{x^2-x-2}$ (c) $\dfrac{x^2-1}{x^3-1}$

Answer (a) $\dfrac{x}{y}$ (b) $\dfrac{x-3}{x+1}$ (c) $\dfrac{x+1}{x^2+x+1}$

Addition and Subtraction of Rational Expressions

Converting parts (a) and (b) of Theorem 1.7 into rational-expression notation, we have the following theorem concerning the addition and subtraction of rational expressions.

Theorem 2.4 If P, Q, and R are polynomials, then

(a) $\dfrac{P}{Q}+\dfrac{R}{Q}=\dfrac{P+R}{Q}.$

(b) $\dfrac{P}{Q}-\dfrac{R}{Q}=\dfrac{P-R}{Q}.$

for those values of the variables for which $Q \neq 0$.

Using Theorem 2.4, we can add or subtract rational expressions that have *the same denominator.*

EXAMPLE 3

Express

$$\frac{x^2+3x}{x+1}+\frac{x-1}{x+1}-\frac{x^2-3}{x+1}$$

as a single fraction.

Solution Using Theorem 2.4, we have

$$\frac{x^2+3x}{x+1}+\frac{x-1}{x+1}-\frac{x^2-3}{x+1}=\frac{(x^2+3x)+(x-1)-(x^2-3)}{x+1}=\frac{4x+2}{x+1}. \quad\blacksquare$$

Before adding or subtracting rational expressions having *different denominators*, the given rational expressions are replaced with equivalent rational expressions all of which have a common denominator. This is done by using Theorem 2.3(b), since this theorem permits us to multiply both the numerator and the denominator of a rational expression by the same *non-*

zero factor. Although any common denominator will lead to a correct sum or difference, the work involved in adding or subtracting rational expressions will be easier when the *least* common denominator is used. This least common denominator (LCD) is determined as follows:

1. Factor each denominator completely over *I*.
2. Form a product using each distinct factor the largest number of times each such factor appears in any *one* denominator.

EXAMPLE 4

Determine the LCD of

$$\frac{1}{x^2-4}, \quad \frac{x}{x^2-4x+4}, \quad \frac{1}{x}, \quad \text{and} \quad \frac{x+1}{x^3}.$$

Solution   With the denominators factored, the fractions are

$$\frac{1}{(x-2)(x+2)}, \quad \frac{1}{(x-2)^2}, \quad \frac{1}{x}, \quad \text{and} \quad \frac{x+1}{x^3}. \qquad \blacksquare$$

The distinct factors of the denominators are $x - 2$, $x + 2$, and x. Thus the LCD is $(x - 2)^2(x + 2)x^3$.

EXAMPLE 5

Express

$$\frac{x+1}{x^2-x}+\frac{1}{x^2}$$

as a single fraction.

Solution   Factoring each denominator, we find that the LCD is $x^2(x-1)$. Thus we have

$$\frac{x+1}{x^2-x}+\frac{1}{x^2}=\frac{x+1}{x(x-1)}+\frac{1}{x^2}=\frac{(x+1)(x)}{x(x-1)(x)}+\frac{1(x-1)}{x^2(x-1)}$$
$$=\frac{(x+1)x+1(x-1)}{x^2(x-1)}=\frac{x^2+2x-1}{x^2(x-1)}. \qquad \blacksquare$$

EXERCISE 2

Perform the indicated operations and simplify.

(a) $\dfrac{5x}{x-1} + \dfrac{x+1}{x-1} - \dfrac{6}{x-1}$ (b) $\dfrac{1}{x^2} - \dfrac{1}{x} + \dfrac{x+2}{x^2-x}$

Answer   (a) $\dfrac{6x-5}{x-1}$ (b) $\dfrac{4x-1}{x^2(x-1)}$

Multiplication and Division of Rational Expressions

Converting parts (d) and (f) of Theorem 1.7 into rational-expression notation, we have the following theorem concerning the multiplication and division of rational expressions.

Theorem 2.5   If P, Q, R, and S are polynomials, then

(a) $\dfrac{P}{Q} \cdot \dfrac{R}{S} = \dfrac{PR}{QS}$.

(b) $\dfrac{P}{Q} \div \dfrac{R}{S} = \dfrac{P}{Q} \cdot \dfrac{S}{R} = \dfrac{PS}{QR}$.

for those values of the variables for which the denominators have nonzero values.

EXAMPLE 6

Express

$$\frac{x^2-x}{x^2-x-2} \cdot \frac{x^2-1}{x^2-2x+1}$$

as a single fraction.

Solution   Using Theorem 2.5(a), we get

$$\frac{x^2-x}{x^2-x-2} \cdot \frac{x^2-1}{x^2-2x+1} = \frac{x(x-1)}{(x-2)(x+1)} \cdot \frac{(x-1)(x+1)}{(x-1)(x-1)}$$
$$= \frac{x(x-1)(x-1)(x+1)}{(x-2)(x+1)(x-1)(x-1)} = \frac{x}{x-2}. \qquad ■$$

EXAMPLE 7

Express

$$\frac{x^3 - 64}{x^2 - 3x} \div \frac{x^2 + 4x + 16}{x - 3}$$

as a single fraction.

Solution   Using Theorem 2.5(b), we get

$$\frac{x^3 - 64}{x^2 - 3x} \div \frac{x^2 + 4x + 16}{x - 3} = \frac{x^3 - 64}{x^2 - 3x} \cdot \frac{x - 3}{x^2 + 4x + 16}$$

$$= \frac{(x - 4)(x^2 + 4x + 16)}{x(x - 3)} \cdot \frac{x - 3}{x^2 + 4x + 16}$$

$$= \frac{(x - 4)(x^2 + 4x + 16)(x - 3)}{x(x - 3)(x^2 + 4x + 16)} = \frac{x - 4}{x}. \qquad \blacksquare$$

EXERCISE 3

Perform the indicated operations and simplify.

(a) $\dfrac{x^2 - 1}{x^2 - 3x + 2} \cdot \dfrac{x^2 + 3x - 10}{x^2 - 25}$ (b) $(x - 2) \div \dfrac{x^2 + x - 6}{x}$

Answer   (a) $\dfrac{x + 1}{x - 5}$ (b) $\dfrac{x}{x + 3}$

Simplifying Compound Fractions

A fraction that contains one or more fractions in its numerator or denominator is called a **compound fraction**. For example,

$$\frac{x^2 + (1/x)}{x - 1 - (1/x)}$$

is a compound fraction. Such fractions can be reduced to rational expressions in lowest terms by using the procedures discussed in this section.

EXAMPLE 8

Reduce

$$\frac{x^2 + (1/x)}{x - 1 + (1/x)}$$

to lowest terms.

Solution

$$\frac{x^2 + (1/x)}{x - 1 + (1/x)} = \frac{(x^3 + 1)/x}{(x^2 - x + 1)/x} = \frac{x^3 + 1}{x} \cdot \frac{x}{x^2 - x + 1}$$
$$= \frac{(x + 1)(x^2 - x + 1)}{x} \cdot \frac{x}{x^2 - x + 1} = \frac{(x + 1)(x^2 - x + 1)x}{x(x^2 - x + 1)} = x + 1. \ \blacksquare$$

EXAMPLE 9

Reduce

$$\frac{1}{1 - \dfrac{1}{1 - (1/x)}}$$

to lowest terms.

Solution

$$\frac{1}{1 - \dfrac{1}{1 - (1/x)}} = \frac{1}{1 - \dfrac{1}{(x - 1)/x}} = \frac{1}{1 - \dfrac{x}{x - 1}}$$
$$= \frac{1}{\dfrac{(x - 1) - x}{x - 1}} = \frac{1}{\dfrac{-1}{x - 1}} = \frac{x - 1}{-1} = 1 - x. \qquad \blacksquare$$

EXERCISE 4

Express

$$\frac{1 - (1/x)}{1 - (1/x^2)}$$

in lowest terms.

Answer $\dfrac{x}{x + 1}$

Problems 2.4

In problems 1–12, reduce the given rational expression to lowest terms.

1. $\dfrac{x^3yz^2}{xy^2z^3}$

2. $\dfrac{x+3(x-1)}{x+3}$

3. $\dfrac{(x-1)^2+4x-4}{x-1}$

4. $\dfrac{x^2+2xy-3y^2}{y^2-x^2}$

5. $\dfrac{8+2y-y^2}{y^2-5y+4}$

6. $\dfrac{x^2-16}{x^2-3x-4}$

7. $\dfrac{x^2-4}{x^2+2x-8}$

8. $\dfrac{x-x^2}{x^2+4x-5}$

9. $\dfrac{x^3+8}{x^2-2x+4}$

10. $\dfrac{x^3-y^3}{x-y}$

11. $\dfrac{x^2-2xy+y^2-1}{x-y-1}$

12. $\dfrac{xy-2y+3x-6}{xy+2y+3x+6}$

In problems 13–18, express the given rational expression as an equivalent rational expression with the given denominator. Specify those values of the variables for which the fractions are equivalent.

13. $\dfrac{xy}{2}=\dfrac{?}{8x^2y}$

14. $\dfrac{y}{x}=\dfrac{?}{3x^3y}$

15. $\dfrac{5}{x-y}=\dfrac{?}{x^2+2xy-3y^2}$

16. $\dfrac{b}{x+y}=\dfrac{?}{x^2-y^2}$

17. $\dfrac{x-2}{x+1}=\dfrac{?}{x^2-3x-4}$

18. $\dfrac{a}{x+y}=\dfrac{?}{x^3+y^3}$

In problems 19–54, perform the indicated operations and simplify.

19. $\dfrac{3x-1}{x}-\dfrac{x+1}{x}+\dfrac{1}{x}$

20. $\dfrac{x-y}{xy}+\dfrac{1}{xy}-\dfrac{x+y}{xy}$

21. $\dfrac{x}{b}-\dfrac{x-1}{b}+\dfrac{2x-3}{b}$

22. $x+\dfrac{1}{x}$

23. $x+1-\dfrac{1}{x-3}$

24. $2+\dfrac{x-1}{x+3}$

25. $\dfrac{x}{x+1}+\dfrac{x-3}{x-2}$

26. $\dfrac{y-5}{y}-\dfrac{y-2}{y+3}$

27. $\dfrac{y}{y-1}-\dfrac{y}{y+1}$

28. $\dfrac{1}{x^2y}-\dfrac{x+1}{x^2}+\dfrac{y+1}{xy}$

29. $1-\dfrac{1}{x}+\dfrac{2}{x^2-2x}$

30. $1-\dfrac{y}{x}+\dfrac{1}{x^2y}$

31. $\dfrac{1}{x^2}-\dfrac{2x+1}{x^2-x}+\dfrac{2}{x-1}$

32. $\dfrac{1}{x^2-4}-\dfrac{1}{x^2+2x}$

33. $\dfrac{2x-4}{x^3+8}+\dfrac{1}{x+2}$

34. $\dfrac{x^2-25}{x^2-x-2}\cdot\dfrac{x^2-1}{x^2-6x+5}$

35. $\dfrac{x^3-8}{x^2-4}\cdot\dfrac{x^2+2x}{x^2+2x+4}$

36. $\dfrac{x^2-4x+4}{x^2-2x+1}\cdot\dfrac{x^2-1}{x^2-4}$

37. $\left(\dfrac{1}{x}-\dfrac{1}{x^2}\right)\cdot\dfrac{x^2+x}{x^2-1}$

38. $\left(\dfrac{x}{x+3}+\dfrac{2x^2}{x^2-9}\right)\cdot\dfrac{x-3}{x^2-x}$

39. $\left(\dfrac{x}{x-1}-\dfrac{x^2}{x^2-1}\right)\cdot\dfrac{x^3+1}{x^2-x+1}$

40. $(1-x)\div\dfrac{x^3-1}{x^2+x+1}$

41. $\dfrac{x-1}{x+1} \div \dfrac{x^3-1}{x^3+1}$

42. $(x^2+3x-10) \div \dfrac{x^2+2x-15}{6-2x}$

43. $\dfrac{x^3+1}{x^2+3x+2} \div \dfrac{x^2-x+1}{x^2-4}$

44. $\dfrac{x^2+x-12}{x^2-x-12} \div \dfrac{x^2+2x-15}{x-4}$

45. $\dfrac{xy+2x-y-2}{x^2-6x+5} \div \dfrac{y^2-y-6}{x^2-3x-10}$

46. $\dfrac{1}{(1/x)-(1/y)}$

47. $\dfrac{(x/y)-(y/x)}{x-y}$

48. $1-\dfrac{1}{1-(1/x)}$

49. $\dfrac{x-(1/x)}{x^2+(1/x)}$

50. $\dfrac{(1/y)-(2/x)}{(1/y^2)-(4/x^2)}$

51. $x-\dfrac{x-1}{1-(1/x^2)}$

52. $1-\dfrac{x-(1/x)}{x+(1/x)}$

53. $\dfrac{x}{1-\dfrac{1}{1-[x/(x-1)]}}$

54. $1-\dfrac{1}{1+\dfrac{x}{1+(1/x)}}$

Answers 2.4

1. $\dfrac{x^2}{yz}$

2. $\dfrac{4x-3}{x+3}$

4. $-\dfrac{x+3y}{x+y}$

5. $\dfrac{2+y}{1-y}$

7. $\dfrac{x+2}{x+4}$

8. $\dfrac{-x}{x+5}$

10. x^2+xy+y^2

11. $x-y+1$

13. $4x^3y^2$

14. $3x^2y^2$

16. $bx-by$

17. x^2-6x+8

19. $\dfrac{2x-1}{x}$

20. $\dfrac{1-2y}{xy}$

22. $\dfrac{x^2+1}{x}$

23. $\dfrac{x^2-2x-4}{x-3}$

25. $\dfrac{2x^2-4x-3}{x^2-x-2}$

26. $\dfrac{-15}{y^2+3y}$

28. $\dfrac{1-y+x}{x^2y}$

29. $\dfrac{x^2-3x+4}{x^2-2x}$

31. $\dfrac{-1}{x^3-x^2}$

32. $\dfrac{2}{x^3-4x}$

34. $\dfrac{x+5}{x-2}$

35. x

37. $\dfrac{1}{x}$

38. $\dfrac{3}{x+3}$

40. -1

41. $\dfrac{x^2-x+1}{x^2+x+1}$

43. $x-2$

44. $\dfrac{x+4}{(x+3)(x+5)}$

46. $\dfrac{xy}{y-x}$

47. $\dfrac{x+y}{xy}$

49. $\dfrac{x-1}{x^2-x+1}$

50. $\dfrac{xy}{x+2y}$

52. $\dfrac{2}{x^2+1}$

53. 1

2.5 Integers As Exponents

In Section 2.1, we defined the meaning of the symbol a^n for positive integer exponents. In this section we shall extend the definition of a^n to include all integers as exponents. Thus we must define a^0 and a^{-n}, where $n \in N$. In so doing, it would seem desirable to define these symbols in such a way that the laws of exponents will hold for all integers.

If Theorem 2.1(a) is to hold for $n = 0$, we must have

$$a^m a^0 = a^{m+0} = a^m,$$

and hence

$$a^0 = \frac{a^m}{a^m} = 1 \qquad \text{when } a \neq 0.$$

Thus we are led to the following definition of a^0.

Definition 2.2   If $a \in R$ with $a \neq 0$, then

$$a^0 = 1.$$

EXAMPLE 1

(a) $4x^0 = 4(1) = 4$.

(b) $(4x)^0 = 1$.

Similarly, if Theorem 2.1(a) is to hold when $n = -m$, we must have

$$a^m a^{-m} = a^{m-m} = a^0 = 1$$

and hence

$$a^{-m} = \frac{1}{a^m} \qquad \text{when } a \neq 0.$$

Thus we arrive at the following definition of a^{-n} when $n \in N$.

Definition 2.3   If $a \in R$ with $a \neq 0$ and if $n \in N$, then

$$a^{-n} = \frac{1}{a^n} = \left(\frac{1}{a}\right)^n.$$

EXAMPLE 2

(a) $x^{-5} = 1/x^5$.

(b) $1/x^{-2} = 1/(1/x^2) = x^2$.

(c) $y^2 x^{-3} = y^2(1/x^3) = y^2/x^3$.

EXERCISE 1

Remove all negative and zero exponents and simplify.

(a) $x^{-2} y^0$ (b) a/x^{-4} (c) $(x^2)^0$

Answer (a) $1/x^2$ (b) ax^4 (c) 1

Using the previous definitions and Theorems 2.1 and 2.2, it can be shown that the laws of exponents are valid for all integers. These laws are restated as Theorem 2.6. Note that the first three parts of Theorem 2.2 have been combined into a single law, namely part (d) of Theorem 2.6. This was possible since zero and negative exponents have been defined in this section.

Theorem 2.6   If $a,b \in R$ with $a,b \neq 0$, and if $m,n \in I$, then
(a) $a^m a^n = a^{m+n}$.
(b) $(a^m)^n = a^{mn}$.
(c) $(ab)^m = a^m b^m$.
(d) $a^m / a^n = a^{m-n}$.
(e) $(a/b)^m = a^m / b^m$.

EXAMPLE 3

Remove all negative and zero exponents and simplify.
(a) $x^2 x^{-5} = x^{2+(-5)} = x^{-3} = 1/x^3$.
(b) $(x^2 y^{-3})^{-2} = (x^2)^{-2}(y^{-3})^{-2} = x^{-4} y^6 = (1/x^4) y^6 = y^6 / x^4$.
(c) $(x^{-2}/x^3)^{-2} = (x^{-2})^{-2}/(x^3)^{-2} = x^4 / x^{-6} = x^{4-(-6)} = x^{10}$.
(d) $(x^3 y^{-9})(2x^{-1}y^2)^3 = (x^3 y^{-9})[2^3(x^{-1})^3(y^2)^3] = (x^3 y^{-9})(8x^{-3}y^6) = 8(x^3 x^{-3})$
$(y^{-9} y^6) = 8x^{3+(-3)} y^{(-9)+6} = 8x^0 y^{-3} = 8(1)(1/y^3) = 8/y^3$.
(e) $(1+x^{-1})^{-1} = \left(1+\dfrac{1}{x}\right)^{-1} = \left(\dfrac{x+1}{x}\right)^{-1} = \dfrac{1}{(x+1)/x} = \dfrac{x}{x+1}$.

EXERCISE 2

Remove all negative and zero exponents and simplify.

(a) $(x^{-3}y^5)^{-2}$ (b) $\left(\dfrac{2x^2 y^{-1}}{x^{-1}y^3}\right)^3$ (c) $\dfrac{x^{-1}}{x^{-1}+y^{-1}}$

Answer   (a) x^6 / y^{10} (b) $8x^9 / y^{12}$ (c) $y/(y+x)$

Problems 2.5

In problems 1–36, remove all zero and negative exponents and simplify the given expression.

1. $2^0 + 2^{-1}$	2. $2^0 / 3^{-1}$	3. $5^{-2}/3^0$
4. $(\frac{2}{5})^{-2}$	5. $(\frac{3}{2})^{-3}$	6. $(\frac{4}{3})^{-3}$
7. $x^{-7}x^2$	8. $2y^6 y^{-10}$	9. $7^0 / x^5 x^{-7}$
10. $(-2x^3 y^{-2})^4$	11. $(-3x^{-2}y^4)^2$	12. $(-4x^{-3}y^3)^5$
13. $(2^0 x^{-2} y^3)^{-2}$	14. $(3^{-2}x^0 y^3)^{-3}$	15. $(2^{-3}x^4 y^{-2})^{-2}$
16. $(x^{-3}y^7)(2x^3 y^{-9})$	17. $(3xy^7)(2x^{-5}y^{-7})$	18. $(2^0 x^5 y^{-2})(x^{-6}y^{-3})$
19. $\left(\dfrac{2x}{y^{-1}}\right)^{-2}$	20. $\left(\dfrac{3x^{-5}}{y^{-3}}\right)^{-3}$	21. $\left(\dfrac{x^{-3}}{3y^4}\right)^{-2}$
22. $\dfrac{(x^{-1}y^2)^3}{x^{-2}y^{-3}}$	23. $\dfrac{(xy^{-2})^{-3}}{x^2 y^{-3}}$	24. $\dfrac{(xy^{-2})^2}{(x^3 y)^{-3}}$

25. $\left(\dfrac{x^{-1}y^0}{2xy^{-2}}\right)^{-3}$

26. $\left(\dfrac{3x^{-2}y^2}{x^3y^{-2}}\right)^{-2}$

27. $\left(\dfrac{x^3y^{-4}}{2x^0y^{-2}}\right)^{-4}$

28. $x^{-1} - y^{-2}$

29. $xy^{-1} + x^{-1}$

30. $x^{-2} - y^{-2}$

31. $(xy)^{-1} + (x/y)^{-1}$

32. $(y^{-1}/x^{-1}) - (x/y)^{-1}$

33. $(x^{-1} + y^{-1})^{-1}$

34. $\dfrac{y^{-1}}{(x+y)^{-1}}$

35. $\dfrac{x^{-1} + y^{-1}}{(xy)^{-1}}$

36. $\dfrac{x^{-1} + y^{-1}}{x^{-1} - y^{-1}}$

Answers 2.5

1. $\frac{3}{2}$

2. 3

4. $\frac{25}{4}$

5. $\frac{8}{27}$

7. $1/x^5$

8. $2/y^4$

10. $16x^{12}/y^8$

11. $9y^8/x^4$

13. x^4/y^6

14. $729/y^9$

16. $2/y^2$

17. $6/x^4$

19. $1/4x^2y^2$

20. $x^{15}/27y^9$

22. y^9/x

23. y^9/x^5

25. $8x^6/y^6$

26. $x^{10}/9y^8$

28. $\dfrac{y^2 - x}{xy^2}$

29. $\dfrac{x^2 + y}{xy}$

31. $\dfrac{y^2 + 1}{xy}$

32. $\dfrac{x^2 - y^2}{xy}$

34. $\dfrac{x + y}{y}$

35. $y + x$

2.6 Roots; Rational Numbers As Exponents

So far we have defined the symbol a^n for integer exponents only. In this section we extend the definition of a^n to include all rational numbers as exponents. As before, it would seem desirable to extend the definition of a^n in such a way that the laws of exponents hold for all rational numbers. However, before we can do this, we must consider two preliminary definitions.

Definition 2.4   If a and b are numbers such that $a^n = b$, where $n \in N$, then a is said to be an ***n*th root** of b. In particular, a is called a **square root** of b when $n = 2$ and a **cube root** when $n = 3$.

If $b > 0$ and n is even, then b has exactly two real nth roots. For example, the square roots of 4 are 2 and -2 since $(2)^2 = 4$ and $(-2)^2 = 4$.

If $b < 0$ and n is even, then b has no real nth roots. For example, there exists no real number a such that $a^2 = -1$.

If n is odd, then b has exactly one real nth root, with the sign of the root being the same as the sign of b. As examples, the real cube root of 27 is 3, since $(3)^3 = 27$, and the real fifth root of -32 is -2, since $(-2)^5 = -32$.

If $b = 0$, then b has exactly one real nth root, namely 0.

As mentioned above, b has two real nth roots when $b > 0$ and n is even. We will find it convenient to choose one of these two roots as the *principal* nth root.

Definition 2.5 The **principal nth root** of a positive number b is defined as the *positive* nth root of b. The **principal nth root** of a negative number b is defined as the nth root of b if n is odd.

Note that we cannot define a principal nth root of a negative number b when n is even, since b has no nth root in this case. It is also important to note that the principal nth root of a number, when it exists, is a *unique* number.

EXAMPLE 1

(a) The principal square root of 4 is 2.
(b) The principal cube root of 27 is 3.
(c) The principal fifth root of -32 is -2.
(d) There is no principal square root of -1.

EXERCISE 1

(a) What are the square roots of 25?
(b) What is the *principal* square root of 25?
(c) Which, if any, of the numbers 0, 9, 10, and -4 fails to have a real square root?
(d) What is the real cube root of 125? of -125?

Answer (a) 5 and -5　(b) 5　(c) -4　(d) $5, -5$

Now we are ready to define a^n for arbitrary rational exponents. We do this in two steps. First we define a^n when n is a rational number of the form $1/n$, where $n \in N$. If Theorem 2.6(b) is to hold when $m = 1/n$, we must have

$$(a^{1/n})^n = a^{(1/n)n} = a^1 = a.$$

Since this means that $a^{1/n}$ is an nth root of a, we are led to the following definition of $a^{1/n}$.

Definition 2.6 If $a \in R$ and $n \in N$, $a^{1/n}$ is defined as the principal nth root of a.

EXAMPLE 2

(a) $4^{1/2} = 2$.
(b) $27^{1/3} = 3$.
(c) $(-32)^{1/5} = -2$.
(d) $(-1)^{1/2}$ is undefined, since there is no principal square root of -1.

Using Definition 2.6, we can finally define a^n when n is any rational number.

Definition 2.7   If $a \in R$, $m \in I$, and $n \in N$,

$$a^{m/n} = (a^{1/n})^m.$$

EXAMPLE 3
(a) $8^{2/3} = (8^{1/3})^2 = (2)^2 = 4$.
(b) $(-32)^{2/5} = [(-32)^{1/5}]^2 = (-2)^2 = 4$.
(c) $9^{-3/2} = (9^{1/2})^{-3} = (3)^{-3} = 1/3^3 = \frac{1}{27}$.
(d) $(-4)^{5/2}$ is undefined, since $(-4)^{1/2}$ is undefined.

EXERCISE 2
Evaluate the following.
(a) $64^{1/2}$ (b) $(-125)^{1/3}$ (c) $81^{3/4}$ (d) $(-16)^{3/2}$

Answer   (a) 8   (b) -5 (c) 27   (d) undefined

Using the definitions of this section we can show that the laws of exponents are valid when m and n are arbitrary rational numbers rather than integers. It is also interesting to note that the laws of exponents are also valid for irrational exponents. We shall not prove the last two statements but will assume them to be true in the remainder of the book.

EXAMPLE 4
Remove all negative and zero exponents and simplify.
(a) $x^2 x^{2/3} = x^{2+(2/3)} = x^{8/3}$.
(b) $(x^{-1/2})^{-1/3} = x^{(-1/2)(-1/3)} = x^{1/6}$.
(c) $x^{2/3}/x^{3/4} = x^{2/3-3/4} = x^{-1/12} = 1/x^{1/12}$.
(d) $\left(\dfrac{x^2 y^{1/2}}{8z}\right)^{2/3} = \dfrac{(x^2)^{2/3}(y^{1/2})^{2/3}}{(8)^{2/3}(z)^{2/3}} = \dfrac{x^{4/3}y^{1/3}}{4z^{2/3}}$.

EXERCISE 3
Remove all negative and zero exponents and simplify.
(a) $(-32x^5)^{1/5}x^{1/2}$ (b) $(x^{10/3}/x^{-2/3})^{-1/2}$ (c) $(27x/y^3)^{1/3}$

Answers   (a) $-2x^{3/2}$ (b) $1/x^2$ (c) $3x^{1/3}/y$

Problems 2.6

In problems 1–12, simplify the given expression.

1. $25^{-1/2}$ 2. $64^{-1/3}$ 3. $32^{-1/5}$
4. $16^{3/4}$ 5. $64^{5/6}$ 6. $(-125)^{2/3}$

7. $(-\frac{27}{8})^{2/3}$ **8.** $(\frac{16}{9})^{3/2}$ **9.** $(\frac{32}{243})^{2/5}$

10. $(\frac{4}{9})^{-3/2}$ **11.** $(-\frac{1}{27})^{-5/3}$ **12.** $(\frac{1}{64})^{-7/6}$

In problems 13–36, remove all zero and negative exponents and simplify the given expression. Assume that all variables represent positive numbers.

13. $x^{1/4}x^{2/3}$ **14.** $x^{1/4}x^{-2/3}$ **15.** $x^{-1/4}x^{2/3}$

16. $x^{4/3}/x^{3/2}$ **17.** $x^{5/4}/x^{5/6}$ **18.** $x^{2/3}/x^{5/2}$

19. $(8x^{-3}y^6)^{2/3}$ **20.** $(9x^6y^{-4})^{3/2}$ **21.** $(16x^{-8}y^{12})^{3/4}$

22. $(x^3y^{-1})^{2/3}(x^{1/2}y^{-2})^{1/2}$ **23.** $(x^2y^{-3})^{4/3}(x^{-1}y^5)^{1/6}$ **24.** $(x^{-3}y^{1/2})^{3/2}(x^3y^{-7})^{1/4}$

25. $\dfrac{(16x^3y^{-2})^{-5/4}}{x^2y^{3/2}}$ **26.** $\dfrac{(8x^{-2}y^3)^{-4/3}}{x^{1/3}y^{2/3}}$ **27.** $\dfrac{(9x^{-2}y^{-5})^{-3/2}}{x^{1/3}y^{-1/2}}$

28. $\left(\dfrac{x^{-3}y^{1/2}}{x^4y^{3/2}}\right)^{-2/3}$ **29.** $\left(\dfrac{x^{2/3}y^{-2}}{x^{-1/3}y^3}\right)^{-1/2}$ **30.** $\left(\dfrac{x^{1/4}y^{-2}}{x^{-5/4}y^{3/2}}\right)^{-3/4}$

31. $(x^{1/2} - y^{1/2})^2$ **32.** $(x^{1/3} + y^{1/3})^2$ **33.** $(x^{1/2} + y^{1/2})(x^{1/2} - y^{1/2})$

34. $(x^{1/4} + 2y^{1/4})(x^{1/4} - 2y^{1/4})$ **35.** $(x^{1/3} + y^{1/3})(x^{2/3} - x^{1/3}y^{1/3} + y^{2/3})$

36. $(x^{2/3} - y^{2/3})(x^{4/3} + x^{2/3}y^{2/3} + y^{4/3})$

37. Explain what, besides the conclusion, is wrong with the following "proof."

$$1 = 1^{1/2} = [(-1)^2]^{1/2} = (-1)^{2/2} = -1.$$

Answers 2.6

1. $\frac{1}{5}$ **2.** $\frac{1}{4}$ **4.** 8 **5.** 32

7. $\frac{9}{4}$ **8.** $\frac{64}{27}$ **10.** $27/8$ **11.** -243

13. $x^{11/12}$ **14.** $1/x^{5/12}$ **16.** $1/x^{1/6}$ **17.** $x^{5/12}$

19. $4y^4/x^2$ **20.** $27x^9/y^6$ **22.** $x^{9/4}/y^{5/3}$ **23.** $x^{5/2}/y^{19/6}$

25. $y/32x^{23/4}$ **26.** $x^{7/3}/16y^{14/3}$ **28.** $x^{14/3}y^{2/3}$ **29.** $y^{5/2}/x^{1/2}$

31. $x - 2x^{1/2}y^{1/2} + y$ **32.** $x^{2/3} - 2x^{1/3}y^{1/3} + y^{2/3}$ **34.** $x^{1/2} - 4y^{1/2}$ **35.** $x + y$

2.7 Radicals

The principal nth root of a real number is often denoted by using a radical instead of a rational exponent.

Definition 2.8   The **radical of order n,** denoted by $\sqrt[n]{a}$, is defined as

$$\sqrt[n]{a} = a^{1/n},$$

where $a \in R$ and $n \in N$. In the radical $\sqrt[n]{a}$, n is called the **index** of the radical, and a is called the **radicand** of the radical. When $n = 2$, we write $\sqrt{a}$ instead of $\sqrt[2]{a}$.

Since $\sqrt[n]{a} = a^{1/n}$, it follows that $\sqrt[n]{a}$ is undefined when $a^{1/n}$ is undefined, and that $\sqrt[n]{a}$, when it exists, is a *unique* real number, since $a^{1/n}$ is a unique real number when it exists.

EXAMPLE 1

Change from radical form to exponent form.
(a) $\sqrt{4} = 4^{1/2} = 2$.
(b) $\sqrt[3]{-27} = (-27)^{1/3} = -3$.
(c) $-\sqrt[5]{x^2} = -(x^2)^{1/5} = -x^{2/5}$.
(d) $\sqrt{x^2 + y^2} = (x^2 + y^2)^{1/2}$.

EXERCISE 1

Change from radical form to exponent form.
(a) $\sqrt[7]{x^5}$ (b) $\sqrt{2x}$ (c) $\sqrt[3]{x^3 + y^3}$

Answer   (a) $x^{5/7}$ (b) $2^{1/2}x^{1/2}$ (c) $(x^3 + y^3)^{1/3}$

EXAMPLE 2

Change from exponent form to radical form.
(a) $9^{1/2} = \sqrt{9} = 3$.
(b) $(x/y^2)^{1/3} = \sqrt[3]{x/y^2}$.
(c) $x^{3/4} = (x^3)^{1/4} = \sqrt[4]{x^3}$.

EXERCISE 2

Change from exponent form to radical form.
(a) $x^{4/5}$ (b) $(x^2/y)^{1/4}$ (c) $3^{1/3}x^{2/3}$

Answer   (a) $\sqrt[5]{x^4}$ (b) $\sqrt[4]{x^2/y}$ (c) $\sqrt[3]{3x^2}$

Using Definition 2.8 and the laws of exponents, we obtain the following laws of radicals.

Theorem 2.7   If $n \in N$ and a is positive, then
(a) $\sqrt[n]{a^m} = (\sqrt[n]{a})^m$ if $m \in I$.
(b) $\sqrt[n]{a^n} = a$.
(c) $\sqrt[n]{\sqrt[m]{a}} = \sqrt[mn]{a}$ if $m \in I$.
(d) $\sqrt[pn]{a^{pm}} = \sqrt[n]{a^m}$ if $p \in N$ and $m \in I$.

Proof of (a)   Using Definition 2.8 and Theorem 2.6(b), we get

$$\sqrt[n]{a^m} = (a^m)^{1/n} = a^{m/n} = (a^{1/n})^m = (\sqrt[n]{a})^m.$$

The proofs of the other parts of the theorem are similar.   ∎

EXAMPLE 3

(a) $\sqrt[5]{x^2}=(\sqrt[5]{x})^2$.

(b) $\sqrt[3]{(2x^2)^3}=2x^2$.

(c) $\sqrt[3]{\sqrt{xy}}=\sqrt[6]{xy}$.

(d) $\sqrt[6]{x^4}=\sqrt[2\cdot3]{x^{2\cdot2}}=\sqrt[3]{x^2}$.

Two other important laws of radicals are given in the following theorem.

Theorem 2.8   If $n \in N$ and $a,b \in R$ such that $\sqrt[n]{a}$ and $\sqrt[n]{b}$ are defined, then

(a) $\sqrt[n]{a}\,\sqrt[n]{b}=\sqrt[n]{ab}$.

(b) $\sqrt[n]{a}/\sqrt[n]{b}=\sqrt[n]{a/b}$ if $b \neq 0$.

Proof of (a)   Using Definition 2.8 and Theorem 2.6(c), we get

$$\sqrt[n]{a}\sqrt[n]{b}=(a^{1/n})(b^{1/n})=(ab)^{1/n}=\sqrt[n]{ab}.$$

The proof of (b) is similar.   ∎

EXAMPLE 4

(a) $\sqrt[3]{x}\,\sqrt[3]{2z}=\sqrt[3]{2xz}$.

(b) $\sqrt{yz}/\sqrt{x}=\sqrt{yz/x}$.

The laws of radicals can be used to simplify radicals. We say that a radical is *simplified* when:

1. The radical has no factor raised to a power that is equal to or greater than the index of the radical.
2. No fractions occur under the radical sign.
3. The index of the radical is as small as possible.

EXAMPLE 5

Use the laws of radicals to simplify the following radicals.

(a) $\sqrt[5]{192}=\sqrt[5]{2^6\cdot3}=\sqrt[5]{2^5\cdot6}=\sqrt[5]{2^5}\sqrt[5]{6}=2\sqrt[5]{6}$.

(b) $\sqrt[3]{x^4y^5}=\sqrt[3]{x^3y^3\cdot xy^2}=\sqrt[3]{(xy)^3(xy^2)}=\sqrt[3]{(xy)^3}\,\sqrt[3]{xy^2}=xy\,\sqrt[3]{xy^2}$.

(c) $\sqrt{\dfrac{x}{y}}=\sqrt{\dfrac{x}{y}\cdot\dfrac{y}{y}}=\sqrt{\left(\dfrac{1}{y}\right)^2(xy)}=\sqrt{\left(\dfrac{1}{y}\right)^2}\,\sqrt{xy}=\dfrac{1}{y}\,\sqrt{xy}$.

(d) $\sqrt{\dfrac{x^4y}{2z}}=\sqrt{\dfrac{x^4y}{2z}\cdot\dfrac{2z}{2z}}=\sqrt{\left(\dfrac{x^4}{2^2z^2}\right)(2yz)}=\sqrt{\left(\dfrac{x^2}{2z}\right)^2(2yz)}=\sqrt{\left(\dfrac{x^2}{2z}\right)^2}\,\sqrt{2yz}=$
$\left(\dfrac{x^2}{2z}\right)\sqrt{2yz}$.

(e) $\sqrt[6]{x^4y^2}=\sqrt[2\cdot3]{(x^2y)^{2\cdot1}}=\sqrt[3]{x^2y}$.

EXERCISE 3

Simplify the following radicals.

(a) $\sqrt[3]{81x^5y^9}$ (b) $\sqrt[4]{y^7/2x^2}$ (c) $\sqrt[4]{x^{10}y^2}$

Answer (a) $3xy^3\sqrt[3]{3x^2}$ (b) $(y/2x)\sqrt[4]{8x^2y^3}$ (c) $x^2\sqrt{xy}$

Problems 2.7

In problems 1–12, change the given radical form to exponent form, but do not simplify.

1. $\sqrt[3]{x^2}$ 2. $\sqrt[5]{y^3}$ 3. $\sqrt[7]{z^4}$

4. $\sqrt[4]{2xy}$ 5. $\sqrt{xy^2}$ 6. $\sqrt[3]{(xy)^2}$

7. $-y/\sqrt{x}$ 8. $-3\sqrt[3]{x/y}$ 9. $2x\sqrt{2y}$

10. $\sqrt[3]{(x+y)^2}$ 11. $\sqrt[3]{x^2}+\sqrt[3]{y^2}$ 12. $\sqrt{x^2+y^2}$

In problems 13–24, change the given exponent form to radical form, but do not simplify.

13. $3^{4/5}$ 14. $x^{3/7}$ 15. $2x^{2/3}$

16. $(2x)^{2/3}$ 17. $(xy^2)^{3/4}$ 18. $(2x^2)^{1/5}$

19. $5(x^2/y)^{1/2}$ 20. $3(1/x^3)^{1/3}$ 21. $-2x^{-1/3}$

22. $(x^2y)^{-1/2}$ 23. $(x^2y)^{-3/5}$ 24. $x^{-1/2}+y^{-1/2}$

In problems 25–60, simplify the given radical. Assume that all variables represent positive numbers.

25. $\sqrt{36}$ 26. $\sqrt[3]{-27}$ 27. $\sqrt[4]{625}$

28. $\sqrt[3]{-64}$ 29. $\sqrt[5]{243}$ 30. $\sqrt[3]{48}$

31. $\sqrt[3]{x^6y^7z^8}$ 32. $\sqrt[4]{x^5y^{11}z^{12}}$ 33. $\sqrt[5]{x^7y^{10}z^{13}}$

34. $\sqrt[3]{32x^7y^9}$ 35. $\sqrt[3]{81x^5y^7}$ 36. $\sqrt{81x^5y^3}$

37. $\sqrt[4]{x^2}$ 38. $\sqrt[9]{y^{12}}$ 39. $\sqrt[8]{x^{10}}$

40. $\sqrt[6]{8x^9y^6}$ 41. $\sqrt[4]{64x^{10}y^8}$ 42. $\sqrt[6]{25x^6y^8}$

43. $\sqrt[3]{\frac{1}{2}}$ 44. $\sqrt[3]{\frac{1}{9}}$ 45. $\sqrt[5]{\frac{1}{8}}$

46. $\sqrt[5]{x^3y^7/z^2}$ 47. $\sqrt{x^3y^5/z^3}$ 48. $\sqrt[4]{x^2y^7/z^5}$

49. $\sqrt{125x^5/y^3z}$ 50. $\sqrt[5]{64x^8/y^3z^4}$ 51. $\sqrt[3]{81x^4/y^4z}$

52. $\sqrt[3]{\sqrt[4]{x}}$ 53. $\sqrt[4]{\sqrt{xy}}$ 54. $\sqrt[3]{\sqrt[3]{xy^4}}$

55. $\sqrt{2\sqrt{2}}$ 56. $\sqrt[3]{3\sqrt{2}}$ 57. $\sqrt[3]{2\sqrt[3]{3}}$

58. $\sqrt[5]{x^2\sqrt{x}}$ 59. $\sqrt{x\sqrt{x}}$ 60. $\sqrt[4]{x^3\sqrt[3]{x^2}}$

61. Prove Theorem 2.7(b). 62. Prove Theorem 2.7(c).

63. Prove Theorem 2.7(d). 64. Prove Theorem 2.8(b).

Answers 2.7

1. $x^{2/3}$ 2. $y^{3/5}$ 4. $(2xy)^{1/4}$ 5. $(xy^2)^{1/2}$

7. $-y/x^{1/2}$ 8. $-3(x/y)^{1/3}$ 10. $(x+y)^{2/3}$ 11. $x^{2/3}+y^{2/3}$

13. $\sqrt[5]{3^4}$ 14. $\sqrt[7]{x^3}$ 16. $\sqrt[3]{(2x)^2}$ 17. $\sqrt[4]{(xy^2)^3}$

19. $5\sqrt{x^2/y}$ 20. $3\sqrt[3]{1/x^3}$ 22. $1/\sqrt{x^2y}$ 23. $1/\sqrt[5]{(x^2y)^3}$

25. 6   **26.** -3 **28.** $-2\sqrt[5]{2}$ **29.** $3\sqrt[4]{3}$

31. $x^2y^2z^2\sqrt[3]{yz^2}$ **32.** $xy^2z^3\sqrt[4]{xy^3}$ **34.** $2xy^2\sqrt[4]{2x^3y}$ **35.** $3xy^2\sqrt[3]{3x^2y}$

37. $\sqrt{x}$ **38.** $y\sqrt[3]{y}$ **40.** $xy\sqrt{2x}$ **41.** $2x^2y^2\sqrt{2x}$

43. $\frac{1}{2}\sqrt[4]{8}$ **44.** $\frac{1}{3}\sqrt[3]{3}$ **46.** $\left(\frac{y}{z}\right)\sqrt[5]{x^3y^2z^3}$ **47.** $(xy^2/z^2)\sqrt{xyz}$

49. $(5x^2/y^2z)\sqrt{5xyz}$ **50.** $(2x/yz)\sqrt[5]{2x^3y^2z}$ **52.** $\sqrt[12]{x}$ **53.** $\sqrt[8]{xy}$

55. $\sqrt[9]{8}$ **56.** $\sqrt[9]{18}$ **58.** $\sqrt{x}$ **59.** $\sqrt[4]{x^3}$

2.8 Basic Operations on Radicals

Addition and Subtraction of Radicals

Radicals having the same order and the same radicand can be combined into a single radical by using the distributive axiom.

EXAMPLE 1

Combine when possible.
(a) $5\sqrt{2}-3\sqrt{2}=(5-3)\sqrt{2}=2\sqrt{2}.$
(b) $x\sqrt[3]{xy}-y\sqrt[3]{xy}+\sqrt[3]{xy}=(x-y+1)\sqrt[3]{xy}.$
(c) $x\sqrt{xy}+\sqrt[3]{xy}$ cannot be combined, since the orders of the radicals are different.
(d) $x\sqrt{xy}+\sqrt{xy^2}$ cannot be combined, since the radicands are different.
Even though radicals having different orders or different radicands cannot, in general, be combined, it is sometimes possible to combine such radicals after they have been simplified.

EXAMPLE 2

Combine when possible.
(a) $\sqrt{x^3y}-3\sqrt{xy^3}=x\sqrt{xy}-3y\sqrt{xy}=(x-3y)\sqrt{xy}.$
(b) $\sqrt{4x^3}-\sqrt[3]{x^4}+\sqrt{x^5}=2x\sqrt{x}-x\sqrt[3]{x}+x^2\sqrt{x}=(x^2+2x)\sqrt{x}-x\sqrt[3]{x}.$
(Since the radicals $\sqrt{x}$ and $\sqrt[3]{x}$ are both simplified, this answer cannot be combined further.)
(c) $3\sqrt{x}+\sqrt[4]{x^2}=3\sqrt{x}+\sqrt{x}=4\sqrt{x}.$

EXERCISE 1

Combine when possible.
(a) $\sqrt{8}-\sqrt{98}+\sqrt[3]{54}$ (b) $\sqrt{8x^3y}-\sqrt{2xy^5}$ (c) $\sqrt[3]{x^5}+\sqrt[6]{x^4}$

Answer   (a) $3\sqrt[3]{2}-5\sqrt{2}$ (b) $(2x-y^2)\sqrt{2xy}$ (c) $(x+1)\sqrt[3]{x^2}$

Multiplication and Division of Radicals

Radicals of the same order can be multiplied and divided by using the laws of radicals that were given in Theorem 2.8.

EXAMPLE 3

Multiply (or divide) and then simplify the resulting radical.
(a) $\sqrt[5]{xy}\ \sqrt[5]{yz}=\sqrt[5]{(xy)(yz)}=\sqrt[5]{xy^2z}.$
(b) $\sqrt[3]{x^2}\ \sqrt[3]{2x^2}=\sqrt[3]{(x^2)(2x^2)}=\sqrt[3]{(x^3)(2x)}=\sqrt[3]{x^3}\ \sqrt[3]{2x}=x\sqrt[3]{2x}.$
(c) $\dfrac{\sqrt{yz}}{\sqrt{x}}=\sqrt{\dfrac{yz}{x}}=\sqrt{\dfrac{yz}{x}\cdot\dfrac{x}{x}}=\sqrt{\left(\dfrac{1}{x}\right)^2(xyz)}=\dfrac{1}{x}\sqrt{xyz}.$
(d) $\sqrt{3}\ (2-\sqrt{5})=2\sqrt{3}-\sqrt{3}\ \sqrt{5}=2\sqrt{3}-\sqrt{15}.$
(e) $(\sqrt{x}-2)(\sqrt{x}+3)=(\sqrt{x}-2)\sqrt{x}+(\sqrt{x}-2)3=\sqrt{x}\ \sqrt{x}-2\sqrt{x}+3\sqrt{x}-6=x+\sqrt{x}-6.$

EXERCISE 2

Multiply (or divide) and simplify.
(a) $\sqrt[4]{x^3}\ \sqrt[4]{x^7y^3}$ (b) $(2-\sqrt{3})(3+\sqrt{3})$ (c) $\sqrt[3]{3x}/\sqrt[3]{yz^2}$

Answer (a) $x^2\sqrt[4]{x^2y^3}$ (b) $3-\sqrt{3}$ (c) $(1/yz)\sqrt[3]{3xy^2z}$

From time to time it will be necessary to eliminate radicals from the denominator of fractions such as

$$\frac{1}{\sqrt{2}+3},\quad \frac{\sqrt{3}+\sqrt{2}}{\sqrt{3}-\sqrt{2}},\quad \text{and}\quad \frac{\sqrt{x}}{\sqrt{x}-\sqrt{y}}.$$

To do this, we multiply both the numerator and the denominator of the fraction by the denominator with the sign between the terms changed. This process is known as *rationalizing the denominator*. The expression that we use to multiply both the numerator and the denominator is called the *conjugate* of the denominator.

EXAMPLE 4

Rationalize denominators and simplify.
(a) $\dfrac{1}{\sqrt{2}+3}=\dfrac{1(\sqrt{2}-3)}{(\sqrt{2}+3)(\sqrt{2}-3)}=\dfrac{\sqrt{2}-3}{2-9}=\dfrac{3-\sqrt{2}}{7}.$ (Note that the factors in the denominator of the second fraction represent the difference of two squares.)
(b) $\dfrac{\sqrt{x}}{\sqrt{x}-\sqrt{y}}=\dfrac{\sqrt{x}\ (\sqrt{x}+\sqrt{y})}{(\sqrt{x}-\sqrt{y})(\sqrt{x}+\sqrt{y})}=\dfrac{x+\sqrt{xy}}{x-y}.$

EXERCISE 3

Rationalize the denominators and simplify.

(a) $\dfrac{3}{\sqrt{x}-5}$ (b) $\dfrac{\sqrt{20}+\sqrt{2}}{\sqrt{20}-3\sqrt{2}}$

Answer   (a) $\dfrac{3\sqrt{x}+15}{x-25}$ (b) $13+4\sqrt{10}$

To multiply or divide radicals with different orders, we must first use Theorem 2.7(d) to express the given radicals as equivalent radicals with the same orders. Having done this, we can then multiply (or divide) the resulting radicals by using Theorem 2.8.

EXAMPLE 5

(a) $\sqrt[3]{x}\,\sqrt[4]{xy}=\sqrt[12]{x^4}\,\sqrt[12]{x^3y^3}=\sqrt[12]{x^7y^3}.$

(b) $\dfrac{\sqrt{x^3y}}{\sqrt[3]{x^2y^5}}=\dfrac{\sqrt[6]{x^9y^3}}{\sqrt[6]{x^4y^{10}}}=\sqrt[6]{\dfrac{x^9y^3}{x^4y^{10}}}=\sqrt[6]{\dfrac{x^5}{y^7}\cdot\dfrac{y^5}{y^5}}=\left(\dfrac{1}{y^2}\right)\sqrt[6]{x^5y^5}.$

EXERCISE 4

Multiply (or divide) and simplify.
(a) $\sqrt{2x}\,\sqrt[4]{x^3y}$ (b) $\sqrt[3]{2}/\sqrt{x}$

Answer   (a) $x\sqrt[4]{4xy}$ (b) $(1/x)\sqrt[6]{4x^3}$

Problems 2.8

In problems 1–12, simplify by combining as many radicals as possible. Assume that all variables represent positive numbers.

1. $\sqrt{3}+\sqrt{27}-\sqrt[3]{3}$
2. $\sqrt[3]{5}-\sqrt{20}+5\sqrt{5}$
3. $\sqrt{18}+\sqrt{50}-4\sqrt{2}$
4. $\sqrt{72}-\sqrt{50}+\sqrt[4]{144}$
5. $\sqrt{27}-\sqrt{162}-\sqrt[6]{1728}$
6. $\sqrt[3]{54}-\sqrt[3]{\frac{1}{4}}-\sqrt[6]{81}$
7. $\sqrt{xy/2}+\sqrt{8xy}$
8. $\sqrt[3]{x/3}-\sqrt[3]{9x^4}$
9. $\sqrt{x^3y^3}+\sqrt{x/y}-\sqrt[3]{xy}$
10. $\sqrt{x^3y}+\sqrt{4xy^5}-\sqrt[3]{x^4y}$
11. $\sqrt[3]{x^5y^4}-\sqrt[3]{x^2/y^2}+\sqrt[4]{16x^4y^2}$
12. $\sqrt[3]{x^6y^2}-\sqrt{x^5y}-\sqrt[6]{x^9y^3}$

In problems 13–33, perform the indicated operations and simplify the resulting radical. Assume that all variables represent positive numbers.

13. $\sqrt{3x^3y}\,\sqrt{6x^2y^5}$
14. $\sqrt[3]{4x^2y^4}\,\sqrt[3]{4x^5y^4}$
15. $\sqrt[4]{8x^5y^7}\,\sqrt[4]{12xy^5}$
16. $\sqrt[5]{x^4y^7}\,\sqrt[5]{x^6y^4}$
17. $\sqrt{xy}\,\sqrt{2xy^7}$
18. $\sqrt{3x^3y}\,\sqrt{6x^4y^3}$
19. $\sqrt[3]{2x^4y^2}\,\sqrt[3]{x^5y^2}$
20. $\sqrt{3x^3y^5}\,\sqrt[3]{x^3y^5}$
21. $\sqrt{x}\,\sqrt[3]{x}\,\sqrt[4]{x}$
22. $\sqrt{2}(3-\sqrt{3})$
23. $\sqrt{3}(\sqrt{2}-\sqrt{5})$
24. $\sqrt{5}(\sqrt{2}-\sqrt{3})$
25. $(2-\sqrt{2})(3+\sqrt{2})$
26. $(\sqrt{3}-4)(2\sqrt{3}-3)$
27. $(\sqrt{3}+1)(3\sqrt{2}-5)$

28. $\dfrac{\sqrt[3]{x^5 y}}{\sqrt[3]{2xy^2}}$ **29.** $\dfrac{\sqrt[4]{x^3 y^2}}{\sqrt[4]{27x^5 y}}$ **30.** $\dfrac{\sqrt{x^2 y^6}}{\sqrt{5x^5 y^3}}$

31. $\dfrac{\sqrt[3]{8x^3 y^7}}{\sqrt{8xy^2}}$ **32.** $\dfrac{\sqrt{x^5 y}}{\sqrt[3]{2xy^3}}$ **33.** $\dfrac{\sqrt[3]{x^4 y}}{\sqrt[4]{x^2 y^3}}$

In problems 34–42, rationalize the denominator and simplify. Assume that all variables represent positive numbers.

34. $\dfrac{2}{1-\sqrt{3}}$ **35.** $\dfrac{4+\sqrt{2}}{2-\sqrt{2}}$ **36.** $\dfrac{3-\sqrt{2}}{3+\sqrt{2}}$

37. $\dfrac{2\sqrt{2}}{\sqrt{3}-\sqrt{2}}$ **38.** $\dfrac{3-\sqrt{3}}{1+\sqrt{3}}$ **39.** $\dfrac{\sqrt{5}+2}{3\sqrt{5}-3}$

40. $\dfrac{\sqrt{x}+1}{\sqrt{x}-1}$ **41.** $\dfrac{\sqrt{y}}{\sqrt{x}+\sqrt{y}}$ **42.** $\dfrac{\sqrt{x}}{\sqrt{x}+3}$

43. Explain what, besides the conclusion, is wrong with the following "proof."

$$1 = \sqrt{1} = \sqrt{(-1)(-1)} = \sqrt{-1}\,\sqrt{-1} = -1.$$

Answers 2.8

1. $4\sqrt{3}-\sqrt[3]{3}$ **2.** $\sqrt[3]{5}+3\sqrt{5}$ **4.** $\sqrt{2}+2\sqrt{3}$ **5.** $\sqrt{3}-9\sqrt{2}$

7. $\frac{5}{2}\sqrt{2xy}$ **8.** $(\frac{1}{3}-x)\sqrt[3]{9x}$ **10.** $(x+2y^2)\sqrt{xy}-x\sqrt[3]{xy}$

11. $[xy-(1/y)]\sqrt[3]{x^2 y}+2x\sqrt{y}$ **13.** $3x^2 y^3\sqrt[3]{2x}$ **14.** $2x^2 y^2\sqrt[3]{2xy^2}$

16. $x^2 y^2\sqrt[5]{y}$ **17.** $xy^4\sqrt{2}$ **19.** $x^2 y\sqrt[12]{16x^7 y^2}$ **20.** $x^2 y^3\sqrt[9]{9xy^3}$

22. $3\sqrt{2}-\sqrt{6}$ **23.** $\sqrt{6}-\sqrt{15}$ **25.** $4-\sqrt{2}$ **26.** $18-11\sqrt{3}$

28. $(x/2y)\sqrt[3]{4xy^2}$ **29.** $(1/3x)\sqrt[4]{3x^2 y}$ **31.** $\frac{1}{2}\sqrt[4]{2xy^3}$ **32.** $(x^2/2y)\sqrt[6]{16xy^3}$

34. $-1-\sqrt{3}$ **35.** $5+3\sqrt{2}$ **37.** $2\sqrt{6}+4$ **38.** $2\sqrt{3}-3$

40. $\dfrac{x+2\sqrt{x}+1}{x-1}$ **41.** $\dfrac{\sqrt{xy}-y}{x-y}$

chapter 2 review problems

1. Perform the indicated operations.
  (a) $(3x^3-2x^2+3)+(3x^2-x-5)$ (b) $(x^2+x-1)-(2x^2-3x+5)$

  (c) $(x^3-x+1)(2x-1)$ (d) $\dfrac{3x^3-3x-15}{x-2}$

2. Factor the following polynomials completely over I.
  (a) $ax^9-a^9 x$ (b) $xy-xr+py-pr$ (c) $6x^2-13x-5$

  (d) $2x^3-5x^2-6x+15$ (e) x^6-27b^3 (f) $x^2+4xy+4y^2-z^2$

3. Perform the indicated operations and express the result in lowest term.

(a) $\dfrac{x+1}{x^3-x^2}+\dfrac{x+2}{x^3-x}-\dfrac{2}{x^2-x}$ (b) $\left(\dfrac{1}{x}-\dfrac{3}{x^2}\right)\dfrac{x^2+3x}{x^2-9}$

(c) $\dfrac{x^3-b^3}{2x^2-bx-b^2}\div\dfrac{x^2+bx+b^2}{2bx+b^2}$ (d) $x-\dfrac{x+(1/x)}{1-(1/x^4)}$

4. Remove all zero and negative exponents and simplify the given expression. Assume that all variables represent positive numbers.

(a) $(9x^{-3}y^4)^{-3/2}$ (b) $(x^{-2/3}y^{1/2})^6\left(\dfrac{x^4}{25y^6}\right)^{1/2}$ (c) $\left(\dfrac{27x^0y^6}{x^3y^{-3}}\right)^{-4/3}$

(d) $x^2y\left(\dfrac{-8}{y^{12}}\right)^{2/3}$ (e) $(x+y^{-1})^{-1}$ (f) $\dfrac{x^{-1}+y^{-1}}{(x+y)^{-1}}$

5. Simplify the given radical, or perform the indicated operations and then simplify the resulting expression. Assume that all variables represent positive numbers.

(a) $\sqrt[4]{32x^3y^{13}}$ (b) $\sqrt[5]{x^7/8y^9}$ (c) $\sqrt[4]{x\sqrt[3]{x}}$

(d) $\sqrt[3]{4x^3y^7}\,\sqrt[6]{8x^2y^7}$ (e) $\dfrac{\sqrt{x^5y^3}}{\sqrt{2x^3y^5}}$ (f) $\sqrt{\dfrac{x}{2}}-\sqrt{\dfrac{2}{x}}+\dfrac{1}{\sqrt{2x}}$

(g) $(\sqrt{x}-3)(2\sqrt{x}+3)$ (h) $\dfrac{\sqrt{2}}{\sqrt{3}-\sqrt{2}}$

6. Which of the following is (are) false?

(a) There are two square roots of 4.

(b) $\sqrt{4}=\pm2$.   (c) $\sqrt{4}=2$.

answers

1. (a) $3x^3+x^2-x-2$ (b) $-x^2+4x-6$ (c) $2x^4-x^3-2x^2+3x-1$
(d) $3x^2+6x+9+[3/(x-2)]$
2. (a) $ax(x^4+a^4)(x^2+a^2)(x+a)(x-a)$ (b) $(x+p)(y-r)$ (c) $(2x-5)(3x+1)$
(d) $(x^2-3)(2x-5)$ (e) $(x^2-3b)(x^4+3bx^2+9b^2)$
(f) $(x+2y+z)(x+2y-z)$
3. (a) $(2x+1)/(x^4-x^2)$ (b) $1/x$ (c) b (d) $-x/(x^2-1)$
4. (a) $x^{9/2}/27y^6$ (b) $1/5x^2$ (c) $x^4/81y^{12}$ (d) $4x^2/y^7$ (e) $y/(xy+1)$
(f) $(x/y)+2+(y/x)$
5. (a) $2y^3\sqrt[4]{2x^3y}$ (b) $\left(\dfrac{x}{2y^2}\right)\sqrt[5]{4x^2y}$ (c) $\sqrt[3]{x^2}$ (d) $2xy^3\sqrt[6]{2x^2y^3}$
(e) $(x/2y)\sqrt{2}$ (f) $(x-1)\sqrt{2x}/2x$ (g) $2x-3\sqrt{x}-9$ (h) $\sqrt{6}+2$
6. Only (b) is false.

3

equations and inequalities
in one variable

3.1 Linear Equations

If $P(x)$ and $Q(x)$ are expressions in the variable x, a statement of the form

$$P(x) = Q(x)$$

is said to be an **equation in the variable x.**

When a number is substituted for the variable in an equation, a statement is obtained that is either true or false. If the resulting statement is *true*, the number is said to be a **solution** or **root** of the equation. For instance, substituting 2 for x in the equation $x^2 = x + 2$ produces the statement $2^2 = 2 + 2$, which is true. Hence 2 is a solution of the equation. On the other hand, substituting 3 for x in the same equation produces the statement $3^2 = 3 + 2$, which is false. Thus 3 is not a solution of the equation.

A **permissible value** of an equation is a number for which both sides of the equation are defined when that number is substituted for the variable throughout the equation. For instance, since both sides of the equation $x^3 - x = 2x^2 + 5$ are defined when any real number is substituted for x throughout the equation, it follows that all real numbers are permissible values of the given equation. As another example, consider the equation $1/x = \sqrt{x}$. In this equation the right side is undefined when x is negative and the left side is undefined when $x = 0$. Hence the only permissible values of $1/x = \sqrt{x}$ are positive numbers.

An equation that is true *for all* the permissible values of the equation is said to be an **identity**. For example, the equation $x^2 - 4 = (x - 2)(x + 2)$ is an identity, since both sides of the equation have the same value when x is replaced by any real number. Similarly, $x(x - 1) = x^2 - x$ is an identity.

On the other hand, an equation that is true *for some, but not all*, of the permissible values of the equation is said to be a **conditional equation**. For example, the equation $x + 2 = 0$ is a conditional equation, since -2 is the only permissible value for which the equation is true. Similarly, $x^2 = 25$ is a conditional equation, since 5 and -5 are the only permissible values for which the equation is true.

To *solve* an equation means to determine all the solutions of the equation. The set consisting of all the solutions of an equation is called the **solution set** of the equation. As examples, the solution set of $x + 2 = 0$ is $\{-2\}$, the solution set of $x^2 = 25$ is $\{-5, 5\}$, and the solution set of the identity $x^2 - 4 = (x - 2)(x + 2)$ is the set R of real numbers.

Two equations are called **equivalent equations** if they have the same solution set. For example, the equations $x + 2 = 6$ and $2x = 8$ are equivalent equations, since the solution set of each is $\{4\}$. One standard method of solving equations is to replace the given equation with other simpler equivalent equations until we obtain an equation whose solution set is obvious. This can be done by using the following theorem, which follows directly from Theorems 1.1 and 1.2.

Theorem 3.1   If $P(x)$, $Q(x)$, and $R(x)$ are expressions in the variable x, then the equation

$$P(x) = Q(x)$$

is equivalent to each of the equations

$$P(x) + R(x) = Q(x) + R(x)$$

and

$$P(x) \cdot R(x) = Q(x) \cdot R(x) \qquad [\text{when } R(x) \neq 0],$$

for all values of x for which $P(x)$, $Q(x)$, and $R(x)$ have real values.

Theorem 3.1 is also valid when P, Q, and R are expressions in two or more variables. We shall use this fact frequently in our work in future chapters.

Linear Equations

An equation that can be expressed in the form

$$ax + b = 0, \qquad\qquad (3-1)$$

with $a \neq 0$ and $a,b \in R$, is called a **linear equation** in the variable x. Equation $(3-1)$ is called the *standard form* for a linear equation.

Theorem 3.2   The linear equation $ax + b = 0$, with $a \neq 0$ and $a,b \in R$, has the unique solution $-b/a$.

Proof   Using Theorem 3.1 to add $-b$ to both sides of the equation

$$ax + b = 0,$$

we obtain the equivalent equations

$$(ax + b) + (-b) = 0 + (-b)$$

and

$$ax = -b.$$

Then using Theorem 3.1 to multiply both sides of the last equation by $1/a$ $(a \neq 0)$, we obtain the equivalent equations

$$\left(\frac{1}{a}\right)(ax) = \left(\frac{1}{a}\right)(-b)$$

and

$$x = \frac{-b}{a}.$$

The last equation obviously has a unique solution, namely $-b/a$. Consequently, it follows from Theorem 3.1 that the linear equation $ax + b = 0$ has the unique solution $-b/a$.   ∎

EXAMPLE 1

Solve $2x - 3 = 0$ for x.

Solution   The given equation is equivalent in turn to each of the following equations:

$$2x - 3 = 0,$$
$$2x = 3,$$
$$x = \tfrac{3}{2}.$$
∎

EXAMPLE 2

Solve $3(x - 1) + 5 = 2(3 - 2x)$ for x.

Solution   The given equation is equivalent in turn to each of the following equations:

$$3(x - 1) + 5 = 2(3 - 2x)$$
$$3x - 3 + 5 = 6 - 4x$$
$$3x + 2 = 6 - 4x$$
$$3x = 4 - 4x$$
$$7x = 4$$
$$x = \tfrac{4}{7}.$$
∎

EXERCISE 1

Solve for x.
(a) $3x + 5 = 0$ (b) $7(1 - 2x) = 1 - 4(4x - 3)$

Answer   (a) $x = -\tfrac{5}{3}$ (b) $x = 3$

Equations Reducible to Linear Equations

According to Theorem 3.1(b), multiplication of both sides of an equation $P(x) = Q(x)$ by an expression $R(x)$ produces an equivalent equation $P(x) \cdot R(x) = Q(x) \cdot R(x)$ when $R(x) \neq 0$. Since the possibility exists that $R(x) = 0$ for the solutions of the given equation, we must check our solutions in the original equation. Stated simply, *when we multiply both sides of an equation by an expression containing the variable, we should check the solutions of the resulting equation in the original equation* to be sure they are actually solutions of the original equation. Keeping this in mind, certain equations that are not linear in form can be solved in a manner similar to that demonstrated in Examples 1 and 2.

EXAMPLE 3

Solve

$$\frac{3x}{x+1} = 2 - \frac{3}{x+1}$$

for x.

Solution   In this problem we multiply through the equation by $(x+1)$. Thus the following are equivalent equations when $x + 1 \neq 0$ (i.e., when $x \neq -1$):

$$\frac{3x}{x+1} = 2 - \frac{3}{x+1}$$
$$\frac{3x}{x+1}(x+1) = 2(x+1) - \frac{3}{x+1}(x+1)$$
$$3x = 2(x+1) - 3$$
$$3x = 2x + 2 - 3$$
$$3x = 2x - 1$$
$$x = -1.$$

Since we multiplied both sides of the original equation by an expression containing the variable, we must check our solution in the original equation. Doing this, we find that $x = -1$ fails to satisfy the original equation. Thus we conclude that the original equation has no solution.   ∎

EXERCISE 2

Solve for x.

(a) $\dfrac{2}{x-1} = \dfrac{3}{x+2}$ (b) $\dfrac{3x}{x-1} = 2 + \dfrac{3}{x-1}$

Answer   (a) 7   (b) no solution

Problems 3.1

In problems 1–6, determine the permissible values for x in the given equation.

1. $3x^2 - x = \sqrt{x}$ 2. $3x^2 + x = 7$ 3. $x^2 + \sqrt{x} = 1$

4. $\dfrac{1}{x} = \sqrt{x+2}$ 5. $\dfrac{1}{2x-2} = \dfrac{1}{x+3}$ 6. $\dfrac{1}{\sqrt{x}} = x + \dfrac{1}{x}$

In problems 7–12, determine if the given equation is an identity or a conditional equation.

7. $x^2 - 3x - 4 = (x-4)(x+1)$ 8. $x^2 - 9 = (x-3)(x+3)$

9. $(2-x)^2 = 4 - x^2$ 10. $2x - 5 = 0$

11. $(x-2)(x+3)=0$ **12.** $x/x=1.$

13. For what values of x is $3x = 2x + 7$ equivalent to $9x = 3(2x + 7)$?

14. For what values of x is $x = 1$ equivalent to $x^2 = x$?

15. For what values of x is $(x - 1)/(x + 3) = \frac{2}{3}$ equivalent to $3(x - 1) = 2(x + 3)$?

In problems $16-36$, determine the solution set of the given equation.

16. $3x + 7 = 0$ **17.** $4x - 5 = 0$ **18.** $5x - 9 = 0$

19. $4x - 5 = 2x + 3$ **20.** $6x + 7 = 3x - 2$ **21.** $3(2 - x) = 2(x - 7)$

22. $ax = a - x$ **23.** $\dfrac{x}{a} = \dfrac{x+b}{c}$ **24.** $(x - 2)(a + 1) = 2a$

25. $\dfrac{1}{x} - \dfrac{1}{a} = b$ **26.** $\dfrac{1}{a} + \dfrac{1}{b} = \dfrac{1}{x}$ **27.** $\dfrac{a}{b} - \dfrac{1}{bx} = a$

28. $\dfrac{3x+1}{2x-3} = \dfrac{1}{8}$ **29.** $\dfrac{2x-1}{x+1} = \dfrac{3}{2}$ **30.** $\dfrac{5x+4}{3x-2} - \dfrac{3}{4} = 0$

31. $\dfrac{2}{x-3} = \dfrac{3}{x+2}$ **32.** $\dfrac{5}{x+1} + \dfrac{16}{x-6} = 0$ **33.** $\dfrac{3}{2x-1} = \dfrac{5}{x+3}$

34. $\dfrac{x+1}{x-2} = 3 + \dfrac{3}{x-2}$ **35.** $\dfrac{4x}{2x-3} = \dfrac{6}{2x-3} - 1$ **36.** $\dfrac{x+1}{x-2} = 3 + \dfrac{3}{x-2}$

37. Determine k so that $2x + 3 = k$ is equivalent to $3x - 5 = 0$.

38. Determine k so that the solution set of $3/(x - 2) = k/(x + 1)$ is $\{1\}$.

Answers 3.1

1. $x \geq 0$ **2.** $x \in R$ **4.** $x \geq -2, x \neq 0$

5. $x \in R, x \neq 1, -3$ **7.** identity   **8.** identity

10. conditional equation   **11.** conditional equation   **13.** $x \in R$

14. $x \in R, x \neq 0$ **16.** $\{-7/3\}$ **17.** $\{5/4\}$

19. $\{4\}$ **20.** $\{-3\}$ **22.** $\left\{\dfrac{a}{a+1}\right\}$ if $a \neq -1$

23. $\left\{\dfrac{ab}{c-a}\right\}$ if $c \neq a$ **25.** $\left\{\dfrac{a}{ab+1}\right\}$ if $ab \neq -1$ **26.** $\left\{\dfrac{ab}{a+b}\right\}$ if $a \neq -b$

28. $\{-1/2\}$ **29.** $\{5\}$ **31.** $\{13\}$

32. $\{2/3\}$ **34.** $\varnothing$ **35.** $\varnothing$

37. 19/3   **38.** -6

3.2 Quadratic Equations

An equation that can be expressed in the form

$$ax^2 + bx + c = 0, \qquad (3-2)$$

with $a \neq 0$ and $a,b,c \in R$, is called a **quadratic equation** in the variable x. Equation $(3-2)$ is called the *standard form* for a quadratic equation.

Solving Quadratic Equations by Factoring

When the left side of Eq. (3 – 2) can be factored by inspection, the quadratic equation can be solved by using the following theorem, which follows directly from Theorem 1.3(b).

Theorem 3.3   If $P(x)$ and $Q(x)$ are expressions in the variable x, then

$$P(x) \cdot Q(x) = 0$$

if and only if

$$P(x) = 0 \qquad \text{or} \qquad Q(x) = 0.$$

EXAMPLE 1
Solve $6x^2 - 7x - 5 = 0$ for x.

Solution   Factoring the left side of $6x^2 - 7x - 5 = 0$, we get

$$(3x - 5)(2x + 1) = 0.$$

Using Theorem 3.3, it follows that $(3x - 5)(2x + 1) = 0$ if and only if

$$3x - 5 = 0 \qquad \text{or} \qquad 2x + 1 = 0.$$

Since the solution of $3x - 5 = 0$ is 5/3 and the solution of $2x + 1 = 0$ is $-1/2$, it follows by Theorem 3.3 that the solutions of $6x^2 - 7x - 5 = (3x - 5)(2x + 1) = 0$ are 5/3 and $-1/2$. ∎

EXAMPLE 2
Solve $(x - 2)(x + 1) = 4$ for x.

Solution   Expressing the given equation in standard form, we get

$$x^2 - x - 6 = 0.$$

Then, factoring the left side, we have

$$(x - 3)(x + 2) = 0.$$

Using Theorem 3.3, it follows that $(x - 3)(x + 2) = 0$ if and only if

$$x - 3 = 0 \qquad \text{or} \qquad x + 2 = 0.$$

Hence the solutions are 3 and -2. ∎

EXERCISE 1

Solve for x.
(a) $x^2 - 4x - 21 = 0$.   (b) $6x^2 - x - 2 = 0$.

Answer   (a) $7, -3$ (b) $2/3, -1/2$

Solving Quadratic Equations by Completing the Square

Since it is not always obvious how to factor the left side of Eq. $(3-2)$, it seems desirable to find another method of solving quadratic equations. One such method depends upon the process, known as *completing the square*, of expressing $x^2 + px$ as a perfect square by adding and subtracting the square of half the coefficient of x. That is, we complete the square on $x^2 + px$ by adding and subtracting $(p/2)^2$.

EXAMPLE 3

Complete the square.

(a) $x^2 + 2x = x^2 + 2x + (1)^2 - (1)^2 = (x + 1)^2 - 1$.
(b) $x^2 - 5x = x^2 - 5x + (-\frac{5}{2})^2 - (-\frac{5}{2})^2 = (x - \frac{5}{2})^2 - \frac{25}{4}$.
(c) $2x^2 - 8x = 2[x^2 - 4x] = 2[x^2 - 4x + (-2)^2 - (-2)^2] = 2[(x - 2)^2 - 4] = 2(x - 2)^2 - 8$.

EXERCISE 2

Complete the square on the following expressions.
(a) $x^2 + 6x$ (b) $3x^2 - 9x$

Answer   (a) $(x + 3)^2 - 9$ (b) $3(x - \frac{3}{2})^2 - \frac{27}{4}$

EXAMPLE 4

Solve $x^2 - 4x - 21 = 0$ for x by completing the square.

Solution   Completing the square on $x^2 - 4x$, we get

$$[x^2 - 4x + (-2)^2 - (-2)^2] - 21 = 0,$$

which is equivalent in turn to each of the following equations:

$$[(x - 2)^2 - 4] - 21 = 0$$
$$(x - 2)^2 - 25 = 0$$
$$[(x - 2) - 5][(x - 2) + 5] = 0$$

and

$$(x - 7)(x + 3) = 0$$

Hence the solutions are $x = 7$ and $x = -3$.   ∎

EXAMPLE 5

Solve $2x^2 + 5x - 3 = 0$ for x by completing the square.

Solution Completing the square on $2x^2 + 5x$, we get

$$2[x^2 + \tfrac{5}{2}x + (\tfrac{5}{4})^2 - (\tfrac{5}{4})^2] - 3 = 0$$

which is equivalent in turn to each of the following equations:

$$2[(x + \tfrac{5}{4})^2 - \tfrac{25}{16}] - 3 = 0$$
$$2(x + \tfrac{5}{4})^2 - \tfrac{25}{8} - 3 = 0$$
$$2(x + \tfrac{5}{4})^2 - \tfrac{49}{8} = 0$$
$$(x + \tfrac{5}{4})^2 - \tfrac{49}{16} = 0$$
$$[(x + \tfrac{5}{4}) - \tfrac{7}{4}][(x + \tfrac{5}{4}) + \tfrac{7}{4}] = 0$$

and

$$(x - \tfrac{1}{2})(x + 3) = 0.$$

Hence the solutions are $x = \tfrac{1}{2}$ and $x = -3$.   ∎

Solving Quadratic Equations by the Quadratic Formula

By completing the square on $ax^2 + bx$ in Eq. (3–2), we can derive a simple formula that can be used to determine the solutions of any quadratic equation. This formula will follow directly from the next theorem.

Theorem 3.4   The solutions of the quadratic equation $ax^2 + bx + c = 0$, when $a,b,c \in R$ with $a \neq 0$, are

$$\frac{-b + \sqrt{b^2 - 4ac}}{2a} \quad \text{and} \quad \frac{-b - \sqrt{b^2 - 4ac}}{2a}.$$

Proof The following are equivalent equations:

$$ax^2 + bx + c = 0$$
$$a\left[x^2 + \frac{b}{a}x\right] + c = 0$$
$$a\left[x^2 + \frac{b}{a}x + \left(\frac{b}{2a}\right)^2 - \left(\frac{b}{2a}\right)^2\right] + c = 0$$
$$a\left[\left(x + \frac{b}{2a}\right)^2 - \frac{b^2}{4a^2}\right] + c = 0$$

$$a\left(x+\frac{b}{2a}\right)^2-\frac{b^2}{4a}+c=0$$

$$a\left(x+\frac{b}{2a}\right)^2-\frac{b^2-4ac}{4a}=0$$

$$\left(x+\frac{b}{2a}\right)^2-\frac{b^2-4ac}{4a^2}=0$$

$$\left(x+\frac{b}{2a}\right)^2-\left(\frac{\sqrt{b^2-4ac}}{2a}\right)^2=0$$

$$\left[\left(x+\frac{b}{2a}\right)-\left(\frac{\sqrt{b^2-4ac}}{2a}\right)\right]\left[\left(x+\frac{b}{2a}\right)+\left(\frac{\sqrt{b^2-4ac}}{2a}\right)\right]=0$$

and

$$\left(x-\frac{-b+\sqrt{b^2-4ac}}{2a}\right)\left(x-\frac{-b-\sqrt{b^2-4ac}}{2a}\right)=0.$$

Therefore, the solutions of the quadratic equation $ax^2+bx+c=0$ are

$$x=\frac{-b+\sqrt{b^2-4ac}}{2a}\qquad\text{and}\qquad x=\frac{-b-\sqrt{b^2-4ac}}{2a}.\qquad\blacksquare$$

Using Theorem 3.4, it follows that substituting the values of a, b, and c from the quadratic equation $ax^2+bx+c=0$ into the equation

$$x=\frac{-b\pm\sqrt{b^2-4ac}}{2a}\qquad\qquad(3-3)$$

gives those values of x which are solutions of $ax^2+bx+c=0$. Using Eq. $(3-3)$, which is known as the **quadratic formula,** we can now solve any quadratic equation for its solutions.

EXAMPLE 6

Solve $8x^2+6x-9=0$ for x by using the quadratic formula.

Solution   Substituting 8 for a, 6 for b, and -9 for c in the quadratic formula, we get

$$x=\frac{-(6)\pm\sqrt{(6)^2-4(8)(-9)}}{2(8)}=\frac{-6\pm\sqrt{324}}{16}=\frac{-6\pm18}{16}.$$

Thus the solutions of $8x^2+6x-9=0$ are

$$x=\frac{-6+18}{16}=\frac{3}{4}\qquad\text{and}\qquad x=\frac{-6-18}{16}=-\frac{3}{2}.\qquad\blacksquare$$

EXERCISE 3

Solve for x by using the quadratic formula.
(a) $x^2 - 2x - 2 = 0$.   (b) $18x^2 + 9x - 2 = 0$.

Answer   (a) $x = 1 + \sqrt{3}, x = 1 - \sqrt{3}$ (b) $x = \frac{1}{6}, x = -\frac{2}{3}$

The expression $b^2 - 4ac$ which appears under the radical in the quadratic formula is called the **discriminant** of the quadratic equation $ax^2 + bx + c = 0$. An examination of the discriminant $b^2 - 4ac$ produces the following facts concerning the two solutions of the quadratic equation $ax^2 + bx + c = 0$:

1. If $b^2 - 4ac = 0$, the two solutions are equal real numbers.
2. If $b^2 - 4ac > 0$, the two solutions are unequal real numbers.
3. If $b^2 - 4ac < 0$, there are no real solutions.

EXAMPLE 7

Determine the values of k for which $4x^2 + kx + 9 = 0$ has exactly one root.

Solution   In this case, $a = 4$, $b = k$, and $c = 9$. The quadratic equation $4x^2 + kx + 9 = 0$ has exactly one solution if and only if

$$b^2 - 4ac = (k)^2 - 4(4)(9) = 0.$$

Therefore, $4x^2 + kx + 9 = 0$ has exactly one solution when $k^2 - 144 = 0$ and hence when $k = 12$ or -12.   ∎
Even though the quadratic equation $ax^2 + bx + c = 0$ has no real solutions when the discriminant $b^2 - 4ac$ is negative, we shall see in the next section that it does have solutions (however, these solutions are *not* real numbers).

Problems 3.2

In problems 1-9, determine the solution set of the given equation by factoring.

1. $x^2 - 3x = 0$ 2. $2x^2 - x - 21 = 0$ 3. $10x^2 - 3x - 1 = 0$
4. $x^2 + x = 20$ 5. $x^2 + 3x = 5x + 15$ 6. $6x^2 - 6x = 7x - 6$
7. $x(2x - 1) = 6$ 8. $(x - 5)(x + 2) = 8$ 9. $(2x + 1)(x + 2) = 5$.

In problems 10-15, determine the solution set of the given equation by completing the square.

10. $x^2 + 10x + 21 = 0$ 11. $x^2 + 5x - 14 = 0$ 12. $x^2 - x - 12 = 0$
13. $2x^2 + x = 6$ 14. $4x^2 + 15x = 4$ 15. $3x^2 + x - 4 = 0$

In problems 16-27, determine the solution set of the given equation by using the quadratic formula.

16. $3x^2 + 8x - 3 = 0$ 17. $2x^2 - 3x - 2 = 0$ 18. $3x^2 + 7x - 6 = 0$

19. $2x^2 + \sqrt{3}\,x - 9 = 0$ **20.** $x^2 - \sqrt{2}\,x - 12 = 0$ **21.** $x^2 + 2\sqrt{2}\,x + 2 = 0$

22. $x^2 - 10x + 23 = 0$ **23.** $x^2 - 6x + 6 = 0$ **24.** $x^2 + 12x + 24 = 0$

25. $2x + 5 = \dfrac{3}{x}$ **26.** $\dfrac{2x}{x-1} = \dfrac{3x-1}{x+1}$ **27.** $\dfrac{1}{x^2-1} - \dfrac{x}{x-1} = \dfrac{3}{x+1}$

28. Determine the value of k for which $kx^2 - 20x + 25 = 0$ has exactly one solution.

29. Determine the values of k for which $x^2 + 3x + k + 2 = 0$ has two distinct real roots.

30. Determine the values of k for which $4x^2 + kx + 9 = 0$ has no real solutions.

Answers 3.2

1. $\{0,3\}$ **2.** $\{7/2, -3\}$ **4.** $\{4, -5\}$

5. $\{5, -3\}$ **7.** $\{2, -3/2\}$ **8.** $\{6, -3\}$

10. $\{-3, -7\}$ **11.** $\{2, -7\}$ **13.** $\{3/2, -2\}$

14. $\{1/4, -4\}$ **16.** $\{1/3, -3\}$ **17.** $\{2, -1/2\}$

19. $\{\sqrt{3}, -\tfrac{3}{2}\sqrt{3}\}$ **20.** $\{3\sqrt{2}, -2\sqrt{2}\}$ **22.** $\{5 + \sqrt{2}, 5 - \sqrt{2}\}$

23. $\{3 + \sqrt{3}, 3 - \sqrt{3}\}$ **25.** $\{1/2, -3\}$ **26.** $\{3 + 2\sqrt{2}, 3 - 2\sqrt{2}\}$

28. $k = 4$ **29.** $k < \tfrac{1}{4}$

3.3 Complex Numbers and Imaginary Roots of Quadratic Equations

The Algebra of Complex Numbers

Since the quadratic equation $ax^2 + bx + c = 0$ has no real solutions when the discriminant $b^2 - 4ac$ is negative, it seems desirable to develop a new kind of number so that $ax^2 + bx + c = 0$ will have solutions when $b^2 - 4ac < 0$. We do this as follows.

Definition 3.1   A **complex number** is a number of the form

$$a + bi,$$

where a and b are real numbers and i is defined as $\sqrt{-1}$.

When $b = 0$, the complex number $a + bi = a + 0i$ is the real number a. Thus it follows that the set of real numbers is a subset of the set of complex numbers.

When $b \neq 0$, we refer to the complex number $a + bi$ as an **imaginary number.** When $a = 0$ and $b \neq 0$, we refer to the complex number $a + bi = 0 + bi = bi$ as a **pure imaginary number.** As a matter of convenience, we usually write the complex number $a + (-b)i$ as $a - bi$.

In the complex number $a + bi$, the real number a is referred to as the **real**

part of $a + bi$ and the real number b is referred to as the **imaginary part** of $a + bi$.

Definition 3.2   Two complex numbers $a + bi$ and $c + di$ are said to be equal, written $a + bi = c + di$, if and only if $a = c$ and $b = d$.

EXAMPLE 1

Determine the values of x and y such that $2x - 5yi = 8 + 15i$.

Solution   Using Definition 3.2,

$$2x - 5yi = 8 + 15i \quad \text{if and only if} \quad 2x = 8 \text{ and } -5y = 15.$$

Therefore, $x = 4$ and $y = -3$.   ∎

EXERCISE 1

For what values of x and y is $3x - 12i = 12 + 15yi$?

Answer $x = 4$, $y = -4/5$

The pure imaginary number i is referred to as the **imaginary unit.** As properties of i, we have

$$i^2 = i \cdot i = \sqrt{-1}\,\sqrt{-1} = -1,$$
$$i^3 = i^2 \cdot i = (-1)i = -i,$$

and

$$i^4 = i^3 \cdot i = (-i)i = -i^2 = -(-1) = 1, \text{ etc.}$$

Addition, subtraction, and multiplication of complex numbers are defined as follows.

Definition 3.3   If $a + bi, c + di$ are complex numbers, then
(a) $(a + bi) + (c + di) = (a + c) + (b + d)i.$ (3–4)
(b) $(a + bi) - (c + di) = (a - c) + (b - d)i.$ (3–5)
(c) $(a + bi)(c + di) = (ac - bd) + (ad + bc)i.$ (3–6)

It is important to note that the complex number on the right side of Eq. (3–4) can be obtained by algebraically adding the complex numbers on the left side of Eq. (3–4) in the usual manner while treating i like any other constant. A similar remark can be made concerning Eqs. (3–5) and (3–6). In other words, complex numbers can be added, subtracted, or multiplied by treating them as if they are polynomials, with i being treated like any other constant. For this reason it is *not* necessary to memorize the formulas in Definition 3.3.

EXAMPLE 2

Perform the indicated operations.
(a) $(3 - 4i) + (2 + 7i) = (3 + 2) + (-4i + 7i) = 5 + 3i.$
(b) $(3 - 4i) - (2 + 7i) = (3 - 2) + (-4i - 7i) = 1 - 11i.$
(c) $(3 - 4i)(2 + 7i) = 3(2 + 7i) - 4i(2 + 7i) = 6 + 21i - 8i - 28i^2 = 6 + 21i - 8i - 28(-1) = 34 + 13i.$

EXERCISE 2

Perform the indicated operations.
(a) $(3 - 7i) - (-3 - 5i)$ (b) $(3 - 7i)(-3 - 5i)$

Answer (a) $6 - 2i$ (b) $-44 + 6i$
Before defining division of complex numbers, we must define the conjugate of a complex number.

Definition 3.4   The **conjugate** of the complex number $a + bi$ is the complex number $a - bi.$
As an example, the conjugate of $3 - 7i$ is $3 + 7i.$

Definition 3.5   If $a + bi$ and $c + di$ are complex numbers with $c + di \neq 0 + 0i$, then

$$\frac{a + bi}{c + di} = \left(\frac{ac + bd}{c^2 + d^2}\right) + \left(\frac{bc - ad}{c^2 + d^2}\right)i. \qquad (3-7)$$

The expression on the right side of Eq. (3-7) can be obtained from the expression on the left side by multiplying both the numerator and the denominator of the left side by the conjugate of the denominator and then simplifying in the usual manner.

EXAMPLE 3

Express

$$\frac{3 + 4i}{1 - i}$$

as a complex number.

Solution   Since the conjugate of the denominator is $1 + i$, we multiply both the numerator and the denominator of the given expression by $1 + i$. This gives

$$\frac{3 + 4i}{1 - i} = \frac{(3 + 4i)(1 + i)}{(1 - i)(1 + i)} = \frac{3 + 3i + 4i + 4i^2}{1 + i - i - i^2} = \frac{-1 + 7i}{2} = -\frac{1}{2} + \frac{7}{2}i. \qquad \blacksquare$$

EXERCISE 3

Express

$$\frac{4+2i}{1-2i}$$

as a complex number.

Answer 2*i*

Imaginary Roots of Quadratic Equations

Before solving quadratic equations that have imaginary roots, we must define the principal square root of a negative real number.

Definition 3.6   If $a > 0$, the **principal square root of** $-a$, denoted by $\sqrt{-a}$, is defined as

$$\sqrt{-a} = i\sqrt{a}.$$

EXAMPLE 4

(a) $\sqrt{-4} = i\sqrt{4} = 2i$.
(b) $\sqrt{-625} = i\sqrt{625} = 25i$.
(c) $\sqrt{-8} = i\sqrt{8} = i\sqrt{4}\sqrt{2} = 2\sqrt{2}\,i$.

Now we are prepared to solve quadratic equations that have imaginary roots.

EXAMPLE 5

Solve $x^2 - 4x + 5 = 0$ for x using the quadratic formula.

Solution   Substituting 1 for a, -4 for b, and 5 for c in the quadratic formula, we get

$$x = \frac{-(-4) \pm \sqrt{(-4)^2 - 4(1)(5)}}{2(1)} = \frac{4 \pm \sqrt{-4}}{2} = \frac{4 \pm 2i}{2} = 2 \pm i.$$

Thus the solutions of $x^2 - 4x + 5 = 0$ are $x = 2 + i$ and $x = 2 - i$.   ∎

EXERCISE 4

Solve for x using the quadratic formula.
(a) $x^2 + 4 = 0$.   (b) $x^2 + 2x + 2 = 0$.

Answer   (a) $x = 2i$, $x = -2i$ (b) $x = -1 + i$, $x = -1 - i$

Problems 3.3

In problems 1–6, determine the values of the real numbers x and y that satisfy the given equations.

1. $3x + i = 9 - 3yi$

2. $8 - 6yi = 2x + 18i$

3. $30 + 7i = 10x - 14yi$

4. $(x - i)(2 + 2i) = 8 + yi$

5. $(1 - xi)(3 + i) = 6 - yi$

6. $(x + i)(1 - i) = 4 + yi$

In problems 7–24, perform the indicated operations and write the result as a complex number.

7. $(2 + i) + (-3 - 3i)$

8. $(5 + i) + (3 - 6i)$

9. $(5 - 7i) + (3 - 8i)$

10. $(2 + i) - (-3 - 3i)$

11. $(5 + i) - (3 - 6i)$

12. $(5 - 7i) - (3 - 8i)$

13. $(2 + i)(-3 - 3i)$

14. $(5 + i)(3 - 6i)$

15. $(5 - 7i)(3 - 8i)$

16. $(3 + 5i)(2 - 3i)$

17. $(2 - i)(4 + i)$

18. $(1 - 3i)(3 + i)$

19. $(3 - 2i)/(1 + i)$

20. $(1 - 2i)/(1 - i)$

21. $(2 + i)/(1 - i)$

22. $(2 - 3i)/(1 - 2i)$

23. $(4 + i)/(2 + 3i)$

24. $(6 - 5i)/(3 + 2i)$

In problems 25–30, determine the solution set of the given equation by using the quadratic formula.

25. $x^2 + 36 = 0$

26. $x^2 + 9 = 0$

27. $x^2 + 25 = 0$

28. $x^2 - 4x + 13 = 0$

29. $x^2 + 4x + 8 = 0$

30. $x^2 + 2x + 10 = 0$

31. Is the set of complex numbers a field? If so, what is the additive identity? What is the multiplicative identity? What is the additive inverse of $a + bi$? When it exists, what is the multiplicative inverse of $a + bi$?

32. Is the set of complex numbers an ordered field? If so, is $i > 0$, $i = 0$, or $i < 0$?

Answers 3.3

1. $x = 3, y = -\frac{1}{3}$

2. $x = 4, y = -3$

4. $x = 3, y = 4$

5. $x = 3, y = 8$

7. $-1 - 2i$

8. $8 - 5i$

10. $5 + 4i$

11. $2 + 7i$

13. $-3 - 9i$

14. $21 - 27i$

16. $21 + i$

17. $9 - 2i$

19. $\frac{1}{2} - \frac{5}{2}i$

20. $\frac{3}{2} - \frac{1}{2}i$

22. $\frac{8}{5} + \frac{1}{5}i$

23. $\frac{11}{13} - \frac{10}{13}i$

25. $\{6i, -6i\}$

26. $\{3i, -3i\}$

28. $\{2 + 3i, 2 - 3i\}$

29. $\{-2 + 2i, -2 - 2i\}$

31. Yes, $0 + 0i$, $1 + 0i$, $-a - bi$, $\dfrac{a - bi}{a^2 + b^2}$

32. No

3.4 Applied Problems

In this section we shall examine various kinds of applied problems. We shall find there are two main challenges involved in solving such problems. First, we must translate the verbal language of the problem into mathematical terms and equations. Second, we must solve the resulting equation and check our answers to make sure they fit the physical situation described in the problem. The following steps are recommended in solving applied problems:

1. Read the entire problem to get the general idea.
2. While rereading the problem, determine the unknown quantities and represent each of them by a variable. (Since we have only dealt with equations involving one variable so far, each unknown quantity should be expressed in terms of a single variable at this point in the text.)
3. While rereading the problem again, translate the conditions of the problem into equations involving the chosen variables.
4. Solve the equations.
5. Check each solution to make sure it fits the physical situation described in the verbal statement of the problem.

EXAMPLE 1

The sum of two numbers is 36. If the square of the larger number is 216 greater than the square of the smaller number, determine the numbers.

Solution   In this case, the unknown quantities are the two numbers. If we let

$$x = \text{larger number,}$$

then

$$36 - x = \text{smaller number.}$$

Translating the condition that the square of the larger number, namely x^2, is 216 greater than the square of the smaller number, namely $(36 - x)^2$, into an equation, we have

$$x^2 - (36 - x)^2 = 216.$$

Solving the previous equation for x, we get

$$x^2 - (1296 - 72x + x^2) = 216$$
$$72x - 1296 = 216$$
$$72x = 1512$$
$$x = 21.$$

Hence the larger number x is 21, and the smaller number $36 - x$ is $36 - 21 = 15$. Checking the solution, we find that

$$(21)^2 - (15)^2 = 441 - 225 = 216. \qquad \blacksquare$$

EXAMPLE 2

A chemist has two mixtures of alcohol solution available to him. One contains 60 percent alcohol and the other contains 20 percent alcohol. How many liters of the 60 percent solution should be added to 8 liters of the 20 percent solution to obtain a solution containing 45 percent alcohol?

Solution Let $x =$ the number of liters of 60 percent solution required. Using the fact that the amount of alcohol in the two original solutions must equal the amount of alcohol in the mixture,

$$\left(\begin{array}{c}\text{amount of alcohol}\\ \text{in the 60\% solution}\end{array}\right) + \left(\begin{array}{c}\text{amount of alcohol}\\ \text{in the 20\% solution}\end{array}\right) = \left(\begin{array}{c}\text{amount of alcohol}\\ \text{in the 45\% solution}\end{array}\right),$$

the conditions of the problem are translated into the equation

$$(.6)(x) + (.2)(8) = (.45)(x + 8).$$

Solving for x, we have

$$.6x + 1.6 = .45x + 3.6$$
$$.15x = 2$$
$$x = \frac{2}{.15} = \frac{200}{15} = 13\tfrac{1}{3}.$$

Checking the solution, we have

$$(.6)(13\tfrac{1}{3}) + (.2)(8) = 9.6 = (.45)(21\tfrac{1}{3}).$$ ∎

EXAMPLE 3

A bricklayer can do a certain job in 9 hours less time than his apprentice can do the same job. If they can do the job together in 20 hours, how long would it take the bricklayer alone?

Solution If we let

$$x = \text{time (in hours) for bricklayer to do job alone,}$$

then

$$x + 9 = \text{time (in hours) for apprentice to do job alone.}$$

Since

$$\begin{pmatrix} \text{portion of job} \\ \text{done alone by} \\ \text{bricklayer in 1 hour} \end{pmatrix} + \begin{pmatrix} \text{portion of job} \\ \text{done alone by} \\ \text{apprentice in 1 hour} \end{pmatrix} = \begin{pmatrix} \text{portion of job} \\ \text{done by both} \\ \text{workers in 1 hour} \end{pmatrix},$$

the conditions of the problem require that

$$\frac{1}{x} + \frac{1}{x+9} = \frac{1}{20}.$$

Solving for x, we have

$$20(x+9) + 20x = x(x+9)$$
$$20x + 180 + 20x = x^2 + 9x$$
$$x^2 - 31x - 180 = 0$$
$$(x-36)(x+5) = 0$$

$$x = 36, \qquad x = -5.$$

The solution $x = -5$ is impossible, since the bricklayer cannot possibly do the job alone in -5 hours. The solution $x = 36$ hours is correct, since

$$\frac{1}{36} + \frac{1}{36+9} = \frac{1}{20}. \qquad\qquad ∎$$

EXAMPLE 4

It takes 2 hours for a man in a motorboat to travel 8 miles downstream and 4 miles back upstream. If the river flows at a rate of 2 miles per hour (mph), determine the rate at which the motorboat would travel in still water.

Solution   If we let

$$x = \text{speed of boat in still water,}$$

then

$$x + 2 = \text{speed of boat downstream,}$$

and

$$x - 2 = \text{speed of boat upstream.}$$

Since

$$\text{time} = \frac{\text{distance}}{\text{rate}}$$

and

$$\left(\begin{matrix}\text{time going}\\\text{downstream}\end{matrix}\right) + \left(\begin{matrix}\text{time going}\\\text{upstream}\end{matrix}\right) = \left(\begin{matrix}\text{total time}\\\text{of trip}\end{matrix}\right),$$

the conditions of the problem require that

$$\frac{8}{x+2} + \frac{4}{x-2} = 2.$$

Solving for x, we get

$$8(x-2) + 4(x+2) = 2(x-2)(x+2)$$
$$8x - 16 + 4x + 8 = 2x^2 - 8$$
$$2x^2 - 12x = 0$$
$$2(x-6)x = 0,$$
$$x = 0, \qquad x = 6.$$

The solution $x = 0$ is impossible, since it means that the time required to go upstream is $4/(0-2) = -2$ hours. However, the solution $x = 6$ checks, since

$$\frac{8}{6+2} + \frac{4}{6-2} = 1 + 1 = 2. \qquad\blacksquare$$

Problems 3.4

1. Determine three consecutive integers whose sum is 357.
2. Determine two consecutive positive integers such that the difference of their squares is 159.
3. Determine four consecutive odd integers such that the sum of the three smallest integers is 30 greater than the largest integer.
4. Determine two consecutive positive integers such that the sum of their squares is 613.
5. Determine two consecutive positive odd integers whose product is 1443.
6. Determine two integers that differ by 3 and have a product of 154.
7. A student's grades on the first two of three tests are 72 and 82. What grade must be made on the third test to bring the average up to 80?
8. A total of $2400 is invested at simple interest, part at 4 percent and the rest at

5 percent. Determine the amount invested at 4 percent if the yearly interest is $102.

9. A total of 2400 tickets to a basketball game were sold. If an adult's ticket costs $3 and a child's ticket costs $2, determine how many adult tickets were sold if the total income from the ticket sales was $6200.

10. A vending machine contains $17.35 in nickels, dimes, and quarters. If there are three more quarters than nickels and twice as many dimes as quarters, how many quarters are in the machine?

11. A rectangular field is 28 feet longer than it is wide. If the field has an area of 5280 square feet, determine the dimensions of the field.

12. A 2-inch square is cut out of each corner from a rectangular piece of tin that is 8 inches longer than it is wide. If an open box whose volume is 1536 cubic inches is then formed from the resulting piece of tin by turning up the sides, determine the dimensions of the piece of tin.

13. How many ounces of pure silver should be added to 12 ounces of silver that is 55 percent pure to produce an alloy that is 70 percent pure?

14. A merchant plans to mix hazelnuts worth 90 cents a pound with walnuts worth 65 cents a pound. How many pounds of each kind of nut does he need to end up with 100 pounds of a mixture worth 79 cents a pound?

15. A chemist has two mixtures of alcohol solution available to him; one contains 35 percent alcohol and the other contains 75 percent alcohol. How many liters of the 35 percent solution should be added to 5 liters of the 75 percent solution to obtain a solution containing 60 percent alcohol?

16. A chemist has two mixtures of sulfuric acid solution available to him. One contains 18 percent acid and the other contains 30 percent acid. How many liters of each should be combined to obtain 15 liters of 26 percent acid?

17. A 10-gallon can contains 4 gallons of solution that has a 40 percent concentration of a certain chemical mixed in water. How much pure water must be added to the can to reduce the concentration of the chemical to 25 percent?

18. A 20-quart radiator is filled with a solution that is 15 percent antifreeze. How much of the solution should be drained out and replaced with pure antifreeze to obtain a solution that is 40 percent antifreeze in the radiator?

19. Bruce can do a certain job alone in 6 hours. Working together with his roommate, they can do the job in 2 hours. How long would it take his roommate to do the job alone?

20. It takes Jim 9 hours to paint a room by himself. Bill can paint the same room alone in 7 hours. How long will it take Jim and Bill to paint the room together?

21. Mary can do a certain job in 9 hours less time than it takes Sue to do the same job alone. If they can complete the job in 20 hours by working together, how long would it take each to do the job alone?

22. One input pipe can fill a swimming pool in 12 hours. A second input pipe can fill the same pool in 9 hours. How long would it take to fill the pool if both input pipes are used at the same time?

23. Two pipes together can fill a swimming pool in 4 hours. The larger of the two

pipes can fill the swimming pool alone in 6 hours less time than the smaller pipe. Determine how long it would take for the smaller pipe to fill the pool alone.

24. A swimming pool holds 2400 cubic feet of water. The pool can be drained 10 cubic feet per minute faster than it can be filled. If it takes 20 minutes longer to fill it than to drain it, determine how long it would take to fill the pool with water.

In problems 25 – 30, remember that

$$rate \times time = distance.$$

25. Jim ran a certain distance 4 minutes faster than Ronnie. If Jim runs 10 mph and Ronnie runs 9 mph, determine the distance.

26. On a trip that takes 6 hours, a man travels 110 miles by car and the remaining 1254 miles of his trip by plane. If the plane travels 280 mph faster than the car, determine the speed of the plane.

27. An airplane travels twice as fast as a car. If the car travels 560 miles in 2 hours more time than it takes the airplane to travel 840 miles, determine the rate of the car.

28. It takes $2\frac{1}{2}$ hours for a man in a motorboat at full speed to travel 18 miles downstream and 8 miles back upstream. If the full speed of the boat in still water is 10 mph, determine the speed of the current.

29. At full speed a motorboat requires 4 hours to travel 18 miles upstream and 21 miles back downstream. If the current flows at 2 mph, determine the full speed of the motorboat in still water.

Answers 3.4

1. 118, 119, 120	**2.** 79, 80	**4.** 17, 18	**5.** 37, 39
7. 86	**8.** $1800	**10.** 35	**11.** 60 by 88
13. 6 oz		**14.** 44 lb of walnuts, 56 lb of hazelnuts	
16. 5 liters of 18% acid, 10 liters of 30% acid		**17.** 2.4 gal	
19. 3 hr	**20.** $3\frac{13}{16}$ hr	**22.** $5\frac{1}{7}$ hr	**23.** 12 hr
25. 6 miles	**26.** 330 mph	**28.** 2 mph	**29.** 10 mph

3.5 Equations in Quadratic Form

If $a,b,c \in R$ with $a \neq 0$, an equation of the form

$$av^2 + bv + c = 0,$$

where v is an expression involving another variable, is said to be an **equation in quadratic form.** Some equations of this type can be solved by the methods that we have discussed previously.

EXAMPLE 1

Solve $x^4 - 5x^2 + 4 = 0$ for x.

Solution   Since $x^4 - 5x^2 + 4 = 0$ can be rewritten as $(x^2)^2 - 5(x^2) + 4 = 0$, the given equation is an equation in quadratic form with $v = x^2$. Substituting v for x^2, the given equation becomes

$$v^2 - 5v + 4 = 0,$$

which is equivalent to

$$(v - 4)(v - 1) = 0.$$

Thus

$$v - 4 = 0 \qquad \text{or} \qquad v - 1 = 0,$$

and hence

$$v = 4 \qquad \text{or} \qquad v = 1.$$

Since $v = x^2$, it follows that

$$x^2 = 4 \qquad \text{or} \qquad x^2 = 1.$$

Thus the solutions are $2, -2, 1$, and -1.   ∎

EXAMPLE 2

Solve $(x^2 - 2x)^2 - 4(x^2 - 2x) + 3 = 0$ for x.

Solution   The given equation is an equation in quadratic form with $v = x^2 - 2x$. Replacing $x^2 - 2x$ with v, the given equation becomes

$$v^2 - 4v + 3 = 0,$$

which is equivalent to

$$(v - 3)(v - 1) = 0.$$

Consequently,

$$v - 3 = 0 \qquad \text{or} \qquad v - 1 = 0,$$

and hence

$$v = 3 \qquad \text{or} \qquad v = 1.$$

Since $v = x^2 - 2x$, it follows that

$$x^2 - 2x = 3 \quad \text{or} \quad x^2 - 2x = 1.$$

Using the quadratic formula to solve the last two equations, we find that the solutions are -1, 3, $1 + \sqrt{2}$, and $1 - \sqrt{2}$.   ∎

EXERCISE 1

Solve for x.

(a) $x^{-2} + 2x^{-1} - 3 = 0$.   (b) $x^4 - 5x^2 - 36 = 0$.

Answer   (a) $1, -1/3$ (b) $3, -3, 2i, -2i$

Problems 3.5

In problems 1–24, determine the solution set of the given equation.

1. $x^4 - 13x^2 + 36 = 0$
2. $4x^4 - 17x^2 + 4 = 0$
3. $x^4 - 12x^2 + 27 = 0$
4. $x^4 + 8x^2 - 9 = 0$
5. $x^4 + 21x^2 - 100 = 0$
6. $9x^4 + 143x^2 - 16 = 0$
7. $2x^{-2} + 9x^{-1} - 5 = 0$
8. $3x^{-2} - 5x^{-1} - 2 = 0$
9. $4x^{-2} + 11x^{-1} - 3 = 0$
10. $9x^{-4} - 37x^{-2} + 4 = 0$
11. $x^{-4} - 5x^{-2} + 4 = 0$
12. $8x^{-4} - 14x^{-2} - 9 = 0$
13. $x - 6x^{1/2} + 8 = 0$
14. $2x - 13x^{1/2} + 15 = 0$
15. $x - 9x^{1/2} + 8 = 0$
16. $2x^{2/3} + 5x^{1/3} - 3 = 0$
17. $x^{2/3} + 2x^{1/3} - 8 = 0$
18. $x^{2/3} - 5x^{1/3} + 6 = 0$
19. $(x^2 + 2x)^2 - 2(x^2 + 2x) - 3 = 0$
20. $(x^2 - 4x)^2 - 3(x^2 - 4x) - 10 = 0$
21. $4(x^2 - x)^2 - 11(x^2 - x) + 6 = 0$
22. $(x^2 + 4x)^2 + 3(x^2 + 4x) - 40 = 0$
23. $(x^2 - 2x)^2 - (x^2 - 2x) - 6 = 0$
24. $\left(x + \dfrac{2}{x}\right)^2 - \left(x + \dfrac{2}{x}\right) - 6 = 0$

Answers 3.5

1. $\{2, -2, 3, -3\}$
2. $\{2, -2, \frac{1}{2}, -\frac{1}{2}\}$
4. $\{1, -1, 3i, -3i\}$
5. $\{2, -2, 5i, -5i\}$
7. $\{2, -1/5\}$
8. $\{-3, 1/2\}$
10. $\{3, -3, \frac{1}{2}, -\frac{1}{2}\}$
11. $\{1, -1, \frac{1}{2}, -\frac{1}{2}\}$
13. $\{4, 16\}$
14. $\{9/4, 25\}$
16. $\{1/8, -27\}$
17. $\{8, -64\}$
19. $\{1, -1, -3\}$
20. $\{-1, 5, 2 \pm \sqrt{2}\}$
22. $\{-2 \pm 2i, 1, -5\}$
23. $\{1 \pm i, -1, 3\}$

3.6 Equations Containing Radicals

An equation that involves one or more radicals, each of which contains the variable x in its radicand, is called a **radical equation** in the variable x. For example,

$$\sqrt{2x - 1} - 1 = x, \quad \sqrt[3]{2x - 1} = \sqrt[4]{x}, \quad \text{and} \quad \sqrt{x - 5} + \sqrt{2x - 3} = \sqrt{x}$$

are radical equations.

To solve radical equations, we need the following theorem.

Theorem 3.5 If $P(x)$ and $Q(x)$ are expressions involving the variable x, and if a is a solution of the equation

$$P(x) = Q(x), \tag{3-8}$$

then a is also a solution of the equation

$$[P(x)]^n = [Q(x)]^n, \tag{3-9}$$

where $n \in N$.

It is important to note that Theorem 3.5 states that every solution of Eq. (3–8) is also a solution of Eq. (3–9). Therefore, we can determine the solutions of Eq. (3–8) by solving Eq. (3–9) and checking its roots in Eq. (3–8). A solution of Eq. (3–9) that is not a root of Eq. (3–8) is called an **extraneous root** of Eq. (3–8).

EXAMPLE 1

Solve $\sqrt{1-6x} - 1 = x$ for x.

Solution When using Theorem 3.5 to solve a radical equation, we begin by placing the most complicated radical on a side by itself. Thus the given equation is replaced with the equivalent equation,

$$\sqrt{1-6x} = x+1.$$

Using Theorem 3.5, it follows that every solution of the previous equation is also a solution of the equation

$$(\sqrt{1-6x})^2 = (x+1)^2.$$

The last equation is equivalent in turn to each of the following equations:

$$1 - 6x = x^2 + 2x + 1$$
$$x^2 + 8x = 0$$

and

$$x(x+8) = 0.$$

Since the solutions of the last equation are 0 and −8, we now know by Theorem 3.5 that 0 and −8 are the only possible solutions of the original equation. Checking each of these possible solutions in the original equation, we find that 0 satisfies the original equation, while -8 does not. Thus the only solution of the original equation is $x=0$. ∎

It is necessary in some problems to apply Theorem 3.5 several times to obtain an equation free of radicals which we can solve.

EXAMPLE 2

Solve $\sqrt{4-3x}+\sqrt{1-2x}=3$ for x.

Solution The given equation is equivalent to the equation

$$\sqrt{4-3x}=3-\sqrt{1-2x}.$$

Squaring both sides of this equation, we get

$$(\sqrt{4-3x})^2=(3-\sqrt{1-2x})^2$$

and

$$4-3x=9-6\sqrt{1-2x}+(1-2x).$$

Replacing the last equation with the equivalent equation

$$x+6=6\sqrt{1-2x}$$

and squaring both sides, we get

$$(x+6)^2=(6\sqrt{1-2x})^2$$
$$x^2+12x+36=36(1-2x)$$
$$x^2+84x=0$$

and

$$x(x+84)=0.$$

Thus the possible solutions of the original equation are 0 and -84. Checking each of these possible solutions in the original equation, we find that the solution set of the given equation is $\{0\}$. ∎

EXERCISE 1

Solve for x.
(a) $3\sqrt{x}+9=2x$.   (b) $\sqrt{7-2x}-\sqrt{3-x}=1$.

Answer (a) 9   (b) 3, -1

Problems 3.6

In problems 1–18, determine the solution set of the given equation.

1. $\sqrt[3]{2x-1}=3$
2. $\sqrt[4]{3x+7}=2$
3. $\sqrt[5]{3x+1}=-2$
4. $\sqrt{1-5x+1}=x$
5. $\sqrt{6x+1}-1=x$
6. $\sqrt{4-5x+2}=x$
7. $\sqrt{2x-2}=\sqrt{x}+1$
8. $\sqrt{3x-11}=\sqrt{x}+1$
9. $\sqrt{2x+17}=\sqrt{x}+3$
10. $\sqrt{2x+4}-\sqrt{x-5}=3$
11. $\sqrt{x+20}-\sqrt{x+4}=2$
12. $\sqrt{x+22}-\sqrt{x+6}=2$
13. $\sqrt{x+11}+\sqrt{2x+6}=\sqrt{9x+19}$
14. $\sqrt{x+4}+\sqrt{3x+1}=\sqrt{9x+4}$
15. $\sqrt{2x+1}+\sqrt{x+5}=\sqrt{6x+12}$
16. $\sqrt{7+\sqrt{x}}=\sqrt{x}+1$
17. $\sqrt{7+6\sqrt{x}}=\sqrt{x}+2$
18. $\sqrt{5+11\sqrt{x}}=\sqrt{x}+3$

Answers 3.6

1. $\{14\}$ 2. $\{3\}$ 4. $\varnothing$ 5. $\{0, 4\}$ 7. $\{9\}$ 8. $\{9\}$
10. $\{6, 30\}$ 11. $\{5\}$ 13. $\{5\}$ 14. $\{5\}$ 16. $\{4\}$ 17. $\{9\}$

3.7 Linear Inequalities

If $P(x)$ and $Q(x)$ are expressions involving the variable x, then a statement of the form

$$P(x) > Q(x), \quad P(x) < Q(x), \quad P(x) \geq Q(x), \quad \text{or} \quad P(x) \leq Q(x)$$

is said to be an **inequality in the variable x.**

If a true statement is obtained when a number is substituted for the variable in an inequality, the number is said to be a **solution** of the inequality. For example, 3 is a solution of $x^2 > 2x + 1$, since $3^2 > 2(3) + 1$ is a true statement. On the other hand, 2 is not a solution of $x^2 > 2x + 1$, since $2^2 > 2(2) + 1$ is a false statement. To *solve* an inequality means to determine all the solutions of the inequality. The set consisting of all the solutions of an inequality is called the **solution set** of the inequality.

Two inequalities are called **equivalent inequalities** if they have the same solution set. As with equations, the standard method of solving inequalities is to replace the given inequality with other equivalent inequalities until we obtain an inequality whose solution set is obvious. This can be done by using the following theorem, which follows from Theorem 1.10.

Theorem 3.6 If $P(x)$, $Q(x)$, and $R(x)$ are expressions in the variable x, then the inequality

$$P(x) > Q(x)$$

is equivalent to each of the inequalities

$$P(x) + R(x) > Q(x) + R(x),$$
$$P(x) \cdot R(x) > Q(x) \cdot R(x) \qquad [\text{when } R(x) > 0],$$

and

$$P(x) \cdot R(x) < Q(x) \cdot R(x) \qquad [\text{when } R(x) < 0],$$

for all values of x for which $P(x)$, $Q(x)$, and $R(x)$ have real values.

The previous theorem remains true when $>$ and $<$ are interchanged throughout the theorem. The theorem also remains true when $>$ and $<$ are replaced with $\geq$ and $\leq$, or with $\leq$ and $\geq$, respectively. These results are also true when P, Q, and R are expressions in two or more variables.

Two inequalities are said to have the *same sense* if they both involve the same inequality relation. For instance, $a > b$ and $c > d$ have the same sense, whereas $a > b$ and $c < d$ do *not* have the same sense. To *reverse the sense* of an inequality means to replace $>$ with $<$, $\geq$ with $\leq$, and so on.

Comparing Theorem 3.6 with Theorem 3.1, we note that working with inequalities is almost like working with equations. The principal difference between solving inequalities and solving equations is contained in that portion of the theorems which involves the multiplication of both sides of an equation or inequality by a particular expression. This difference is summarized in the following statements. If we multiply (or divide) both sides of an inequality by the same *positive* expression, *the sense of the inequality remains the same.* On the other hand, if we multiply (or divide) both sides of an inequality by the same *negative* expression, *the sense of the inequality is reversed.*

EXAMPLE 1

The following examples follow from Theorem 3.6.
(a) If $x > 2$, then $x + 7 > 2 + 7$. (The sense of the inequality remains the same when adding the same expression to both sides of an inequality.)
(b) If $x > 2$, then $3x > 3 \cdot 2$ and $-2x < (-2)2$. (The sense of the inequality remains the same when multiplying both sides of an inequality by a *positive* expression, and the sense of an inequality is reversed when multiplying both sides of an inequality by a *negative* expression.)

EXERCISE 1

Fill in the blanks with the correct inequality sign.
(a) If $x > -3$, then $x + 7$ ____ 4.
(b) If $x \geq -1$, then $3x$ ____ -3.
(c) If $x < 5$, then $5x$ ____ 25.
(d) If $3x \leq 9$, then $-x$ ____ -3.

Answer (a) $>$ (b) $\geq$ (c) $<$ (d) $\geq$

Linear Inequalities

An inequality that can be expressed in the form

$$ax + b > 0, \quad ax + b < 0, \quad ax + b \geq 0, \quad \text{or} \quad ax + b \leq 0,$$

with $a \neq 0$ and $a,b \in R$, is called a **linear inequality** in the variable x.

EXAMPLE 2

Solve $1 - 3x > 4$ for x.

Solution The given inequality is equivalent in turn to each of the following inequalities:

$$1 - 3x > 4$$
$$(1 - 3x) + (-1) > 4 + (-1)$$
$$-3x > 3$$
$$(-\tfrac{1}{3})(-3x) < (-\tfrac{1}{3})(3)$$
$$x < -1.$$

Thus any $x < -1$ satisfies the original inequality.   ∎

The **graph** of an inequality (or equation) in the variable x is the set of all points $P(x)$ of a coordinate line whose coordinates are solutions of the inequality (or equation). In sketching the graph of an inequality, it is customary to *darken* (or to *color*) that portion of the coordinate line which corresponds to the solution set of the inequality. For example, the graph of the inequality in Example 2 is as follows:

The *empty circle* indicates that the endpoint -1 *does not* belong to the solution set. On the other hand, a *filled circle* would have meant that the endpoint -1 *does* belong to the solution set.

EXAMPLE 3

Determine the solution set and graph of $5x - 2 \leq 7x - (4 - x)$.

Solution The following inequalities are each equivalent to the given inequality:

$$5x - 2 \leq 7x - (4 - x)$$
$$5x - 2 \leq 8x - 4$$
$$5x - 2 + (-8x + 2) \leq 8x - 4 + (-8x + 2)$$
$$-3x \leq -2$$
$$(-\tfrac{1}{3})(-3x) \geq (-\tfrac{1}{3})(-2)$$
$$x \geq \tfrac{2}{3}.$$

Thus the solution set is $\{x \mid x \geq \tfrac{2}{3}\}$, and the graph is

EXAMPLE 4

Determine the solution set and graph of $-2 \leq 7 - 3x \leq 10$.

Solution Recall that x satisfies the double inequality $a \leq x \leq b$ only if it satisfies both of the inequalities $a \leq x$ and $x \leq b$. Therefore, in this problem, x must satisfy both of the inequalities

$$-2 \leq 7 - 3x \qquad \text{and} \qquad 7 - 3x \leq 10.$$

The following pairs of inequalities are equivalent to the previous pair of inequalities:

$$0 \leq 7 - 3x + 2 \qquad \text{and} \qquad -3x \leq 10 - 7$$
$$3x \leq 9 \qquad \text{and} \qquad -3x \leq 3$$
$$x \leq 3 \qquad \text{and} \qquad x \geq -1.$$

Thus the solution set is $\{x \mid -1 \leq x \leq 3\}$, since any solution of $-1 \leq x \leq 3$ satisfies *both* of the inequalities $x \leq 3$ and $x \geq -1$ and hence *both* of the inequalities $-2 \leq 7 - 3x$ and $7 - 3x \leq 10$. The graph is

EXERCISE 2

Determine the solution set and graph.
(a) $3x + 17 \leq 2(1 - x)$. (b) $-2 < 1 - 3x < 7$.

Answer (a) $\{x \mid x \leq -3\}$
(b) $\{x \mid -2 < x < 1\}$

Problems 3.7

In problems 1–6, fill in the blank with the correct inequality sign.

1. If $2 < x + 3$, then -1 ____ x.   2. If $x + 5 \geq -3$, then x ____ -8.
3. If $x > -3$, then $5x$ ____ -15.   4. If $3x \leq 12$, then x ____ 4.
5. If $2x < 14$, then $-x$ ____ -7.   6. If $-5x \geq 10$, then x ____ -2.

In problems 7–30, determine the solution set and graph of the given inequality.

7. $3x > 5$
8. $2x \leq 3$
9. $5x < -4$
10. $-2x \leq 6$
11. $-3x \geq 12$
12. $-x > 4$
13. $3x - 2 < 8 - 7x$
14. $4x \leq 3 - 2x$
15. $-2x + 1 \leq 3x + 11$
16. $5x - 2 > 5x + 3$
17. $-2x + 3 \leq 2(3 - x)$
18. $2(5 - 3x) \geq 6(1 - x)$
19. $x + [(4x + 3)/2] \leq 5x - 1$
20. $5x - \frac{1}{3} < 8(x - 2)$
21. $4x - (2 - x) \leq -(3 - 5x)$
22. $-6 \leq 3x \leq 9$
23. $-8 < -4x \leq 12$
24. $8 \leq -2x < 14$
25. $-2 < 4x - 3 < 7$
26. $-1 \leq 3x + 5 < 8$
27. $-5 < 7x - 3 < -2$
28. $-1 < 3 - 2x \leq 5$
29. $-3 < 2 - 5x < 8$
30. $-4 < 5 - 3x \leq 14$

31. A student must average between 70 and 80 on five tests to receive a C in the course. If his grades on the first four tests are 62, 79, 67, and 82, what range of grades on the fifth test will result in a C in the course?

32. Fahrenheit and centrigrade temperatures are related by the formula $C = \frac{5}{9}(F - 32)$. If the directions for a certain chemical experiment require that the temperature of a particular solution be kept between 25 and 30° C, what range of temperatures in degrees Fahrenheit will satisfy the temperature restrictions of the solution?

33. A company manufactures electronic pocket calculators. If the company is to show a profit, the revenue obtained from sales of the calculators must certainly be greater than the cost of producing them. If the parts for each calculator cost $12 and if it costs $1500 a week to keep the production line going, how many calculators must be sold each week at $30 each for the company to show a profit?

Answers 3.7

1. $<$ 2. $\geq$ 4. $\leq$

5. $>$ 7. $\{x \mid x > \frac{5}{3}\}$ 8. $\{x \mid x \leq \frac{3}{2}\}$

10. $\{x \mid x \geq -3\}$ 11. $\{x \mid x \leq -4\}$ 13. $\{x \mid x < 1\}$

14. $\{x \mid x \leq \frac{1}{2}\}$ 16. $\varnothing$ 17. R

19. $\{x \mid x \geq \frac{5}{4}\}$ 20. $\{x \mid x > \frac{47}{9}\}$ 22. $\{x \mid -2 \leq x \leq 3\}$

23. $\{x \mid -3 \leq x < 2\}$ 25. $\{x \mid \frac{1}{4} < x < \frac{5}{2}\}$ 26. $\{x \mid -2 \leq x < 1\}$

28. $\{x \mid -1 \leq x < 2\}$ 29. $\{x \mid -\frac{6}{5} < x < 1\}$ 31. 60 or more

32. 77 to 86° F

3.8 Inequalities Involving Products or Quotients

Quadratic Inequalities

An inequality that can be expressed in the form

$$ax^2 + bx + c > 0, \quad ax^2 + bx + c < 0, \quad ax^2 + bx + c \geq 0, \quad \text{or}$$
$$ax^2 + bx + c \leq 0,$$

with $a \neq 0$ and $a,b,c \in R$, is called a **quadratic inequality** in the variable x. Such inequalities can be solved by using Theorem 3.6 and the following theorem, the proof of which follows directly from Theorem 1.11.

Theorem 3.7 If $P(x)$ and $Q(x)$ are expressions in the variable x, then
(a) $P(x) \cdot Q(x) > 0$ if and only if $(P(x) > 0$ and $Q(x) > 0)$ or $(P(x) < 0$ and $Q(x) < 0)$.
(b) $P(x) \cdot Q(x) < 0$ if and only if $(P(x) > 0$ and $Q(x) < 0)$ or $(P(x) < 0$ and $Q(x) > 0)$.

In words, Theorem 3.7 states that *the product of two expressions is positive if and only if both expressions have positive values or both expressions have negative values, and the product of two expressions is negative if and only if the expressions have values that are opposite in sign.*

EXAMPLE 1

Determine the solution set and graph of $2x^2 - 7x - 4 > 0$.

Solution Factoring the left side of the given inequality, we get

$$(2x + 1)(x - 4) > 0.$$

Applying Theorem 3.7, it follows that $(2x + 1)(x - 4) > 0$ if and only if $2x + 1$ and $x - 4$ are both positive or both negative. Since $2x + 1$ and $x - 4$ are both positive when $x > 4$ and both negative when $x < -\frac{1}{2}$, it follows that $(2x + 1)$ $(x - 4) > 0$ when $x > 4$ or when $x < -\frac{1}{2}$. Thus the solution set is $\{x | x < -\frac{1}{2}$ or $x > 4\}$. The graph is

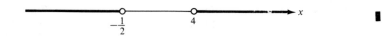

There is an easier method, called the *graphical method,* of solving quadratic inequalities. The procedure used in the graphical method depends for its justification upon Theorem 3.7. We demonstrate this procedure in the following example.

EXAMPLE 2

Determine the solution set and graph of $3x^2 - 8x > 3$.

Solution   We begin by using Theorem 3.6 to rewrite the given inequality as

$$3x^2 - 8x - 3 > 0.$$

Then factoring the left side, we get

$$(3x + 1)(x - 3) > 0.$$

Above the following coordinate line, we have indicated where each of the factors $x - 3$ and $3x + 1$ is positive and where each is negative:

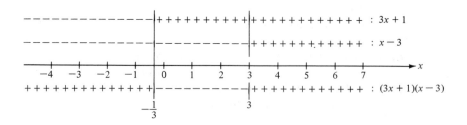

We can then use Theorem 3.7 to determine where $(3x + 1)(x - 3)$ is positive and where it is negative by observing where the factors $x - 3$ and $3x + 1$ have the same signs and where they have opposite signs. Having determined where $(3x + 1)(x - 3)$ is positive and where it is negative, we indicate this information below the previous coordinate line. It is then clear from the coordinate line that the solution set of $(3x + 1)(x - 3) > 0$ and hence of $3x^2 - 8x - 3 > 0$ is $\{x \mid x < -\frac{1}{3} \text{ or } x > 3\}$. The graph is

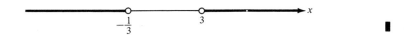

EXERCISE 1

Use the graphical method to determine the solution set and graph.
(a) $x^2 - 10x + 21 < 0$.   (b) $2x^2 + 5x - 3 \geq 0$.

Answer (a) $\{x \mid 3 < x < 7\}$
(b) $\{x \mid x \leq -3 \text{ or } x \geq \frac{1}{2}\}$

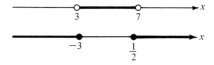

Other Inequalities Involving Products or Quotients

The graphical method demonstrated in Example 2 can also be used to solve inequalities involving products or quotients of more than two factors.

EXAMPLE 3

Determine the solution set and graph of $x(x - 2)(x + 3) < 0$.

Solution Above the following coordinate line, we have indicated where each of the factors $x - 2$, x, and $x + 3$ is positive and where each is negative:

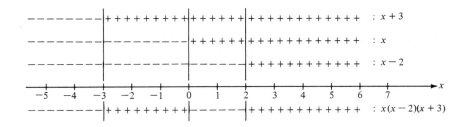

Below the coordinate line, we have indicated where $x(x - 2)(x + 3)$ is positive and where it is negative. Thus the solution set of $x(x - 2)(x + 3) < 0$ is $\{x \mid x < -3 \text{ or } 0 < x < 2\}$, and the graph is

EXAMPLE 4

Determine the solution set and graph of

$$\frac{2}{x-1} > \frac{1}{x-2}.$$

Solution First we rewrite the given inequality as follows:

$$\frac{2}{x-1} - \frac{1}{x-2} > 0$$

$$\frac{2(x-2) - 1(x-1)}{(x-1)(x-2)} > 0$$

and

$$\frac{x-3}{(x-1)(x-2)} > 0.$$

Above the following coordinate line, we have indicated where each of the factors $x - 3$, $x - 2$, and $x - 1$ is positive and where each is negative:

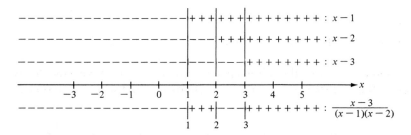

Below the coordinate line, we have indicated where $(x - 3)/[(x - 1)(x - 2)]$ is positive and where it is negative. Thus the solution set of

$$\frac{x-3}{(x-1)(x-2)} > 0,$$

and hence of $2/(x - 1) > 1/(x - 2)$, is $\{x \mid 1 < x < 2 \text{ or } x > 3\}$, and the graph is

EXERCISE 2

Use the graphical method to determine the solution set and graph.
(a) $(x-2)(x+1)(x+4) \le 0.$ (b) $3/(x-2) > 2/x.$

Answer
(a) $\{x|x \leq -4 \text{ or } -1 \leq x \leq 2\}$
(b) $\{x|-4 < x < 0 \text{ or } x > 2\}$

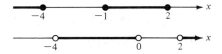

Problems 3.8

In problems 1–30, determine the solution set and graph of the given inequality.

1. $x^2 + 11x + 10 > 0$ 2. $x^2 - x - 6 \leq 0$
3. $x^2 - 3x - 10 < 0$ 4. $2x^2 - x \geq 10$
5. $3x^2 - 5x > 2$ 6. $2x^2 - 3x \leq 9$
7. $x(x + 2) < -1$ 8. $x(x - 2) \geq 3$
9. $x(x - 1) > 12$ 10. $x^3 + 6x^2 + 9x < 0$
11. $x^3 + 2x^2 > 0$ 12. $x^3 - 25x \geq 0$
13. $x^3 - x^2 - 9x + 9 \geq 0$ 14. $x^3 - 3x^2 - x + 3 \leq 0$
15. $x^3 - 2x^2 - 9x + 18 < 0$ 16. $(x - 2)^2(x - 3)(x - 4) \geq 0$
17. $(x - 2)(x - 3)^2(x - 4) \geq 0$ 18. $(x - 2)(x - 3)(x - 4)^2 \geq 0$

19. $\dfrac{2}{x - 2} \leq 1$ 20. $\dfrac{3}{x + 3} \geq 2$

21. $\dfrac{-2}{x - 4} > \frac{1}{2}$ 22. $\dfrac{5}{2x - 3} < -2$

23. $\dfrac{12}{3x + 2} \leq -3$ 24. $\dfrac{1}{2x - 1} \geq -1$

25. $\dfrac{2x}{x - 1} \leq 1$ 26. $\dfrac{4x - 3}{x + 2} > 3$

27. $\dfrac{3x - 2}{x + 4} < 2$ 28. $\dfrac{4}{x - 3} \geq \dfrac{3}{x + 4}$

29. $\dfrac{1}{x} > \dfrac{2}{x - 5}$ 30. $\dfrac{3}{x - 7} < \dfrac{5}{x + 7}$

Answers 3.8

1.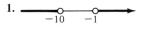
2.
4.

5.
7.
8.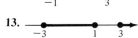

10.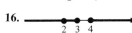
11.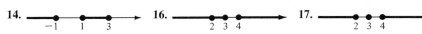
13.

14.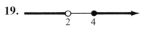
16.
17.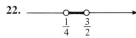

19.
20.
22.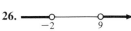

23.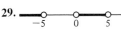
25.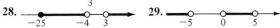
26. (graph)

28. (graph)
29. (graph)

3.9 Equations and Inequalities Involving Absolute Value

Corresponding to each real number x there is a nonnegative value that represents the distance of x from the origin (i.e., the number of unit lengths between the number and the origin) on a coordinate line. This distance, called the *absolute value* of the number, can be represented algebraically as follows.

Definition 3.7 The **absolute value** of a real number x, denoted by $|x|$, is defined as

$$|x| = \begin{cases} x & \text{if } x \geq 0, \\ -x & \text{if } x < 0. \end{cases} \qquad (3-10)$$

Note that the absolute value (i.e., the distance to the origin) of every non-zero real number is positive.

EXAMPLE 1

(a) $|7| = 7$, since $7 \geq 0$.
(b) $|0| = 0$, since $0 \geq 0$.
(c) $|-5| = -(-5) = 5$, since $-5 < 0$.

Since absolute value represents distance on a coordinate line, we can define the distance between any two points on a coordinate line as follows.

Definition 3.8 If $P_1(x_1)$ and $P_2(x_2)$ are any two points on a coordinate line, then the **distance** between P_1 and P_2, denoted by $D(P_1, P_2)$, is defined as

$$D(P_1, P_2) = |x_2 - x_1|. \qquad (3-11)$$

EXAMPLE 2

The distance between 3 and -2 is $|3 - (-2)| = 5$.

Certain basic properties of real numbers involving absolute values are given in the following theorem.

Theorem 3.8 If $a, b \in R$, then
(a) $\sqrt{a^2} = |a|$.
(b) $|-a| = |a|$.
(c) $|a - b| = |b - a|$.
(d) $|ab| = |a||b|$.
(e) $|a/b| = |a|/|b|$ if $b \neq 0$.

Proof of (a) We consider two cases.

Case 1. If $a \geq 0$, then $\sqrt{a^2} = a = |a|$.

Case 2. If $a < 0$ (i.e., if $-a > 0$), then $\sqrt{a^2} = \sqrt{(-a)^2} = -a = |a|$.

Proof of (d) Using the first part of this theorem and Theorem 2.8(a), we get

$$|ab| = \sqrt{(ab)^2} = \sqrt{a^2 b^2} = \sqrt{a^2}\,\sqrt{b^2} = |a||b|.$$

The proofs of the remaining parts of the theorem are left as problems. ∎

EXAMPLE 3

(a) $\sqrt{(-3)^2} = |-3| = 3$.

(b) $|-(x+3)| = |x+3|$.

(c) $|2-x| = |x-2|$.

(d) $|-3x| = |-3||x| = 3|x|$.

(e) $|x/3| = |x|/|3| = |x|/3$.

Equations Involving Absolute Value

Using the following theorem, we can solve certain equations involving absolute value.

Theorem 3.9

If $a \geq 0$, then

$$|p| = a \quad \text{if and only if} \quad p = a \text{ or } p = -a.$$

Proof The proof follows from Definition 3.7 and Theorem 3.8(b). ∎

EXAMPLE 4

Solve $|3x-2| = 7$ for x.

Solution Using Theorem 3.9, the given equation,

$$|3x-2| = 7,$$

is equivalent to the pair of equations

$$3x - 2 = 7 \quad \text{and} \quad 3x - 2 = -7.$$

Solving each of these equations for x, we get

$$3x = 9 \quad \text{or} \quad 3x = -5$$
$$x = 3 \quad \text{or} \quad x = -\tfrac{5}{3}.$$

Hence the solution set is $\{3, -\tfrac{5}{3}\}$.   ∎

EXERCISE 1

Solve $|2x - 3| = 5$ for x.

Answer $4, -1$

Inequalities Involving Absolute Value

In advanced mathematics, you will find that many important inequalities involve absolute values. For this reason, we shall now consider two important theorems which can be used to replace inequalities that involve absolute values with equivalent inequalities of the types considered in the previous sections.

Theorem 3.10   If $a \geq 0$, then

$$|p| \leq a \quad \text{if and only if} \quad -a \leq p \leq a.$$

Proof

Proof of: if $a \geq 0$ and $|p| \leq a$, then $-a \leq p \leq a$ We consider two cases.
Case 1. If $p \geq 0$, then $|p| = p$. Since $|p| = p$ and $|p| \leq a$, we have $p \leq a$. Since $p \geq 0$ and $a \geq 0$ (and hence $-a \leq 0$), it follows that $-a \leq p$. Thus $-a \leq p \leq a$ when $p \geq 0$.
Case 2. If $p < 0$, then $|p| = -p$. Since $|p| = -p$ and $|p| \leq a$, we have $-p \leq a$ and hence $p \geq -a$. Since $p < 0$ and $a \geq 0$, it follows that $p \leq a$. Thus $-a \leq p \leq a$ when $p < 0$.

Proof of: if $a \geq 0$ and $-a \leq p \leq a$, then $|p| \leq a$ We consider two cases.
Case 1. If $p \geq 0$, then $p = |p|$. Since $p = |p|$ and $p \leq a$, it follows that $|p| \leq a$.
Case 2. If $p < 0$, then $-p = |p|$ and hence $p = -|p|$. Since $p = -|p|$ and $-a \leq p$, it follows that $-a \leq -|p|$ and hence $|p| \leq a$.   ∎

Theorem 3.11   If $a \geq 0$, then

$$|p| \geq a \quad \text{if and only if} \quad p \geq a \quad \text{or} \quad p \leq -a.$$

Proof The proof, which is similar to that of Theorem 3.10, is left as a problem. ∎

The previous two theorems are each valid when p is replaced with any expression. For instance, it follows from Theorem 3.10 that

$$|2x-3|\leq 2 \quad \text{if and only if} \quad -2\leq 2x-3\leq 2.$$

As another example, it follows from Theorem 3.11 that

$$|3x-5|\geq 3 \quad \text{if and only if} \quad 3x-5\geq 3 \quad \text{or} \quad 3x-5\leq -3.$$

We now illustrate how to use the previous theorems in solving inequalities involving absolute values.

EXAMPLE 5

Determine the solution set and graph of $|x-3|\leq 7$.

Solution Using Theorem 3.10, the given inequality,

$$|x-3|\leq 7,$$

is equivalent to

$$-7\leq x-3\leq 7,$$

which is equivalent in turn to each of the following pairs of inequalities:

$$-7\leq x-3 \quad \text{and} \quad x-3\leq 7$$
$$-4\leq x \quad \text{and} \quad x\leq 10.$$

Thus the solution set is $\{x|-4\leq x\leq 10\}$, and its graph is

EXAMPLE 6

Determine the solution set and graph of $|2x-3|\geq 5$.

Solution The following inequalities (or pairs of inequalities) are equivalent in turn to one another:

$$|2x-3|\geq 5$$
$$2x-3\geq 5 \quad \text{or} \quad 2x-3\leq -5$$
$$2x\geq 8 \quad \text{or} \quad 2x\leq -2$$
$$x\geq 4 \quad \text{or} \quad x\leq -1.$$

Thus the solution set is $\{x|x\le-1 \text{ or } x\ge 4\}$, and its graph is

EXERCISE 2

Determine the solution set and graph.
(a) $|x-7|<3$.   (b) $|3x-4|>5$.

Answer (a) $\{x|4<x<10\}$
(b) $\{x|x<-\frac{1}{3} \text{ or } x>3\}$

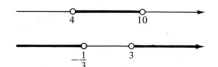

Problems 3.9

In problems 1–6, determine the distance between the given points of a coordinate line.

1. $P(5)$, $P(-2)$ **2.** $P(-3)$, $P(-4)$ **3.** $P(3)$, $P(10)$
4. $P(-7)$, $P(\frac{3}{2})$ **5.** $P(\frac{5}{2})$, $P(-\frac{2}{3})$ **6.** $P(-\frac{3}{2})$, $P(-\frac{19}{4})$

In problems 7–15, determine the solution set of the given equation.

7. $|x-3|=5$ **8.** $|x+2|=3$ **9.** $|x-2|=-2$
10. $|2x+3|=-3$ **11.** $|3x-7|=4$ **12.** $|3x-5|=3$
13. $|3x+1|=2$ **14.** $|2x-1|=-1$ **15.** $|2x+1|=4$

In problems 16–36, determine the solution set and graph of the given inequality.

16. $|x-5|<3$ **17.** $|x+2|\le 4$ **18.** $|x-3|\le 2$
19. $|3x-1|\le 4$ **20.** $|2x+5|<2$ **21.** $|4x-3|<3$
22. $|x+1|\ge 3$ **23.** $|x-2|>2$ **24.** $|x+4|>4$
25. $|2x+1|>5$ **26.** $|5x-2|\ge 3$ **27.** $|3x+2|\ge 6$
28. $|2x+1|<-2$ **29.** $|3x+4|>-1$ **30.** $|2x-5|\ge-1$
31. $\dfrac{2}{|x-3|}>5$ **32.** $\dfrac{3}{|x+1|}\le\frac{1}{2}$ **33.** $\dfrac{2}{|x-5|}\le\frac{1}{3}$
34. $\left|\dfrac{x-5}{3x-2}\right|<1$ **35.** $\left|\dfrac{x+2}{x-5}\right|>4$ **36.** $\left|\dfrac{2x+1}{x-2}\right|\ge 3$
37. Prove Theorem 3.8(b).   **38.** Prove Theorem 3.8(c).
39. Prove Theorem 3.8(e).   **40.** Prove Theorem 3.11.

Answers 3.9

1. 7   **2.** 1   **4.** $\frac{17}{2}$ **5.** $\frac{19}{6}$
7. $\{8,-2\}$ **8.** $\{1,-5\}$ **10.** $\varnothing$
11. $\{1,\frac{11}{3}\}$ **13.** $\{\frac{1}{3},-1\}$ **14.** $\varnothing$

16. $\{x\,|\,2<x<8\}$

17. $\{x\,|\,-6\le x\le 2\}$

19. $\{x\,|\,-1\le x\le\frac{5}{3}\}$

20. $\{x\,|\,-\frac{7}{2}<x<-\frac{3}{2}\}$

22. $\{x\,|\,x\le-4\text{ or }x\ge 2\}$

23. $\{x\,|\,x<0\text{ or }x>4\}$

25. $\{x\,|\,x<-3\text{ or }x>2\}$

26. $\{x\,|\,x\le-\frac{1}{5}\text{ or }x\ge 1\}$

28. $\varnothing$

29. R

31.

32. ![number line with open circle at -7 and closed circle at 5]

34. ![number line with open circles at -3/2 and 7/4]

35. ![number line with open circles at 18/5, 5, and 22/3]

chapter 3 review problems

1. Determine the solution set of the given equation:
   (a) $3x+1=0$
   (b) $3(1-2x)=2(x+6)$
   (c) $\dfrac{3}{x-1}+\dfrac{5}{x+3}=0$
   (d) $\dfrac{6x}{2x-1}=2+\dfrac{3}{2x-1}$
   (e) $x^2-5x-6=0$
   (f) $(x-3)(x+5)=20$
   (g) $x^2-4x-1=0$
   (h) $x^2+4x+5=0$
   (i) $x^4-12x^2-64=0$
   (j) $x^{-2}+2x^{-1}-3=0$
   (k) $\sqrt{x+32}-\sqrt{x+5}=3$
   (l) $\sqrt{9-2x}+\sqrt{1-x}=22$

2. The sum of two integers is 79. If the larger integer is divided by the smaller integer, the quotient is 4 and the remainder is 9. Determine the two integers.

3. Determine how many ounces of pure silver should be added to 16 ounces of an alloy that is 45 percent silver to produce a new alloy that is 65 percent silver.

4. Bill and Jim can plant a lawn in 8 hours. If it takes Bill 12 hours more to plant the lawn alone than it takes Jim to do the same job alone, determine how long it would take Jim to plant the lawn by himself.

5. Perform the indicated operations and write the result as a complex number.
   (a) $(2-i)+(-3+2i)$
   (b) $(2-i)-(-3+2i)$
   (c) $(2-i)(-3+2i)$
   (d) $\dfrac{-3+2i}{2-i}$

6. Determine the solution set and graph of the given inequality:
   (a) $3x-5\le x-13$
   (b) $2x^2-5x-12>0$
   (c) $x^3+3x^2-4x-12>0$
   (d) $(x-5)(x-2)(x+3)\le 0$
   (e) $(x-5)(x-1)^2(x+2)\ge 0$
   (f) $\dfrac{(x-5)(x-1)}{x+2}\ge 0$
   (g) $\dfrac{1}{x-3}>2$
   (h) $\dfrac{2}{x-3}\le\dfrac{3}{x+2}$
   (i) $|x+2|\le 5$
   (j) $|2x-3|>3$
   (k) $|5x-1|\le-3$
   (l) $|x-5|<\frac{3}{2}$

answers

1. (a) $\{-\frac{1}{3}\}$ (b) $\{-\frac{9}{8}\}$ (c) $\{-\frac{1}{2}\}$ (d) $\varnothing$ (e) $\{6,-1\}$ (f) $\{5,-7\}$
(g) $\{2\pm\sqrt{5}\}$ (h) $\{-2\pm i\}$ (i) $\{4,-4,2i,-2i\}$ (j) $\{1,-\frac{1}{3}\}$
(k) $\{4\}$ (l) $\{-80\}$

2. 14 and 65   **3.** $9\frac{1}{7}$ ounces   **4.** 12 hours

5. (a) $-1+i$ (b) $5-3i$ (c) $-4+7i$ (d) $-\frac{8}{5}+\frac{1}{5}i$

6. (a)

(b)

(c)

(d)

(e)

(f)

(g)

(h)

(i)

(j)

(k)

(l)

4

relations

4.1 Cartesian Coordinate Systems and the Distance Formula

In the set $\{a, b\}$, the elements do not have to be listed in any particular order. That is, the sets $\{a, b\}$ and $\{b, a\}$ are one and the same. On the other hand, an **ordered pair**, denoted by (a, b), is a pair of elements in which a is the *first element* and b is the *second element*. Because of the ordering, the ordered pairs (a, b) and (b, a) are not the same unless $a = b$. In general, two ordered pairs are said to be **equal** if and only if the two ordered pairs have equal first elements and equal second elements.

Definition 4.1 The **Cartesian product** of two sets X and Y, written $X \times Y$, is defined as

$$X \times Y = \{(x, y) | x \in X \text{ and } y \in Y\}.$$

That is, the Cartesian product of two sets X and Y is the set consisting of all possible ordered pairs (x, y) such that $x \in X$ and $y \in Y$.

EXAMPLE 1

If $X = \{0, 1\}$ and $Y = \{-1, 0\}$, then

$$X \times Y = \{(0, -1), (0, 0), (1, -1), (1, 0)\},$$

and

$$Y \times X = \{(-1, 0), (0, 0), (-1, 1), (0, 1)\}.$$

121

EXERCISE 1

If $X = \{1, 3, 5\}$ and $Y = \{2, 4\}$, describe $X \times Y$ by the roster method.

Answer $X \times Y = \{(1, 2), (1, 4), (3, 2), (3, 4), (5, 2), (5, 4)\}$

EXAMPLE 2

If $X = R$ and $Y = R$, then $X \times Y = R \times R$, where $R \times R$ is the set of all possible ordered pairs of real numbers.

Cartesian Coordinate Systems

Just as it is possible to set up a one-to-one correspondence between the real numbers and the points of a line, it is also possible to set up a one-to-one correspondence between the ordered pairs of real numbers and the points of a plane. This can be done as follows. Consider two mutually perpendicular coordinate lines which intersect such that the point of intersection, called the **origin,** represents the real number zero on both coordinate lines. We assume the unit length to be the same on each of the coordinate lines. We follow the usual convention of drawing one of the coordinate lines as a horizontal line with its positive direction toward the right, and the other coordinate line as a vertical line with positive direction upward. Together the two coordinate lines are called the **coordinate axes** of the plane. In particular, the horizontal line is called the **x-axis,** and the vertical line is called the **y-axis.**

When P is any point of the plane formed by the coordinate axes, P has a unique ordered pair (x, y) of real numbers associated with it. This can be

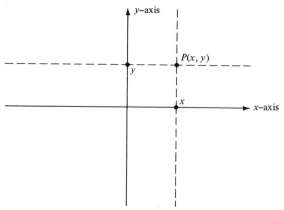

Figure 4.1

seen by drawing a line through P parallel to the x-axis, and then drawing a second line through P parallel to the y-axis. See Figure 4.1. The coordinate of the point of the x-axis at which the vertical line intersects the x-axis represents the first number, x, in the ordered pair (x, y). Similarly, the coordinate of the point of the y-axis at which the horizontal line intersects the y-axis represents the second number, y, in the ordered pair (x, y). The first number, x, is called the **x-coordinate,** or **abscissa,** of P, and the second number, y, is called the **y-coordinate,** or **ordinate,** of P. Together the two numbers x and y, are called the **coordinates** of P. Thus, with each point P of the plane there is associated a unique ordered pair (x, y) of real numbers. Conversely, with each ordered pair (x, y) of real numbers, there is associated a unique point P of the plane.

The one-to-one correspondence described above between the points of a plane and the ordered pairs of real numbers is called a **Cartesian (or rectangular) coordinate system** for the plane. A plane that has such a Cartesian coordinate system is referred to as a **rectangular coordinate plane** (or **coordinate plane,** for short). As in the case of the real number line, we often speak of the point (x, y) when we actually mean the point P whose abscissa is x and whose ordinate is y. That is, we shall frequently follow the customary convention of using the terms *ordered pair* and *point* interchangeably. Some points together with their coordinates are shown on the coordinate plane is Figure 4.2.

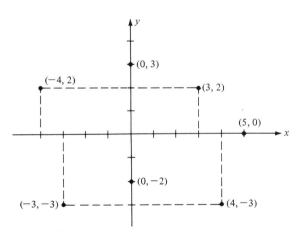

Figure 4.2

A coordinate plane is divided into four regions, called **quadrants,** by the coordinate axes as indicated in Figure 4.3. Thus a point is in quadrant 1 when $x > 0$ and $y > 0$, in quadrant 2 when $x < 0$ and $y > 0$, in quadrant 3 when $x < 0$ and $y < 0$, and in quadrant 4 when $x > 0$ and $y < 0$. If either coordinate of $P(x, y)$ is zero, the point is *not* in any quadrant but is instead a point of one or both of the coordinate axes.

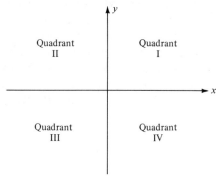

Figure 4.3

The Distance Formula

The distance between any two points of a coordinate plane can be determined by using the simple formula, called the **distance formula**, which appears in the following theorem.

Theorem 4.1   If $P_1(x_1, y_1)$ and $P_2(x_2, y_2)$ are any two points of a coordinate plane, the distance between the points P_1 and P_2, denoted by $D(P_1, P_2)$, is given by

$$D(P_1, P_2) = \sqrt{(x_2 - x_1)^2 + (y_2 - y_1)^2}. \qquad (4-1)$$

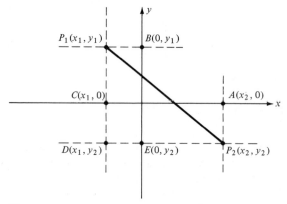

Figure 4.4

Proof Let $P_1(x_1, y_1)$ and $P_2(x_2, y_2)$ be two arbitrary points of a coordinate plane. Draw a line through P_1 parallel to the x-axis and a line through P_2 parallel to the x-axis. Similarly, draw lines through P_1 and P_2 parallel to the y-axis. See Figure 4.4. Since the line segments $\overline{DP_2}$ and $\overline{AC}$ are opposite sides of a rectangle, it follows that $D(D, P_2) = D(A, C)$. Similarly, $D(P_1, D) = D(E, B)$. Since A, B, C, and E are points of coordinate lines, it follows by Definition 3.8 that $D(A, C) = |x_2 - x_1|$ and $D(E, B) = |y_2 - y_1|$. Using the Pythagorean theorem, it follows that

$$
\begin{aligned}
[D(P_1, P_2)]^2 &= [D(P_1, D)]^2 + [D(D, P_2)]^2 \\
&= [D(E, B)]^2 + [D(A, C)]^2 \\
&= |y_2 - y_1|^2 + |x_2 - x_1|^2 \\
&= (y_2 - y_1)^2 + (x_2 - x_1)^2 \\
&= (x_2 - x_1)^2 + (y_2 - y_1)^2.
\end{aligned}
$$

Hence

$$
D(P_1, P_2) = \sqrt{(x_2 - x_1)^2 + (y_2 - y_1)^2},
$$

since distance is always nonnegative.   ∎

EXAMPLE 3

Determine the distance between the points $(3, -2)$ and $(-2, 5)$.

Solution Let $P_1 = (3, -2)$ and $P_2 = (-2, 5)$. Then $x_1 = 3, y_1 = -2, x_2 = -2$, and $y_2 = 5$. Using the distance formula, we get

$$
D(P_1, P_2) = \sqrt{[(-2) - (3)]^2 + [(5) - (-2)]^2} = \sqrt{74}. \qquad ∎
$$

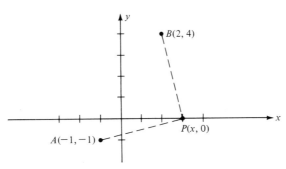

Figure 4.5

EXAMPLE 4

Determine x so that the point $(x, 0)$ will be equidistant from $(2, 4)$ and $(-1, -1)$.

Solution   See Figure 4.5. The point $(x, 0)$ will be equidistant from $(2, 4)$ and $(-1, -1)$ when $D(A, P) = D(B, P)$. Using the distance formula to substitute for $D(A, P)$ and $D(B, P)$,

$$\sqrt{[x-(-1)]^2 + [0-(-1)]^2} = \sqrt{(x-2)^2 + (0-4)^2}.$$

Squaring both sides of this equation gives

$$(x+1)^2 + (1)^2 = (x-2)^2 + (-4)^2$$

and hence

$$x^2 + 2x + 1 + 1 = x^2 - 4x + 4 + 16.$$

Solving for x, we find that $x = 3$.   ∎

Problems 4.1

In problems 1–6, describe $X \times Y$ by the roster method.

1. $X = \{a, b\}$, $Y = \{b, c\}$ **2.** $X = \{a, 1\}$, $Y = \{b, 2\}$
3. $X = \{1, 2, 3\}$, $Y = \{4, 5\}$ **4.** $X = Y = \{-1, 1\}$
5. $X = Y = \{a, b\}$ **6.** $X = Y = \{x, y, z\}$

In problems 7–15, determine those quadrants of a coordinate plane whose points $P(x, y)$ satisfy the given condition.

7. $x < 0$ **8.** $y > 0$ **9.** $y < 0$
10. $1/y > 0$ **11.** $1/x > 0$ **12.** $1/y > 0$
13. $y/x < 0$ **14.** $x/y < 0$ **15.** $x/y > 0$

In problems 16–24, locate the following pairs of points of a coordinate plane and then determine the distance between the points.

16. $(1, 5)$, $(2, 3)$ **17.** $(-2, 1)$, $(-4, 3)$ **18.** $(5, 1)$, $(7, 4)$
19. $(5, -1)$, $(-3, 2)$ **20.** $(4, 1)$, $(-3, -3)$ **21.** $(2, 4)$, $(0, -1)$
22. $(-1, 4)$, $(2, 2)$ **23.** $(1, 3)$, $(5, 0)$ **24.** $(2, 1)$, $(-3, 0)$
25. Determine x so that $(x, 0)$ is equidistant from $(2, 2)$ and $(7, 0)$.
26. Determine y so that $(0, y)$ is equidistant from $(-1, 4)$ and $(3, -3)$.
27. Determine y so that $(0, y)$ is equidistant from $(-1, 5)$ and $(2, -1)$.
28. Use the distance formula to show that the triangle formed by the points $(-1, -3)$, $(6, 1)$, and $(2, -5)$ is a right triangle.
29. Use the distance formula to show that the triangle formed by the points $(2, 1)$, $(6, 1)$, and $(4, 4)$ is an isosceles triangle.
30. Use the distance formula to derive an equation of the circle whose center is $(0, 0)$ and whose radius is 1.

Answers 4.1

1. $\{(a, b), (a, c), (b, b), (b, c)\}$ 2. $\{(a, b), (a, 2), (1, b), (1, 2)\}$
4. $\{(-1, -1), (-1, 1), (1, -1), (1, 1)\}$ 5. $\{(a, a), (a, b), (b, a), (b, b)\}$
7. P is in quadrant 2 or 3   8. P is in quadrant 1 or 2
10. P is in quadrant 1 or 2   11. P is in quadrant 1 or 4
13. P is in quadrant 2 or 4   14. P is in quadrant 2 or 4
16. $\sqrt{5}$ 17. $\sqrt{8}$ 19. $\sqrt{73}$ 20. $\sqrt{65}$
22. $\sqrt{13}$ 23. 5   25. $1/10$ 26. $-1/14$

4.2 Relations Defined by Equations

In much of the remainder of this book, we shall be interested in subsets of Cartesian product sets (in particular, subsets of $R \times R$). Such subsets are called relations.

Definition 4.2   If X and Y are sets, then any nonempty subset S of $X \times Y$ is said to be a **relation from X to Y.** The set of all first elements of the ordered pairs of the relation S, denoted by D_S, is called the **domain** of the relation S. The set of all second elements of the ordered pairs of the relation S, denoted by R_S, is called the **range** of S. A relation from R to R is said to be a **relation on R.**

EXAMPLE 1

The set $S = \{(0, 0), (1, 0), (0, 1), (2, 1)\}$ is a relation on R since S is a subset of $R \times R$. The domain of S is $\{0, 1, 2\}$, since 0, 1, and 2 are the first elements of the ordered pairs of S. Similarly, the range of S is $\{0, 1\}$, since 0 and 1 are the second elements.

EXERCISE 1

What is the domain and the range of $S = \{(0, \pi), (1, \pi), (1, \sqrt{2}), (1, \sqrt{3}), (1, 2)\}$?

Answer $D_S = \{0, 1\}$, $R_S = \{\pi, \sqrt{2}, \sqrt{3}, 2\}$.

Since each subset of $R \times R$ is a collection of ordered pairs of real numbers, each relation on R can be represented graphically as points of a coordinate plane.

Definition 4.3   The **graph of a relation on R** is the set of all points (x, y) of a coordinate plane whose associated ordered pairs belong to the relation.

EXAMPLE 2

Determine the domain and range of the relation $S = \{(1, 1), (1, 2), (2, 2),$ $(2, 3), (2, 4), (3, 3)\}$, and then graph S.

Solution   Note that S is a relation on R since S is a subset of $R \times R$. The domain of S is $\{1, 2, 3\}$, and the range of S is $\{1, 2, 3, 4\}$. The graph of S, which is shown in Figure 4.6, is composed of the six points of the coordinate plane associated with the six ordered pairs that belong to S.   ∎

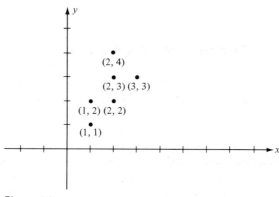

Figure 4.6

Relations on R Defined by Equations

If $P(x, y)$ and $Q(x, y)$ are expressions involving the two variables x and y, then a statement of the form

$$P(x, y) = Q(x, y)$$

is said to be an **equation in the two variables x and y.** For example,

$$2x = 7 - y, \quad y^2 - x = x^2 + 1, \quad \text{and} \quad x^2 + 4y^2 = 1$$

are equations in the two variables x and y.

If a true statement is obtained when the x and y coordinates of an ordered pair (x, y) are substituted for the variables x and y, respectively, in an equation, the ordered pair (x, y) is said to be a **solution** of the equation. For example, $(1, 9)$ is a solution of the equation $2x + 7 = y$, since $2(1) + 7 = 9$. On the other hand, $(9, 1)$ is not a solution of $2x + 7 = y$, since $2(9) + 7 \neq 1$. When (x, y) is a solution of an equation, the coordinates x and y of the ordered pair (x, y) are called *corresponding values* of x and y.

To *solve* an equation in the variables x and y means to determine all the ordered pairs whose coordinates satisfy the equation. However, most equations of interest have an infinite number of such ordered pairs. Although it is actually impossible to list all the solutions of such equations, we can determine as many of the solutions as we desire. Such solutions are obtained by choosing a value of x and then calculating the corresponding value or values of y, if any, from the given equation.

Since the solutions of an equation in the variables x and y are ordered pairs, we can represent the solutions of such an equation as points of a coordinate plane. This process is known as *graphing the equation*. Thus the **graph of an equation** in the variables x and y is the set of all points (x, y) of a coordinate plane whose coordinates satisfy the equation. The geometric figure that is formed by the points of the graph is referred to as a *plane curve*, or simply a *curve*.

Since the solutions of an equation in the variables x and y are ordered pairs of real numbers, we see that an equation defines a collection of ordered pairs and hence a relation on R. When a relation is defined by an equation, the graph of the relation is the same as the graph of the equation, since the ordered pairs that satisfy the equation are the same as the ordered pairs that belong to the graph of the relation.

EXAMPLE 3

Graph the relation S on R defined by the equation $y = x$. That is, graph the relation $S = \{(x, y) \mid y = x\}$.

Solution We begin by choosing some values for x, say $-3, -2, -1, 0, 1, 2$, and 3, and calculating the corresponding values of y from the given equation $y = x$. These values can be shown conveniently in the form of a table of values such as the one that follows:

x	-3	-2	-1	0	1	2	3
y	-3	-2	-1	0	1	2	3

In this table, for a given value of x, the corresponding value of y appears below it. Thus we see that $(-3, -3), (-2, -2), (-1, -1), (0, 0), (1, 1), (2, 2),$ and $(3, 3)$ belong to the graph of the equation $y = x$ and hence to the graph of the relation $S = \{(x, y) \mid y = x\}$. Representing these points on a coordinate plane (Figure 4.7), we find that they all lie in a straight line. Thus we suspect that the graph of the given relation is a straight line. In the next section we shall prove that our assumption is indeed correct. ∎

Since the relation S in Example 2 contained only a finite number of ordered pairs, it was possible to determine the domain and range of S by actually examining each of the ordered pairs of S. On the other hand, however, the relation S in Example 3 contains an infinite number of ordered pairs. Thus it is impossible to determine the domain and range by actually examining each of the ordered pairs of S. In such cases, the graph of S can be used to determine the domain and the range of S.

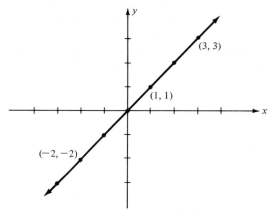

Figure 4.7

Using Definitions 4.2 and 4.3, it follows that the domain of a relation S on R is the set of all real numbers x such that (x, y) is a point of the graph of S, and the range of S is the set of all real numbers y such that (x, y) is a point of the graph of S. The previous fact justifies the following rule for determining the domain and the range of a relation on R from its graph.

The Projection Rule

1. *If we project the graph of a relation vertically (i.e., up or down) onto the x-axis, the domain of the relation consists of that portion of the x-axis which has a point of the graph projected onto it.*
2. *If we project the graph of a relation horizontally (i.e., to the left or to the right) onto the y-axis, the range of the relation consists of that portion of the y-axis which has a point of the graph projected onto it.*

EXAMPLE 4

Use the projection rule to determine the domain and the range of the relation $S = \{(x, y) | y = x\}$.

Solution The graph of S was determined in Example 3 (see Figure 4.7). By projecting the points of the graph of S vertically onto the x-axis (see Figure 4.8), we see that every point of the x-axis has a point of the graph projected onto it. Thus the domain of S is $\{x | x \in R\}$. Projecting the points of the graph of S horizontally onto the y-axis (see Figure 4.9), we see that every point of the y-axis has a point of the graph projected onto it. Thus the range of S is $\{y \mid y \in R\}$.

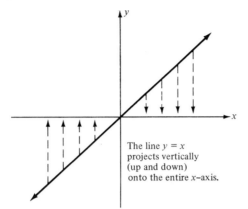

The line $y = x$
projects vertically
(up and down)
onto the entire x–axis.

Figure 4.8

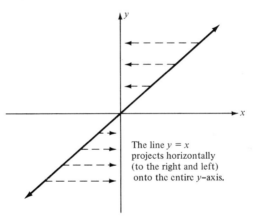

The line $y = x$
projects horizontally
(to the right and left)
onto the entire y–axis.

Figure 4.9

EXERCISE 2

Assuming that the given graph is the graph of the relation S, determine the domain and range of S.

(a)

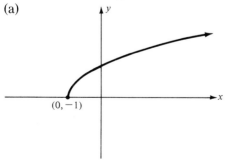

$(0, -1)$

(b)

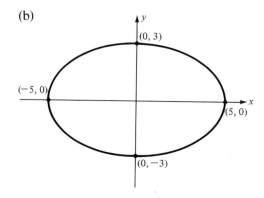

Answer (a) $\{x|x \geq -1\}$, $\{y|y \geq 0\}$ (b) $\{x|-5 \leq x \leq 5\}$, $\{y|-3 \leq y \leq 3\}$

Problems 4.2

1. Determine y so that $(4, y)$ is a solution of $y=x^2-x-4$.
2. Determine y so that $(2, y)$ is a solution of $y^2+xy=3$.
3. Determine y so that $(-2, y)$ is a solution of $y^4=4x^2y^2$.
4. Determine x so that $(x, 1)$ is a solution of $\sqrt{9x+1}-y=x$.
5. Determine x so that $(x, -3)$ is a solution of $y = \sqrt[3]{2x-3}$.
6. Determine x so that $(x, 5)$ is a solution of $y=x^2+4x$.

In problems 7–12, list five ordered pairs that belong to the given relation on R.

7. $\{(x, y)|y=2x-5\}$ 8. $\{(x, y)|y=x^2\}$
9. $\{(x, y)|y=x^2-x\}$ 10. $\{(x, y)|y=x^3\}$
11. $\{(x, y)|y=\sqrt{x-3}\}$ 12. $\{(x, y)|y=|x-3|\}$

In problems 13–21, see if you can discover the pattern for the graph of the relation S defined by the given equation by plotting the points that have the given x-values.

13. $y=x-2$, x-values: $-4, -2, 0, 2, 4$
14. $y=2x+1$, x-values; $-4, -2, 0, 2, 4$
15. $y=x^2$, x-values: $-3, -2, -1, 0, 1, 2, 3$
16. $y=x^2-2x$, x-values: $-2, -1, 0, 1, 2, 3, 4$
17. $y=x^3$, x-values: $-3, -2, -1, 0, 1, 2, 3$
18. $y=\sqrt{x}$, x-values: $0, 1, 2, 3, 4, 9, 16, 25$
19. $y=|x|$, x-values: $-3, -2, -1, 0, 1, 2, 3$
20. $y^2=x$, x-values: $0, 1, 4, 9, 16$
21. $x^2+y^2=9$, x-values: $-3, -2, -1, 0, 1, 2, 3$

In problems 22–30, assuming that the given curve is the graph of the relation S, determine the domain and range of S.

22.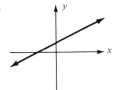

23.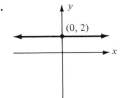

24.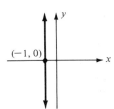

25.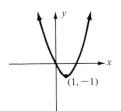

26.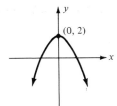

27.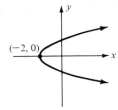

28.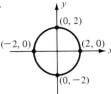

29.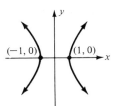

30.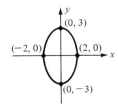

Answers 4.2

1. 8   **2.** 1, −3   **4.** 0. 7   **5.** −12

7. (−2, −9), (−1, −7), (0, −5), (1, −3), (2, −1)

8. (−2, 4), (−1, 1), (0, 0), (1, 1), (2, 4)

10. (−2, −8), (−1, −1), (0, 0), (1, 1), (2, 8)

11. (3, 0), (4, 1), (5, $\sqrt{2}$), (6, $\sqrt{3}$), (7, 2)

13. **14.** 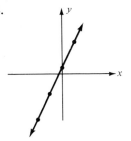 **16.**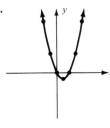

17. 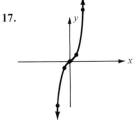 **19.** 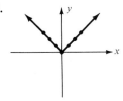 **20.**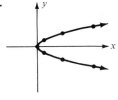

22. $\{x|x \in R\}$, $\{y|y \in R\}$
23. $\{x|x \in R\}$, $\{2\}$
25. $\{x|x \in R\}$, $\{y|y \geq -1\}$
26. $\{x|x \in R\}$, $\{y|y \leq 2\}$
28. $\{x|-2 \leq x \leq 2\}$, $\{y|-2 \leq y \leq 2\}$
29. $\{x|x \geq 1 \text{ or } x \leq -1\}$, $\{y|y \in R\}$

4.3 Relations Whose Graphs Are Lines

In this section, we show that the graph of each relation on R defined by an equation of the form

$$Ax + By + C = 0, \qquad (4-2)$$

where $A,B,C \in R$ with $A \neq 0$ or $B \neq 0$, is a straight line. Any equation that is equivalent to an equation of the form of Eq. (4–2) is called a **linear equation** in the variables x and y. Equation (4–2) is referred to as the *standard form* of a linear equation.

We begin our discussion of lines by introducing a fundamental concept that pertains to lines.

Definition 4.4   Let $P_1(x_1, y_1)$ and $P_2(x_2, y_2)$ be any two points of a straight line with $x_1 \neq x_2$. The number m defined by the equation

$$m = \frac{y_2 - y_1}{x_2 - x_1} \qquad (4-3)$$

is called the **slope** of the line. If $x_1 = x_2$, the line has **no slope**.

EXAMPLE 1

Determine the slope m of the line through the points $(1, -2)$ and $(3, 1)$.

Solution   Let $(x_1, y_1) = (1, -2)$ and $(x_2, y_2) = (3, 1)$. Using Eq. (4–3), we get

$$m = \frac{y_2 - y_1}{x_2 - x_1} = \frac{1 - (-2)}{3 - 1} = \frac{3}{2}.$$

Since

$$\frac{y_2 - y_1}{x_2 - x_1} = \frac{-(y_1 - y_2)}{-(x_1 - x_2)} = \frac{y_1 - y_2}{x_1 - x_2},$$

the order in which the two points (x_1, y_1) and (x_2, y_2) are taken is immaterial in determining the slope of the line through the points. Thus we could have chosen $(x_1, y_1) = (3, 1)$ and $(x_2, y_2) = (1, -2)$ in Example 1.   ∎

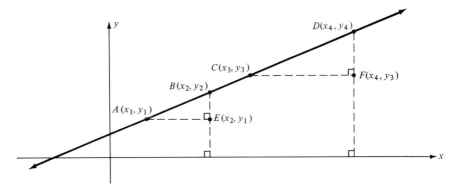

Figure 4.10

It is important to note that the slope of a line is the same regardless of the two points of the line that are used in determining the slope. Using Figure 4.10, this can be seen as follows. Since triangles ABE and CDF are similar, the ratios of the lengths of corresponding sides are equal. Therefore,

$$\frac{y_4 - y_3}{x_4 - x_3} = \frac{y_2 - y_1}{x_2 - x_1}. \qquad (4-4)$$

The ratio on the left side of Eq. (4–4) represents the slope of the line through the points C and D, and the ratio on the right side of Eq. (4–4) represents the slope of the line through the points A and B. Since these two ratios are equal, it follows that the slope of the line is the same regardless of the points used in determining the slope.

EXERCISE 1

Determine the slope of the line through $(1, 2)$ and $(3, -1)$.

Answer $-3/2$

We now turn our attention to the problem of determining an equation of a line. We begin with two simple cases. Since every point of a vertical line has the same x-coordinate (see Figure 4.11), an equation of the vertical line through the point (x_1, y_1) is

$$x = x_1.$$

Since every point of a horizontal line has the same y-coordinate (see Figure 4.12), an equation of the horizontal line through the point (x_1, y_1) is

$$y = y_1.$$

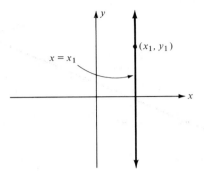

Figure 4.11

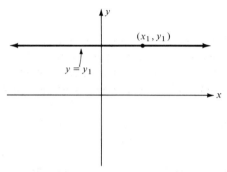

Figure 4.12

Using the following theorem, we can determine an equation of the non-vertical line which passes through a given point with a given slope.

Theorem 4.2   An equation for the line passing through the point (x_0, y_0) with a slope of m is

$$y - y_0 = m(x - x_0). \qquad (4-5)$$

Proof   Let (x, y) be any point of the line except (x_0, y_0). Then the slope m of the line is given by

$$m = \frac{y - y_0}{x - x_0}.$$

Thus $y - y_0 = m(x - x_0)$, since $x \neq x_0$.   ∎

Since Eq. (4-5) involves a point of the line and the slope of the line, it is called the *point-slope form* for the equation of a straight line.

EXAMPLE 2

Find an equation for the line through (−5, 3) with a slope of $-\frac{2}{3}$.

Solution   Using Eq. (4−5) with $(x_0, y_0) = (-5, 3)$ and $m = -\frac{2}{3}$, we get

$$y - 3 = -\tfrac{2}{3}[x - (-5)]$$

as the equation of the line in point-slope form. An equivalent equation in standard form is

$$2x + 3y + 1 = 0.$$

EXERCISE 2

Find an equation for the line through the point $(1, -2)$ with a slope of $-\frac{3}{4}$.

Answer $3x + 4y + 5 = 0$

In general, the **x-intercepts** of the graph of an equation are the values of x at the points, if any, where the graph intersects the x-axis. Similarly, the **y-intercepts** of the graph are the values of y at the points, if any, where the graph crosses the y-axis. Note that every nonvertical line has precisely one x-intercept, which we denote by a, and one y-intercept, which we denote by b (see Figure 4.13).

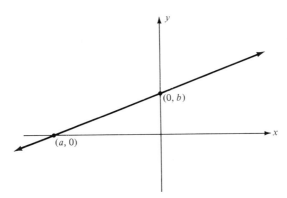

Figure 4.13

The following theorem can be used to determine an equation of the nonvertical line with a given slope and a given y-intercept.

Theorem 4.3   An equation for the line that has a slope of m and a y-intercept of b is

$$y = mx + b. \tag{4-6}$$

Proof   Since b is the y-intercept of the line, $(0, b)$ is a point of the line. Using Eq. (4–5) with $(x_0, y_0) = (0, b)$, we get

$$y - b = m(x - 0)$$

and hence

$$y = mx + b. \qquad \blacksquare$$

Equation (4–6) is called the *slope-intercept form* for the equation of a line.

EXAMPLE 3

Find an equation for the line with a slope of -2 and a y-intercept of 0.

Solution   Using Eq. (4–6) with $m = -2$ and $b = 0$, we get

$$y = (-2)x + 0$$

as the equation of the line in slope-intercept form. An equivalent equation in standard form is $\qquad \blacksquare$

$$2x + y = 0.$$

EXERCISE 3

Find an equation for the line with a slope of -3 and a y-intercept of 2.

Answer $3x + y - 2 = 0$

The slope of a line whose equation is given in standard form can easily be determined by rewriting the equation in slope-intercept form.

EXAMPLE 4

Determine the slope of the line $2x - 3y - 2 = 0$.

Solution   Solving $2x - 3y - 2 = 0$ for y, we get

$$y = (\tfrac{2}{3})x + (-\tfrac{2}{3}).$$

Comparing the last equation with Eq. (4–6), we find that the slope of $2x - 3y - 2 = 0$ is $\tfrac{2}{3}$. $\qquad \blacksquare$

EXERCISE 4

Determine the slope of the line $3x + 5y - 7 = 0$.

Answer $m = -\tfrac{3}{5}$

The following theorem can be used to determine an equation of a slant line with a given nonzero x-intercept and a given nonzero y-intercept.

Theorem 4.4 An equation for the line that has an x-intercept of a, where $a \neq 0$, and a y-intercept of b, where $b \neq 0$, is

$$\frac{x}{a} + \frac{y}{b} = 1. \qquad\qquad (4-7)$$

Proof Since a is the x-intercept of the line, $(a, 0)$ is a point of the line. Since b is the y-intercept of the line, $(0, b)$ is another point of the line. Hence the slope of the line is $m = (b - 0)/(0 - a) = -b/a$. Using Eq. (4–5) with $(x_0, y_0) = (a, 0)$ and $m = -b/a$, we get

$$y - 0 = \left(\frac{-b}{a}\right)(x - a).$$

Rewriting the last equation, we get

$$\frac{x}{a} + \frac{y}{b} = 1. \qquad\qquad ∎$$

Equation (4–7) is called the *intercept form* for the equation of a line.

EXAMPLE 5

Find the equation for the line with an x-intercept of 3 and a y-intercept of -2.

Solution Using Eq. (4–7) with $a = 3$ and $b = -2$, we get

$$\frac{x}{3} + \frac{y}{-2} = 1$$

as the equation of the line in intercept form. An equivalent equation in standard form is

$$2x - 3y - 6 = 0. \qquad\qquad ∎$$

EXERCISE 5

Find the equation for the line with an x-intercept of -2 and a y-intercept of 7.

Answer $7x - 2y + 14 = 0$

We can now prove that the graph of every linear equation in the variables x and y is a line.

Theorem 4.5 The graph of every equation of the form $Ax + By + C = 0$, where $A, B, C \in R$ with $A \neq 0$ or $B \neq 0$, is a straight line.

Proof If $B \neq 0$, then $Ax + By + C = 0$ is equivalent to

$$y = \left(\frac{-A}{B}\right)x + \left(\frac{-C}{B}\right),$$

which is an equation of *the* line that has a slope of $-A/B$ and a y-intercept of $-C/B$. If $B = 0$, then $A \neq 0$, and hence $Ax + By + C = 0$ is equivalent to

$$x = -\frac{C}{A},$$

which is an equation of *the* vertical line whose x-intercept is $-C/A$.   ∎

EXAMPLE 6

Graph the line whose equation is $3x - 4y - 12 = 0$.

Solution Since the graph of a straight line is determined by two points of the line, it is sufficient to determine the x-intercept and the y-intercept of the line. This could be done by expressing the given equation in intercept form. However, it is easier to determine the intercepts by direct substitution. Thus we set up the following table of corresponding values of x and y:

x	0	4
y	-3	0

The graph of $3x - 4y - 12 = 0$ is shown in Figure 4.14.   ∎

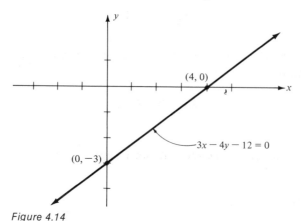

Figure 4.14

Problems 4.3

In problems 1–6, determine the slope of the line through the given points.

1. $(2, -1), (-3, 2)$ 2. $(-2, 3), (4, 1)$ 3. $(-1, 5), (6, 2)$
4. $(5, -2), (6, -1)$ 5. $(-2, 4), (1, -1)$ 6. $(-3, 1), (2, 5)$

In problems 7–12, determine an equation, in standard form, for the line with the given slope that passes through the given point.

7. $m = -3, (2, -3)$ 8. $m = 4, (-1, -3)$ 9. $m = 2, (-3, 1)$
10. $m = \frac{4}{5}, (-2, -\frac{1}{2})$ 11. $m = -\frac{3}{5}, (-5, \frac{1}{4})$ 12. $m = -\frac{2}{7}, (3, -\frac{1}{6})$

In problems 13–18, determine an equation, in standard form, for the line with the given slope and the given y-intercept.

13. $m = -3, b = -1$ 14. $m = 2, b = 7$ 15. $m = -4, b = \frac{3}{5}$
16. $m = \frac{2}{3}, b = -\frac{1}{6}$ 17. $m = -\frac{2}{3}, b = \frac{3}{10}$ 18. $m = \frac{6}{7}, b = -3$

In problems 19–24, determine an equation, in standard form, for the line with the given intercepts.

19. $a = -3, b = 4$ 20. $a = -2, b = -1$ 21. $a = 6, b = -2$
22. $a = -6, b = \frac{4}{3}$ 23. $a = -\frac{2}{3}, b = 3$ 24. $a = -\frac{1}{4}, b = 2$

In problems 25–30, determine the slope of the given line.

25. $2x - 5y + 7 = 0$ 26. $3x - 2y + 6 = 0$ 27. $4x - y - 3 = 0$
28. $x + 3y + 7 = 0$ 29. $5x + y - 3 = 0$ 30. $3x + 4y - 2 = 0$

In problems 31–42, graph the line with the given equation.

31. $2x - 3y + 6 = 0$ 32. $3x + 6y + 6 = 0$ 33. $2x + 8y - 4 = 0$
34. $4x + 5y - 10 = 0$ 35. $2x - 4y - 6 = 0$ 36. $5x - 6y + 15 = 0$
37. $2x + 6 = 0$ 38. $7x - 3 = 0$ 39. $3x - 4 = 0$
40. $4y - 6 = 0$ 41. $5y + 10 = 0$ 42. $6y + 6 = 0$

43. Determine an equation for the line whose slope is -3 and whose x-intercept is 2.
44. Prove that $y = mx - am$ is an equation for the line whose slope is m and whose x-intercept is a.
45. Prove that two nonvertical lines are parallel if and only if their slopes are equal. (*Hint:* Use similar triangles.)
46. Determine an equation for the line passing through $(-1, 3)$ which is parallel to the line $2x - 3y + 1 = 0$. See problem 45.
47. Determine an equation for the line passing through $(2, 2)$ which is parallel to the line $x + 4y - 5 = 0$. See problem 45.
48. Prove that two nonvertical lines are perpendicular if and only if the product of their slopes is -1.
49. Determine an equation for the line passing through $(1, -1)$ which is perpendicular to the line $3x - 4y + 2 = 0$. See problem 48.
50. Determine an equation for the line passing through $(2, -3)$ which is perpendicular to the line $2x + y + 5 = 0$. See problem 48.

Answers 4.3

1. $-\frac{3}{5}$	2. $-\frac{1}{3}$	4. 1
5. $-\frac{5}{3}$	7. $3x+y-3=0$	8. $4x-y+1=0$
10. $8x-6y+13=0$	11. $12x+20y+55=0$	13. $3x+y+1=0$
14. $2x-y+7=0$	16. $4x-6y-1=0$	17. $4x+10y-3=0$
19. $4x-3y+12=0$	20. $x+2y+2=0$	22. $4x-18y+24=0$
23. $9x-2y+6=0$	25. $\frac{2}{5}$	26. $\frac{3}{2}$
28. $-\frac{1}{3}$	29. -5	43. $y=-3x+6$
46. $2x-3y+11=0$	47. $x+4y-10=0$	49. $4x+3y-1=0$
50. $x-2y-8=0$		

4.4 Relations Whose Graphs Are Circles

In this section, we show that the graph, if one exists, of each relation on *R* defined by an equation of the form

$$x^2+y^2+Dx+Ey+F=0, \tag{4-8}$$

where $D,E,F \in R$, is a circle or a point circle. Equation $(4-8)$ is referred to as the *standard form* for the equation of a circle.

Definition 4.5   A **circle** is a set consisting of all points of a plane that are a fixed distance from a fixed point. The fixed distance is called the **radius** of the circle, and the fixed point is called the **center** of the circle.

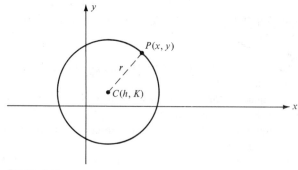

Figure 4.15

The following theorem can be used to determine an equation for the circle with a given center and a given radius.

Theorem 4.6 An equation for the circle with radius r and center $C(h, k)$ is

$$(x-h)^2 + (y-k)^2 = r^2. \tag{4-9}$$

Proof See Figure 4.15. Let $P(x, y)$ be any point of the circle. Since the radius of a circle represents the distance from the center of the circle to any point of the circle, it follows that

$$D(C, P) = r.$$

Therefore,

$$\sqrt{(x-h)^2 + (y-k)^2} = r$$

and hence

$$(x-h)^2 + (y-k)^2 = r^2 \qquad\blacksquare$$

Equation (4-9) is called the *center-radius form* for the equation of a circle.

EXAMPLE 1

Find an equation of the circle with center $C(3, -2)$ and radius 5.

Solution Using Eq. (4-9) with $(h, k) = (3, -2)$ and $r = 5$, we get

$$[x-3]^2 + [y-(-2)]^2 = 25$$

as the equation of the circle in center-radius form. $\qquad\blacksquare$

EXAMPLE 2

Find an equation of the circle with center $C(1,1)$ which passes through $P(2,-3)$.

Solution Since the radius is the distance from the center to any point of the circle we have

$$r = D(C, P) = \sqrt{(2-1)^2 + (-3-1)^2} = \sqrt{17}.$$

Thus an equation of the circle is

$$(x-1)^2 + (y-1)^2 = 17. \qquad\blacksquare$$

EXERCISE 1

Find an equation of the circle with center $(1, -3)$ which passes through $(0, 0)$.

Answer $(x-1)^2+(y+3)^2=10$

If $r^2 > 0$ in Eq. (4–9), the graph of Eq. (4–9) is a circle with radius $|r|$ and center (h, k). If $r^2=0$ in Eq. (4–9), the only ordered pair of real numbers which satisfies

$$(x-h)^2+(y-k)^2=0$$

is (h, k), since the sum of two nonnegative numbers can be zero only when both of the numbers are zero. In this case, we call the graph of Eq. (4–9) a *point circle*. If $r^2 < 0$ in Eq. (4–9), there is no ordered pair of real numbers that satisfies the equation, since the sum of two nonnegative numbers is never negative. In this case, Eq. (4–9) has no graph. Thus we see that the graph, when one exists, of Eq. (4–9) is always a circle or a point circle.

Since each equation of the form

$$x^2+y^2+Dx+Ey+F=0, \tag{4–8}$$

where $D, E, F \in R$, can be rewritten in center-radius form by completing the square on x and on y, it follows that the graph, if one exists, of Eq. (4–8) is a circle or a point circle.

EXAMPLE 3

Graph the circle whose equation is $x^2+y^2+2x-6y-6=0$ after finding its center and radius.

Solution   The given equation can be rewritten as

$$(x^2+2x \quad)+(y^2-6y \quad)=6.$$

Rewriting this equation so that the expression enclosed by each pair of parentheses is a perfect square, we obtain

$$(x^2+2x+1)+(y^2-6y+9)=6+1+9$$

and hence

$$(x+1)^2+(y-3)^2=16.$$

Therefore, the center of the circle is $(-1, 3)$ and its radius is 4. The graph of the circle is shown in Figure 4.16.   ∎

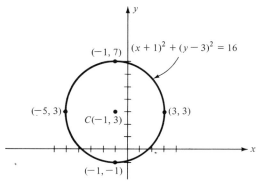

Figure 4.16

EXERCISE 2

Express the equation $x^2 + y^2 - 4x + 2y + 9 = 0$ in center-radius form. Is the graph a circle or a point circle, or is there no graph?

Answer $(x - 2)^2 + (y + 1)^2 = -4$, there is no graph, since $r^2 = -4 < 0$.

Problems 4.4

In problems 1–12, determine the center and the radius of the circle with the given equation, and sketch its graph.

1. $x^2 + y^2 = 1$
2. $x^2 + y^2 = 4$
3. $x^2 + y^2 = 9$
4. $x^2 + y^2 = 7$
5. $x^2 + y^2 = 2$
6. $x^2 + y^2 = 5$
7. $(x + 1)^2 + (y - 2)^2 = 9$
8. $(x - 5)^2 + (y - 1)^2 = 16$
9. $(x + 3)^2 + (y + 2)^2 = 25$
10. $(x - 3)^2 + (y + \frac{1}{5})^2 = 5$
11. $(x + 2)^2 + (y + \frac{1}{2})^2 = 11$
12. $(x + \frac{4}{3})^2 + (y + 3)^2 = 8$

In problems 13–18, express the given equation of a circle in center-radius form. Then determine the center and radius of the circle, and sketch its graph.

13. $x^2 + y^2 - 2x - 10y + 22 = 0$
14. $x^2 + y^2 - 4x + 6y - 12 = 0$
15. $x^2 + y^2 + 2x + 4y - 4 = 0$
16. $x^2 + y^2 + 4x + 2y - 2 = 0$
17. $x^2 + y^2 + 2x - 6y + 2 = 0$
18. $x^2 + y^2 - 4x + 6y = 0$

In problems 19–27, if the given equation has a graph, determine whether it is a circle or a point circle.

19. $x^2 + y^2 - 2x + 6y - 15 = 0$
20. $x^2 + y^2 - 14x - 2y + 50 = 0$
21. $x^2 + y^2 + 4x + 10y + 34 = 0$
22. $x^2 + y^2 - 6x + 4y + 13 = 0$
23. $x^2 + y^2 - 4x + 2y - 4 = 0$
24. $x^2 + y^2 + 4x - 6y - 3 = 0$
25. $x^2 + y^2 - 6x - 10y + 37 = 0$
26. $x^2 + y^2 - 2x - 12y + 41 = 0$
27. $x^2 + y^2 + 10x - 8y + 41 = 0$

In problems 28–36, determine an equation, in standard form, for the circle(s) which satisfies the given conditions.

28. Center $(1, 3)$, radius 2
29. Center $(-2, 2)$, radius 3
30. Center $(-1, 5)$, radius 4
31. Center $(4, -3)$ radius $\sqrt{17}$
32. Center $(-2, -4)$, radius $\sqrt{8}$
33. Center $(-1, -3)$ radius $\sqrt{3}$
34. Center $(2, -3)$, passes through $(1, 2)$
35. Center $(1, -1)$, passes through $(4, 2)$
36. Center $(1, 3)$, passes through $(-1, 5)$

Answers 4.4

1. $C(0, 0), r=1$ **2.** $C(0, 0), r=2$
4. $C(0, 0), r=\sqrt{7}$ **5.** $C(0, 0), r=\sqrt{2}$
7. $C(-1, 2), r=3$ **8.** $C(5, 1), r=4$
10. $C(3, -\frac{1}{3}), r=\sqrt{5}$ **11.** $C(-2, -\frac{1}{2}), r=\sqrt{11}$
13. $C(1, 5), r=2$ **14.** $C(2, -3), r=5$
16. $C(-2, -1), r=\sqrt{7}$ **17.** $C(-1, 3), r=\sqrt{8}$
19. circle   **20.** point circle
22. point circle   **23.** circle
25. no graph   **26.** no graph
28. $x^2+y^2-2x-6y+6=0$ **29.** $x^2+y^2+4x-4y-1=0$
31. $x^2+y^2-8x+6y+8=0$ **32.** $x^2+y^2+4x+8y+12=0$
34. $x^2+y^2-4x+6y-13=0$ **35.** $x^2+y^2-2x+2y-16=0$

4.5 Relations Whose Graphs Are Parabolas

In this section, we show that the graph of each relation on R defined by an equation of the form

$$y=Ax^2+Bx+C \tag{4-10}$$

or

$$x=Ay^2+By+C, \tag{4-11}$$

where $A, B, C \in R$ and $A \neq 0$, is a parabola.

Definition 4.6   A **parabola** is a set consisting of all points of a plane that are the same distance from a fixed point and a fixed line. The fixed point is called the **focus** of the parabola, and the fixed line is called the **directrix** of parabola.

The following theorem can be used to determine an equation for the parabola with focus $(h + a, k)$ and directrix $x = h - a$.

Theorem 4.7   An equation for the parabola with focus $F(h + a, k)$ and directrix $x = h - a$ is

$$(y - k)^2 = 4a(x - h). \qquad (4-12)$$

Proof   See Figure 4.17. Let $P(x, y)$ be any point of the parabola. Now applying Definition 4.6, we have

$$d_1 = d_2.$$

Therefore,

$$|x - (h - a)| = \sqrt{[(x - (h + a)]^2 + (y - k)^2}$$
$$(x - h + a)^2 = (x - h - a)^2 + (y - k)^2$$
$$x^2 + h^2 + a^2 - 2hx + 2ax - 2ah = (x^2 + h^2 + a^2 - 2hx + 2ah - 2ax) + (y - k)^2$$
$$4ax - 4ah = (y - k)^2$$

and hence

$$(y - k)^2 = 4a(x - h). \qquad \blacksquare$$

The point $V(h, k)$ (see Figure 4.17), which is the midpoint of the perpendicular (dotted) line segment from the focus to the directrix, is called the **vertex** of the parabola. The following important facts concerning the constant a of Eq. (4-12) can be observed from Figure 4.17.

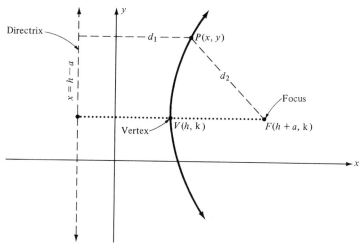

Figure 4.17

1. The parabola opens to the right when $a > 0$, and it opens to the left when $a < 0$.
2. The distance between the focus and the vertex is $|a|$.
3. The distance between the vertex and the directrix is $|a|$.
4. The distance between the focus and the directrix is $|2a|$.

EXAMPLE 1

Determine an equation for the parabola whose focus is $(-3, 2)$ and whose vertex is $(0, 2)$.

Solution Since the vertex $V(h, k)$ is $(0, 2)$, we know that $h = 0$ and $k = 2$. Representing the vertex and focus as points of the plane in Figure 4.18, we see that the distance, $|a|$, between the focus and the vertex is $|a| = 3$. In this case, $a = -3$, since the focus is to the left of the vertex. Replacing h, k, and a with 0, 2, and -3, respectively, in Eq. $(4-12)$, we have

$$(y - 2)^2 = -12x$$

as an equation for the parabola. ∎

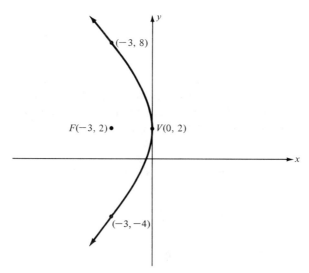

Figure 4.18

Since each equation of the form

$$x = Ay^2 + By + C, \qquad (4-11)$$

where $A, B, C \in R$ with $A \neq 0$, can be rewritten in the form of Eq. $(4-12)$ by completing the square on y, it follows that the graph of Eq. (4–11) is a parabola opening to the right if $A > 0$ and to the left when $A < 0$.

EXAMPLE 2

Determine the vertex of the parabola whose equation is $x = -y^2 - 2y + 3$, and then graph the parabola.

Solution Completing the square on y, we have

$$x = -(y^2 + 2y \qquad) + 3$$

and

$$x = -(y^2 + 2y + 1) + 3 + 1.$$

Hence

$$x = -(y + 1)^2 + 4$$
$$x - 4 = -(y + 1)^2$$

and

$$(y + 1)^2 = (-1)(x - 4).$$

Since the last equation has the form of Eq. (4–12), the vertex $V(h, k)$ is $(4, -1)$. Note that the graph will open to the left since $a = -\frac{1}{4}$ (and since $A = -1$). Using the equation $x = -y^2 - 2y + 3$ to determine a few points of the parabola in addition to the vertex, we get

x	0	3	4	3	0	-5
y	1	0	-1	-2	-3	-4

by choosing the given y-values and then calculating the corresponding x-values. Representing the points in the table and the vertex (which happens to be a point of the table) as points of the coordinate plane in Figure 4.19, we obtain the graph of the parabola as shown in Figure 4.19. ∎

The roles of x and y can be interchanged in Theorem 4.7 to get the following theorem.

Theorem 4.8 An equation for the parabola with focus $F(h, k + a)$ and directrix $y = k - a$ is

$$(x - h)^2 = 4a(y - k). \qquad (4–13)$$

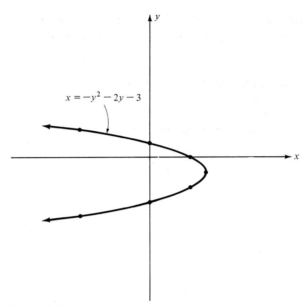

$x = -y^2 - 2y - 3$

Figure 4.19

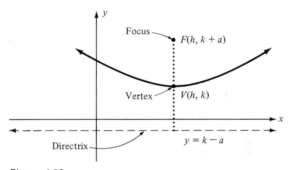

Focus—
$F(h, k + a)$

Vertex—
$V(h, k)$

$y = k - a$

Directrix—

Figure 4.20

With the exception of the first one, all the facts concerning the constant a of Eq. (4–12) are also valid for the constant a of Eq. (4–13). Referring to Figure 4.20, we can see that the first fact should be restated as follows:

1. The parabola opens upward when $a > 0$, and it opens downward when $a < 0$.

EXAMPLE 3

Determine an equation for the parabola whose focus is (3, 4) and whose vertex is (3, 2).

Solution   Since the vertex $V(h, k)$ is (3, 2), we know that $h = 3$ and $k = 2$. Representing the vertex and focus as points of the plane in Figure 4.21, we see that the distance, $|a|$, between the focus and vertex is $|a| = 2$. In this case, $a = 2$, since the focus is above the vertex. Replacing the h, k, and a with 3, 2 and 2, respectively, in Eq. (4–13), we have

$$(x-3)^2 = 8(y-2)$$

as an equation for the parabola.   ∎

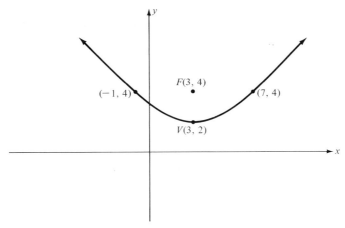

Figure 4.21

Since each equation of the form

$$y = Ax^2 + Bx + C,$$ (4–10)

where $A, B, C \in R$ with $A \neq 0$, can be rewritten in the form of Eq. (4–13) by completing the square on x, it follows that the graph of Eq. (4–10) is a parabola opening upward when $A > 0$ and downward when $A < 0$.

EXAMPLE 4

Determine the vertex of the parabola whose equation is $y = x^2 - 4x + 2$, and then graph the parabola.

Solution   Completing the square on x, we get

$$y = (x^2 - 4x + 4) + 2 - 4.$$

Hence

$$y = (x-2)^2 - 2$$

and

$$(x-2)^2 = y + 2.$$

Since the last equation has the form of Eq. (4–13), the vertex $V(h, k)$ is $(2, -2)$. Note that the graph will open upward since $a = \frac{1}{4}$ (and since $A = 1$).

Using the equation $y = x^2 - 4x + 2$ to determine a few points of the parabola in addition to the vertex, we get

x	0	1	2	3	4	5
y	2	-1	-2	-1	2	7

Plotting these points, we get the graph of the parabola shown in Figure 4.22.   ∎

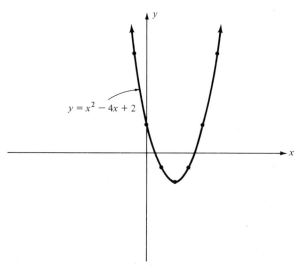

$y = x^2 - 4x + 2$

Figure 4.22

Problems 4.5

In problems 1–12, graph the given equation. Determine the vertex of the graph and whether the graph opens to the right or to the left.

1. $(y-1)^2 = -4(x-2)$ 2. $(y+2)^2 = 4(x+3)$ 3. $(y+3)^2 = 8(x-2)$
4. $x = y^2 - 6$ 5. $x = y^2 - 4$ 6. $x = -2y^2 + 7$
7. $x = -y^2 - 2y + 1$ 8. $x = -y^2 + 2y + 2$ 9. $x = y^2 + 4y - 1$
10. $x = \frac{1}{3}y^2 - 2y - 1$ 11. $x = \frac{1}{2}y^2 + 2y - 1$ 12. $x = -\frac{1}{2}y^2 + 2y + 1$

In problems 13–24, graph the given equation. Determine the vertex of the graph and whether the graph opens upward or downward.

13. $(x-1)^2 = 8(y+1)$ 14. $(x+2)^2 = -8y$ 15. $(x+5)^2 = -4(y-1)$
16. $y = 2x^2 - 3$ 17. $y = -2x^2 + 4$ 18. $y = -x^2 + 4$

19. $y=-x^2+2x+2$ **20.** $y=x^2-4x+2$ **21.** $y=x^2-6x+6$
22. $y=\frac{1}{2}x^2+2x+1$ **23.** $y=-\frac{1}{3}x^2+2x+3$ **24.** $y=-\frac{1}{3}x^2-2x+1$

In problems 25–30, determine an equation of the parabola that satisfies the given conditions.

25. focus, $(2,-7)$; vertex, $(2,-3)$ **26.** focus, $(3,-1)$; vertex, $(-1,-1)$
27. focus, $(3,2)$; directrix, $x=-1$ **28.** focus, $(-3,2)$; directrix, $y=-2$
29. vertex, $(2,-1)$; directrix, $y=2$ **30.** vertex, $(0,-2)$; directrix, $x=3$
31. Prove Theorem 4.8.

Answers 4.5

1. **2.** **4.** **5.**

7. **8.** **10.** **11.**

13. **14.** 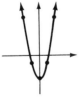 **16.** **17.**

19. **20.** **22.** **23.**

25. $(x-2)^2=-16(y+3)$ **26.** $(y+1)^2=16(x+1)$
28. $(x+3)^2=8y$ **29.** $(x-2)^2=-12(y+1)$

4.6 Relations Whose Graphs Are Ellipses or Hyperbolas

In this section, we show that the graph of each relation on R defined by an equation of the form

$$Ax^2 + By^2 = C, \qquad (4-14)$$

where A, B, and C are nonzero real numbers, is an ellipse or a hyperbola.

Relations Whose Graphs Are Ellipses

Definition 4.7   An **ellipse** is a set consisting of all the points of a plane which satisfy the condition that the sum of the distances to two fixed points is constant. The fixed points are called the **foci** of the ellipse.

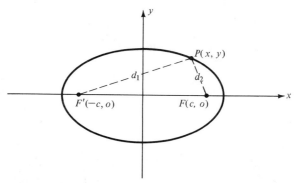

Figure 4.23

The following theorem can be used to determine an equation for the ellipse with foci $F(c, 0)$ and $F(-c, 0)$.

Theorem 4.9   An equation for the ellipse with foci $F(c, 0)$ and $F'(-c, 0)$ is

$$\frac{x^2}{a^2} + \frac{y^2}{b^2} = 1, \qquad (4-15)$$

where $b^2 = a^2 - c^2$.

Proof   See Figure 4.23. Let $P(x, y)$ be any point of the ellipse. Now applying Definition 4.7, we have

$$d_1 + d_2 = 2a,$$

where we have chosen to represent the constant mentioned in the definition as $2a$. Therefore,

$$\sqrt{[x-(-c)]^2+(y-0)^2}+\sqrt{(x-c)^2+(y-0)^2}=2a.$$

Eliminating the radicals in the previous equation, we get

$$(a-c^2)x^2+a^2y^2=a^2(a^2-c^2).$$

Since $2a$ represents the distance between the two x-intercepts of the ellipse according to Definition 4.7, it is easy to see from Figure 4.23 that $2a > 2c > 0$. Hence $a > c > 0$ and $a^2 > c^2$. Now, letting $b^2 = a^2 - c^2$, since $a^2 - c^2 > 0$, we have

$$b^2x^2+a^2y^2=a^2b^2$$

and hence

$$\frac{x^2}{a^2}+\frac{y^2}{b^2}=1. \qquad ∎$$

Interchanging the roles of x and y in Theorem 4.9 and choosing the constant mentioned in the definition of an ellipse as $2b$, we find that Eq. $(4-15)$ also represents the equation of an ellipse whose foci are $F(0, c)$ and $F(0, -c)$.

EXAMPLE 1

Graph (a) $(x^2/9)+(y^2/4)=1$ and (b) $(x^2/4)+(y^2/9)=1$.

Solution Since both equations have the form of Eq. $(4-15)$, we know that each equation has an ellipse as its graph. Thus we can use the x- and y-intercepts of the ellipse to determine its graph. See Figures 4.24 and 4.25 on page 156. ∎

Since each equation of the form

$$Ax^2+By^2=C, \qquad (4-14)$$

where A, B, and C are all positive or all negative, can be rewritten as

$$\frac{x^2}{C/A}+\frac{y^2}{C/B}=1,$$

where C/A and C/B are positive, it follows from Theorem 4.9 that the graph of Eq. $(4-14)$ is an ellipse when A, B, and C are all positive or all negative.

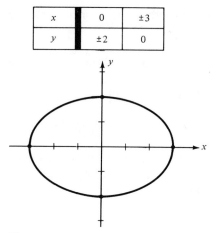

x	0	±3
y	±2	0

Figure 4.24

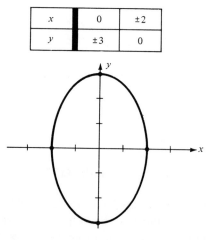

x	0	±2
y	±3	0

Figure 4.25

Relations Whose Graphs Are Hyperbolas

Definition 4.8   A **hyperbola** is a set consisting of all points of a plane which satisfy the condition that the difference of the distances to two fixed points is constant. The fixed points are the **foci** of the hyperbola.

The following theorem can be used to determine an equation for the hyperbola with foci $F(c, 0)$ and $F'(-c, 0)$.

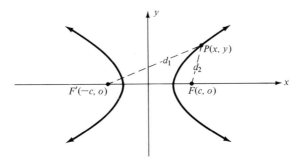

Figure 4.26

Theorem 4.10   An equation for the hyperbola with foci $F(c,\ 0)$ and $F'(-c,\ 0)$ is

$$\frac{x^2}{a^2} - \frac{y^2}{b^2} = 1, \qquad\qquad (4-16)$$

where $b^2 = c^2 - a^2$.

Proof   See Figure 4.26. Let $P(x,\ y)$ be any point of the hyperbola. Now applying Definition 4.8, we have

$$|d_1 - d_2| = 2a,$$

where we have chosen to represent the constant mentioned in the definition as $2a$. Therefore,

$$\left| \sqrt{(x-(-c))^2 + (y-0)^2} - \sqrt{(x-c)^2 + (y-0)^2} \right| = 2a.$$

Eliminating the radicals in the previous equation, we get

$$(a^2 - c^2)x^2 + a^2y^2 = a^2(a^2 - c^2).$$

Since $2a$ represents the distance between the two x-intercepts of the hyperbola according to Definition 4.8, it is easy to see from Figure 4.26 that $2c > 2a > 0$. Hence $c > a > 0$ and $c^2 > a^2$. Now letting $b^2 = c^2 - a^2$, since $c^2 > a^2$, we have

$$(-b^2)x^2 + a^2y^2 = a^2(-b^2)$$

and hence

$$\frac{x^2}{a^2} - \frac{y^2}{b^2} = 1. \qquad\qquad \blacksquare$$

Solving Eq. (4–16) for y, we get

$$y=\pm\frac{bx}{a}\sqrt{1-\frac{a^2}{x^2}}.\qquad(4-17)$$

In Eq. (4–17) we can see that as $|x|$ becomes increasingly larger, the expression under the radical sign approaches 1. Therefore, the y-values of Eq. (4–17) [and hence of Eq. (4–16)] approach the y-values of the equation

$$y=\pm\frac{bx}{a}.\qquad(4-18)$$

Stating this fact in another way, the graph of the hyperbola $(x^2/a^2)-(y^2/b^2)=1$ approaches the graph of the pair of intersecting lines $y=\pm bx/a$, called the **asymptotes** of the hyperbola, as $|x|$ becomes increasingly larger. Thus the asymptotes can be used as an effective aide in graphing hyperbolas.

EXAMPLE 2
Graph $(x^2/9)-(y^2/4)=1$.

Solution   Since the given equation has the form of Eq. (4–16), we know that its graph is a hyperbola. Thus we can use its intercepts and its asymptotes to determine its graph. Setting $y=0$, we find that the x-intercepts are ±3. Setting $x=0$, we find that the graph has no y-intercepts. Applying Eq. (4–18) with $a=3$ and $b=2$, we find that the equations of the asymptotes are $y=2x/3$ and $y=-2x/3$. The graph of the hyperbola is shown in Figure 4.27. Observe that the hyperbola approaches its asymptotes as $|x|$ becomes increasingly larger. ∎

Interchanging the roles of x and y in Theorem 4.10 and choosing the constant in the definition of a hyperbola as $2b$, we get the following theorem.

Theorem 4.11   An equation for the hyperbola with foci $F(0,\ c)$ and $F'(0,-c)$ is

$$\frac{y^2}{b^2}-\frac{x^2}{a^2}=1,\qquad(4-19)$$

where $b^2=c^2-a^2$.
   As we did before, we can show that the asymptotes of those hyperbolas defined by $(y^2/b^2)-(x^2/a^2)=1$ are also $y=\pm bx/a$.

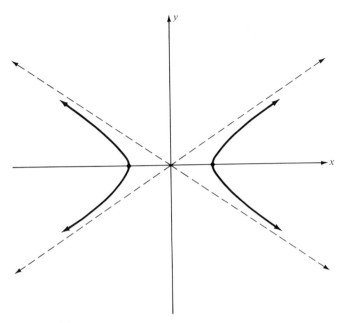

Figure 4.27

EXAMPLE 3

Graph $(y^2/9) - (x^2/4) = 1$.

Solution   Since the given equation has the form of Eq. (4–19), we know that its graph is a hyperbola. In this case the y-intercepts are ± 3 and there are no x-intercepts. Since $b = 3$ and $a = 2$, the equations of the asymptotes are $y = 3x/2$ and $y = -3x/2$. The graph of the hyperbola is shown in Figure 4.28. Observe that the hyperbola approaches its asymptotes as $|x|$ becomes increasingly larger. ∎

Since each equation of the form

$$Ax^2 + By^2 = C, \qquad (4-14)$$

where A and B have opposite signs and $C \neq 0$, can be rewritten as

$$\frac{x^2}{C/A} - \frac{y^2}{C/B} = 1 \quad \text{or} \quad \frac{y^2}{C/B} - \frac{x^2}{C/A} = 1,$$

where C/A and C/B are positive, it follows from Theorems 4.10 and 4.11 that the graph of Eq. (4–14) is a hyperbola when A and B have opposite signs and $C \neq 0$.

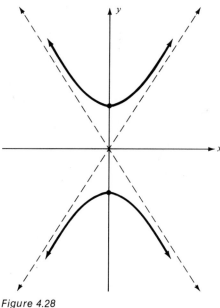

Figure 4.28

Problems 4.6

In problems 1–18, graph the given equation. If the graph is an ellipse, determine its intercepts. If the graph is a hyperbola, determine its intercepts and the equations of its asymptotes.

1. $(x^2/4) + y^2 = 1$
2. $x^2 + (y^2/9) = 1$
3. $(x^2/16) + y^2 = 1$
4. $(x^2/9) - y^2 = 1$
5. $(x^2/16) - y^2 = 1$
6. $(y^2/25) - x^2 = 1$
7. $9x^2 + 4y^2 = 36$
8. $4x^2 + 16y^2 = 16$
9. $25x^2 + 4y^2 = 100$
10. $16x^2 - 4y^2 = -16$
11. $25x^2 - 4y^2 = -100$
12. $4x^2 - 9y^2 = 36$
13. $3x^2 + y^2 = 9$
14. $x^2 + 5y^2 = 25$
15. $8x^2 + y^2 = 16$
16. $5x^2 - y^2 = 5$
17. $8x^2 - 4y^2 = 16$
18. $x^2 - 3y^2 = -3$

In problems 19–21, determine an equation of the ellipse that satisfies the given conditions.

19. foci, $(\pm3, 0)$; x-intercepts, ±5
20. foci, $(0, \pm4)$; y-intercepts, ±5
21. foci, $(\pm12, 0)$; y-intercepts, ±5

In problems 22–24, determine an equation of the hyperbola that satisfies the given conditions.

22. foci, $(0, \pm13)$; y-intercepts, ±5
23. foci, $(\pm13, 0)$; x-intercepts, ±12
24. foci, $(0, \pm5)$; y-intercepts, ±3
25. (a) Graph $4x^2 - 9y^2 = 0$.

    (b) If one of the numbers A and B is positive and the other is negative, and if $C = 0$, discuss the graph of $Ax^2 + By^2 = C$.

26. (a) Graph $-x^2 = -9$.   (b) Graph $9y^2 = 4$.
    (c) If one of the numbers A and B is zero and if the other number has the same sign as C where $C \neq 0$, discuss the graph of $Ax^2 + By^2 = C$.

27. (a) Graph $-x^2 = 0$.   (b) Graph $9y^2 = 0$.
    (c) If exactly one of the numbers A and B is zero and if $C = 0$, discuss the graph of $Ax^2 + By^2 = C$.

28. (a) Graph $x^2 + 4y^2 = 0$.   (b) Graph $-9x^2 - y^2 = 0$.
    (c) If the numbers A and B are both positive or both negative and if $C = 0$, discuss the graph of $Ax^2 + By^2 = C$.

29. (a) Graph $x^2 + 4y^2 = -4$.   (b) Graph $-9x^2 - y^2 = 1$.
    (c) If the numbers A and B are both positive or both negative and if C has the opposite sign of A and B with $C \neq 0$, discuss the graph of $Ax^2 + By^2 = C$.

30. (a) Graph $x^2 = -4$.   (b) Graph $-y^2 = 9$.
    (c) If one of the numbers A and B is zero and if the other number has the opposite sign of C with $C \neq 0$, discuss the graph of $Ax^2 + By^2 = C$.

31. Fill in all missing details in the proof of Theorem 4.9.

32. Fill in all missing details in the proof of Theorem 4.10.

33. Prove Theorem 4.11.

Answers 4.6

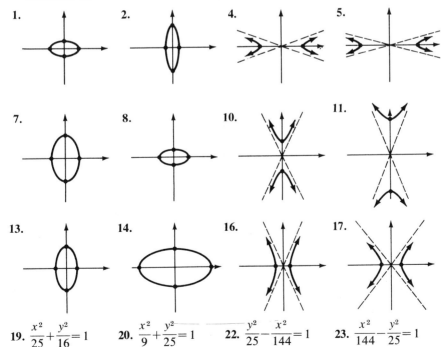

19. $\dfrac{x^2}{25} + \dfrac{y^2}{16} = 1$ **20.** $\dfrac{x^2}{9} + \dfrac{y^2}{25} = 1$ **22.** $\dfrac{y^2}{25} - \dfrac{x^2}{144} = 1$ **23.** $\dfrac{x^2}{144} - \dfrac{y^2}{25} = 1$

4.7 Relations Defined by Inequalities

If $P(x, y)$ and $Q(x, y)$ are expressions involving the two variables x and y, then a statement of the form

$$P(x, y) > Q(x, y), \quad P(x, y) < Q(x, y), \quad P(x, y) \geq Q(x, y), \quad \text{or}$$
$$P(x, y) \leq Q(x, y)$$

is said to be an **inequality in the variables x and y.**

If a true statement is obtained when the x and y coordinates of an ordered pair (x, y) are substituted for the variables x and y, respectively, in an inequality, the ordered pair (x, y) is said to be a **solution** of the inequality. The set consisting of all the solutions of an inequality is called the **solution set** of the inequality.

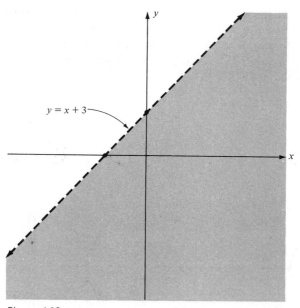

Figure 4.29

As with equations, it is usually impossible to list all the solutions of an inequality. Consequently, we describe the solution set of an inequality by graphing the inequality. As an example, the graph of the inequality $y < x + 3$ is obtained as follows. Choose a value of x, and then calculate the corresponding values of y from the inequality $y < x + 3$. For instance, if $x = 1$, then $y < 4$. Hence every ordered pair $(1, y)$ such that $y < 4$ belongs to the solution set of $y < x + 3$. See Figure 4.29. Note that for a given value of x, each value of y which is less than the corresponding y-value of the equation $y =$

$x + 3$ is a corresponding y-value of the inequality $y < x + 3$. Therefore, the graph of $y < x + 3$ consists of all points (x, y) in the region below the graph of $y = x + 3$. Since the points of the line $y = x + 3$ do not belong to the solution set, we indicate this by means of a *dashed line*. On the other hand, if the points of the line $y = x + 3$ did belong to the solution set, we would indicate this by means of a *solid line*.

When the inequality sign in a given inequality is replaced with an equality sign, the equation obtained is called the *corresponding equation* of the given inequality. It can be shown that the graph of the corresponding equation of a given inequality divides the plane into regions such that every point in a given region satisfies the given inequality or such that every point in the region fails to satisfy the given inequality. Using this fact, we have the following procedure for graphing inequalities:

1. Begin by graphing the corresponding equation,
2. Select a point in each region formed by the corresponding equation and check this point to see whether or not it satisfies the given inequality.
3. Shade the regions corresponding to those points selected in step 2 which satisfy the inequality.

EXAMPLE 1

Graph the solution set of $2x - 3y \leq 9$.

Solution   The graph of the corresponding equation $2x - 3y = 9$ is shown in Figure 4.30. Since $(0, 0)$ is a solution of $2x - 3y \leq 9$, it follows that every point in the region above the line satisfies the given inequality. Hence this region is shaded in Figure 4.30. Since $(5, 0)$ is not a solution of $2x - 3y \leq 9$, it follows that every point in the region below the line fails to satisfy the given inequality. Hence this region is left unshaded in Figure 4.30. Since the points of the line $2x - 3y = 9$ belong to the solution set, the line is shown as a solid line.   ∎

EXAMPLE 2

Graph the solution set of $x^2 + y^2 + 2x - 3 < 0$.

Solution   The graph of the corresponding equation $x^2 + y^2 + 2x - 3 = 0$, which is equivalent to $(x + 1)^2 + y^2 = 4$, is shown in Figure 4.31. Since $(0, 0)$ is a solution of $x^2 + y^2 + 2x - 3 < 0$, it follows that every point in the region inside the circle satisfies the given inequality. Hence this region is shaded in Figure 4.31. Since $(2, 0)$ is not a solution of $x^2 + y^2 + 2x - 3 < 0$, it follows that every point in the region outside the circle fails to satisfy the given inequality. Hence this region is left unshaded in Figure 4.31. Since the points of the circle $x^2 + y^2 - 2x - 3 = 0$ do not belong to the solution set, the circle is shown as a dashed curve. ∎

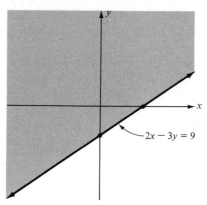

Figure 4.30

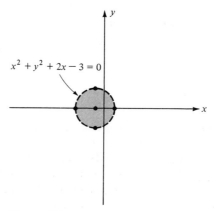

Figure 4.31

Problems 4.7

In problems 1 – 30, graph the solution set of the given inequality.

1. $2x - y > 8$
2. $3x > y + 6$
3. $x - 2y > 4$
4. $3x - y \leq 6$
5. $y + 8 \geq 2x$
6. $6x - 6 \geq y$
7. $2x + 3y < 12$
8. $y - 3x < 9$
9. $x - y < 2$
10. $y - 3 \leq 2x$
11. $2x \leq 6 - 3y$
12. $0 \leq 2x - 5y + 4$
13. $|2x - y| < 2$
14. $|3x + y| \geq 3$
15. $|x - 2y| \leq 4$
16. $x^2 + y^2 < 4$

17. $x^2 + y^2 \geq 9$ **18.** $x^2 + y^2 > 0$
19. $(x-1)^2 + (y-3)^2 \geq 1$ **20.** $(x+2)^2 + (y-1)^2 < 4$
21. $4 \leq (x+1)^2 + (y-2)^2 \leq 9$ **22.** $x^2 + 4y^2 \leq 4$
23. $16x^2 + 9y^2 \geq 144$ **24.** $9x^2 + y^2 > 9$
25. $y^2 - x^2 \leq 4$ **26.** $4x^2 - y^2 \geq 4$
27. $9x^2 - y^2 < 9$ **28.** $x^2 > y$
29. $x^2 > -4y$ **30.** $y^2 \geq -4x$

Answers 4.7

1.   **2.** 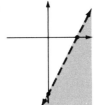 **4.** 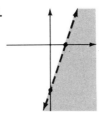 **5.**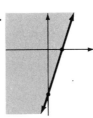

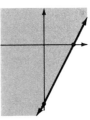

7. 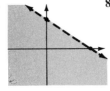 **8.**   **10.**   **11.**

13.   **14.**   **16.**   **17.**

19. 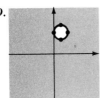 **20.**   **22.**   **23.**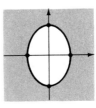

25. 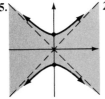 **26.**   **28.** 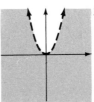 **29.**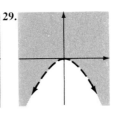

chapter 4 review problems

1. (a) Determine the length of the line segment between the point $(3, 1)$ and $(-2, 5)$.
   (b) Determine the slope of the line segment through the points $(3, 1)$ and $(-2, 5)$.
2. Determine an equation, in standard form, for the line that satisfies the given conditions:
   (a) slope, -3; passes through $(2, -5)$ (b) slope, -1; y-intercept, 5
   (c) slope, $-\frac{1}{2}$; x-intercept, -3 (d) x-intercept, 2; y-intercept, $-\frac{1}{3}$
3. Determine the slope of the line $3x - 4y + 7 = 0$.
4. Determine an equation for the line passing through $(2, -1)$ which is parallel to the line $3x - 4y + 7 = 0$.
5. Determine the center and radius for the circle defined by the given equation:
   (a) $(x-2)^2 + (y+3)^2 = 4$ (b) $x^2 + y^2 - 4x + 6y = 0$
6. Determine an equation, in standard form, for the circle that satisfies the given conditions:
   (a) center, $(2, -3)$; radius, $\sqrt{3}$ (b) center, $(3, 1)$; passes through $(1, 2)$
7. Determine an equation for the parabola with vertex $(3, 5)$ and focus $(0, 5)$.
8. Determine an equation for the ellipse with foci $(\pm 12, 0)$ and y-intercepts ± 5.
9. Determine an equation for the hyperbola with foci $(0, \pm 5)$ and y-intercepts ± 4.
10. Graph the following equations or inequalities:
    (a) $3x - 2y = 6$ (b) $x = -2$
    (c) $x^2 + y^2 = 9$ (d) $x^2 + y^2 - 2x + 4y + 1 = 0$
    (e) $x^2 + y^2 - 6x + 4y + 13 = 0$ (f) $y = x^2$
    (g) $y = x^2 - 2x + 3$ (h) $x = y^2 - 4y$
    (i) $(x-1)^2 = -4(y-1)$ (j) $x^2 + 4y^2 = 4$
    (k) $x^2 - 9y^2 = 9$ (l) $4y^2 - x^2 = 4$
    (m) $2x - y < 2$ (n) $x^2 + (y-1)^2 > 4$
    (o) $9x^2 + y^2 \geq 9$

answers

1. (a) $\sqrt{41}$ (b) $-\frac{4}{5}$
2. (a) $3x + y - 1 = 0$ (b) $x + y - 5 = 0$ (c) $x + 2y + 3 = 0$
   (d) $x - 6y - 2 = 0$
3. $\frac{3}{4}$ 4. $3x - 4y - 10 = 0$ 5. (a) $C(2, -3); r = 2$ (b) $C(2, -3); r = \sqrt{13}$
6. (a) $x^2 + y^2 - 4x + 6y + 10 = 0$ (b) $x^2 + y^2 - 6x - 2y + 5 = 0$
7. $(y-5)^2 = -12(x-3)$ 8. $25x^2 + 169y^2 = 4225$ 9. $9y^2 - 16x^2 = 144$
10. (a)   (b)   (c)   (d)

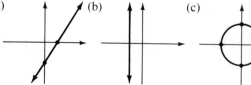
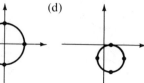

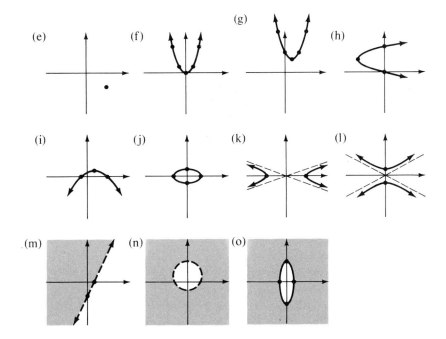

5

functions

5.1 Functions (A Special Kind of Relation)

This chapter deals with a special kind of relation, called a *function*, which plays a very important role in man's attempt to understand the world in which he lives.

Definition 5.1   A **function f from X to Y,** denoted by $f : X \rightarrow Y$, is a relation from X to Y in which no two different ordered pairs of the relation have the same first element. A function from R to R is called a **real-valued function.**

From Definition 5.1, it follows that every function is a relation. However, it is *not* true that every relation is a function. Since every function is a relation, the domain and the range of a function will be the same as the domain and range of the corresponding relation.

For real-valued functions, we can restate Definition 5.1 in the following way. A relation on R is a real-valued function if each real number x in the domain of the relation corresponds with *one and only one* real number y in the range of the relation.

EXAMPLE 1

The relation $\{(0, 1), (1, 2), (3, 5)\}$ is a function, since no two different ordered pairs of the relation have the same first element. On the other hand, the relation $\{(0, 1), (1, 0), (1, 1)\}$ is not a function, since two different ordered pairs, namely $(1, 0)$ and $(1, 1)$, have the same first element.

EXAMPLE 2

The relation $\{(x, y)| y = x^2\}$ is a function, since each element x in the domain of the relation corresponds with *exactly one* element y in the range of the relation. That is to say, no two ordered pairs in the relation have the same first element.

EXAMPLE 3

The relation $\{(x, y)| y^2 = x\}$ is not a function, since certain elements x in the domain of the relation correspond to more than one element y in the range of the relation. For instance, the number 1 in the domain corresponds to both of the numbers 1 and -1 in the range. That is, two ordered pairs, namely $(1, 1)$ and $(1, -1)$, in the relation have the same first element.

EXERCISE 1

Determine which of the following relations are functions. When the relation is not a function, list two ordered pairs that have the same first element.

(a) $\{(1, 1), (2, 5), (2, 3)\}$ (b) $\{(7, \pi), (\pi, 5), (5, 7)\}$

(c) $\{(x, y)| y = 2x - 3\}$ (d) $\{(x, y)| x^2 + y^2 = 1\}$

Answer   (b) and (c) are functions,   (a) $(2, 5)$ and $(2, 3)$ (d) $(0, 1)$ and $(0, -1)$

In mathematics, the real-valued functions of main interest are usually those defined by equations. In such cases, we often speak of the equation that defines the function as being the function itself, since this equation actually defines the association between the numbers in the domain and the numbers in the range. Thus one might speak of the function $y = 2x$ when we really mean the function $\{(x, y)| y = 2x\}$, which is the collection of ordered pairs defined by the equation $y = 2x$.

Unless otherwise specified, when the ordered pairs of a real-valued funcion are defined by an equation, the domain of the function is understood to consist of all real numbers x whose corresponding values are also real numbers.

EXAMPLE 4

Determine the domain of the function $f = \{(x, y)| y = \sqrt{x - 2}\}$.

Solution   First, we recall that the symbol $\sqrt{a}$ is used to indicate the principle (nonnegative) square root of a. Since $\sqrt{x - 2}$ has a real value only when $x - 2 \geq 0$ and hence when $x \geq 2$, it follows that the domain of f is $D_f = \{x| x \geq 2\}$.   ∎

EXAMPLE 5

Determine the domain of the function f defined by $y = 1/x(x-1)$.

Solution Since $1/x(x-1)$ has a real value when x is any real number except 0 or 1, it follows that the domain of f is $D_f = \{x | x \in R, x \neq 0, x \neq 1\}.$ ∎

EXERCISE 2

Determine the domain of the following functions.
(a) $\{(x, y) | y = \sqrt{5-x}\}$ (b) $\{(x, y) | y = 1/(x^2 + 3x)\}$

Answer (a) $\{x | x \leq 5\}$ (b) $\{x | x \in R, x \neq 0, x \neq -3\}$

Since a real-valued function is a special kind of relation on R, we can represent functions graphically as points of a coordinate plane.

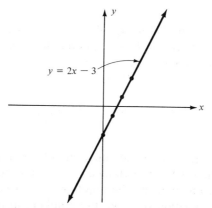

$y = 2x - 3$

Figure 5.1

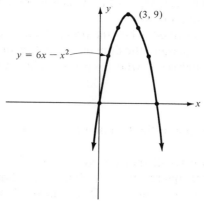

$(3, 9)$

$y = 6x - x^2$

Figure 5.2

EXAMPLE 6

Determine the domain of $f = \{(x, y) \mid y = 2x - 3\}$, graph f, and use the graph of f to determine the range of f.

Solution   The domain of f is $D_f = \{x \mid x \in R\}$, since $2x - 3$ has a real value for each real number x. The graph of f is given in Figure 5.1. By projecting the points of the graph horizontally onto the y-axis, we see that the range of f is $R_f = \{y \mid y \in R\}$.   ∎

EXAMPLE 7

Determine the domain of $f = \{(x, y) \mid y = 6x - x^2\}$, graph f, and use the graph of f to determine the range of f.

Solution   The domain of f is $D_f = \{x \mid x \in R\}$, since $6x - x^2$ has a real value for each real number x. The graph of f is given in Figure 5.2. By projecting the points of the graph of f horizontally onto the y-axis, it follows that $R_f = \{y \mid y \leq 9\}$.   ∎

Using Definitions 4.3 and 5.1, we obtain the following rule for deciding whether or not a relation on R is a function

Vertical-Line Rule

A relation on R is a function if and only if no vertical line intersects the graph of the relation more than once.

Using this rule, we observe from the graphs of the last two examples that the relations defined in those examples are functions.

EXERCISE 3

Assuming that the given graph is the graph of a particular relation, use the vertical-line rule to determine whether or not the relation is a function.

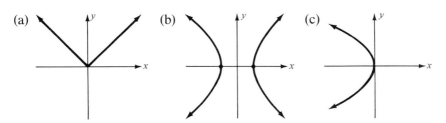

(a)   (b)   (c)

Answer   The graph in (a) represents a function, those in (b) and (c) do not.

In the discussion so far, we have used the symbol f exclusively to represent a function. However, a function (and also a relation) can be denoted by any convenient symbol. For example, we might use any one of the symbols f, g, h, F, or G to represent a particular function.

The symbol representing a function is used together with the variable representing an arbitrary element of the domain as follows. When f is a function, the symbol $f(x)$, which is read "f of x," is used to represent the *unique* element of the range of f, which is associated with the element x in the domain of f. Thus, when we write $y = f(x)$, (x, y) is an ordered pair belonging to the function f.

EXAMPLE 8

When we speak of the function defined by $f(x) = 2x + 3$, we mean the function $f = \{(x, y) \mid y = 2x + 3\}$.

EXAMPLE 9

If f is defined by $f(x) = x^2 - 6x + 5$, determine $f(0)$, $f(-2)$, and $f(a + 1)$.

Solution   In this case we can think of the equation that defines the function f as

$$f(\ ) = (\ )^2 - 6(\ ) + 5,$$

where any number $x \in D_f$ can be substituted in the parentheses throughout the equation. Thus

$$f(0) = (0)^2 - 6(0) + 5 = 5,$$
$$f(-2) = (-2)^2 - 6(-2) + 5 = 21,$$

and

$$f(a + 1) = (a + 1)^2 - 6(a + 1) + 5 = a^2 - 4a. \qquad \blacksquare$$

Problems 5.1

In problems 1–9, determine the domain of the function defined by the given equation.

1. $y = 3x + 5$ 2. $y = 2x - x^2$ 3. $y = \sqrt{4 - x}$
4. $f(x) = \sqrt{x + 5}$ 5. $f(x) = \sqrt{x^2 - 4}$ 6. $f(x) = \sqrt{9 - x^2}$
7. $f(x) = \sqrt[3]{x - 2}$ 8. $f(x) = 1/(x - 3)$ 9. $f(x) = 1/(x + 2)$

In problems 10–15, determine the domain of each function, graph the function, and use the graph of the function to determine the range of the function.

10. $\{(x, y) \mid y = 3x - 1\}$ 11. $\{(x, y) \mid y = x^2\}$ 12. $\{(x, y) \mid y = x^2 - 2x\}$
13. $\{(x, y) \mid y = \sqrt{x}\}$ 14. $\{(x, y) \mid y = |x|\}$ 15. $\{(x, y) \mid y = x^3\}$

In problems 16–24, explain why the given relation is (or is not) a function.

16. $\{(1, 1), (2, 1), (2, -2)\}$ 17. $\{(4, 2), (4, 1), (7, 5)\}$
18. $\{(15, 5), (7, 5), (0, 5)\}$ 19. $\{(x, y) \mid y^2 = x\}$

20. $\{(x, y) \mid y = 5x - 2\}$ **21.** $\{(x, y) \mid x^2 + y^2 = 4\}$
22. $\{(x, y) \mid xy = 4\}$ **23.** $\{(x, y) \mid x^2 - 4y^2 = 4\}$
24. $\{(x, y) \mid y = \sqrt{x}\}$
25. If $f(x) = 3 - 5x$, determine $f(-2)$, $f(a - 1)$, and $f[f(2)]$.
26. If $g(x) = x^2 - 2x - 3$, determine $g(3)$, $g(a - 1)$, and $g[g(2)]$.
27. If $h(x) = \sqrt{x + 3}$, determine $h(1)$, $h(6)$, and $h[h(6)]$.
28. If $F(x) = \sqrt{(x - 2)(x - 4)}$, determine $F(\tfrac{1}{3})$ and $1/F(6)$.
29. If $G(x) = x/(x - 4)$, determine $G[G(5)]$ and $[G(5)]^2$.
30. If $H(x) = 1/(x - 6)$, what can be said about $H(6)$?

Answers 5.1

1. $\{x \mid x \in R\}$ **2.** $\{x \mid x \in R\}$ **4.** $\{x \mid x \geq -5\}$
5. $\{x \mid x \leq -2 \text{ or } x \geq 2\}$ **7.** $\{x \mid x \in R\}$ **8.** $\{x \mid x \in R, x \neq 3\}$
10. $D = \{x \mid x \in R\}$, $R = \{y \mid y \in R\}$ **11.** $D = \{x \mid x \in R\}$, $R = \{y \mid y \geq 0\}$
13. $D = \{x \mid x \geq 0\}$, $R = \{y \mid y \geq 0\}$ **14.** $D = \{x \mid x \in R\}$, $R = \{y \mid y \geq 0\}$
16. is not   **17.** is not   **19.** is not   **20.** is
22. is   **23.** is not   **25.** 13, $8 - 5a$, 38
26. 0, $a^2 - 4a$, 12 **28.** $\sqrt{253}/6$, $\sqrt{2}/4$ **29.** 5, 25

5.2 Polynomial Functions

We begin by defining a polynomial function.

Definition 5.2   A function f defined by an equation of the form

$$f(x) = a_0 x^n + a_1 x^{n-1} + \cdots + a_{n-1} x + a_n,$$

where n is a nonnegative integer and $a_0, a_1, \cdots, a_n \in R$ with $a_0 \neq 0$, is called a **polynomial function of degree n.**

Constant Functions

A polynomial function of degree 0 is called a **constant function.** Thus a constant function f is defined by an equation of the form

$$f(x) = a_0,$$

where $a_0 \in R$ with $a_0 \neq 0$. For obvious reasons, we shall also call the **zero function,** $f(x) = 0$, a constant function. Note that the constant function $f(x) = a_0$ associates the real number a_0 with each real number x. Hence the graph of a constant function is a line parallel to the x-axis. As an example, the graph of the constant function $f(x) = 3$ is shown in Figure 5.3.

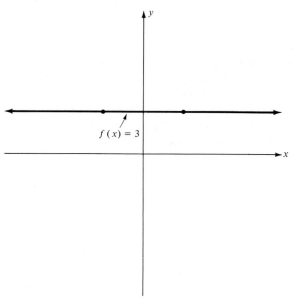

Figure 5.3

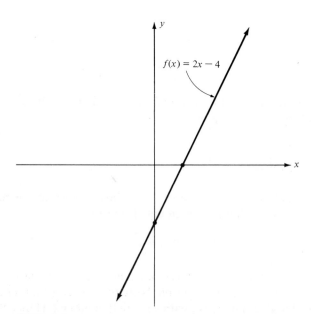

Figure 5.4

Linear Functions

A polynomial function of degree 1 is called a **linear function.** Thus a linear function f is defined by an equation of the form

$$f(x) = a_0 x + a_1,$$

where $a_0, a_1 \in R$ with $a_0 \neq 0$. Since $y = f(x) = a_0 x + a_1$ has the form of Eq. (4–6), it follows that the graph of the linear function $f(x) = a_0 x + a_1$ is a straight line whose slope is a_0 and whose y-intercept is a_1. For example, the graph of the linear function $f(x) = 2x - 4$ is shown in Figure 5.4.

Quadratic Functions

A polynomial function of degree 2 is called a **quadratic function.** Thus a quadratic function f is defined by an equation of the form

$$f(x) = a_0 x^2 + a_1 x + a_2,$$

where $a_0, a_1, a_2 \in R$ with $a_0 \neq 0$. Since $y = f(x) = a_0 x^2 + a_1 x + a_2$ has the form of Eq. (4–10), it follows that the graph of the quadratic function $f(x) = a_0 x^2 + a_1 x + a_2$ is a parabola opening upward if $a_0 > 0$ and opening downward if $a_0 < 0$.

EXAMPLE 1

Graph $f(x) = x^2 - 2x - 3$.

Solution We begin by setting up a table of corresponding values for x and $f(x)$:

x	-2	-1	0	1	2	3	4
$f(x)$	5	0	-3	-4	-3	0	5

Representing the ordered pairs determined by the previous table as points, we obtain the parabola shown in Figure 5.5 as the graph of $f(x) = x^2 - 2x - 3$. Note that $(1, -4)$ is the vertex of the parabola. ∎

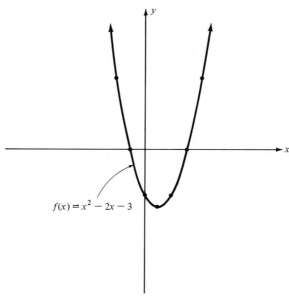

$$f(x) = x^2 - 2x - 3$$

Figure 5.5

Polynomial Functions of Degree n where $n \geq 3$

Polynomial functions of degree n, where $n \geq 3$, can also be graphed by setting up a table of corresponding values of x and $f(x)$ after using some educated guessing in choosing our values of x. In fact, we have no alternative in this course. However, better methods will become available when you take a calculus course. Before considering some examples, we consider several definitions and some information from calculus which we will be unable to prove in this course.

A point of a graph that is higher than any neighboring point of the graph is called a **local maximum point** of the graph. Similarly, a point of a graph that is lower than any neighboring point of the graph is called a **local minimum point** of the graph. For example, in Figure 5.6, the points P and R are local maximum points, and the points Q and S are local minimum points.

In the case of a polynomial function f, a local maximum point or a local minimum point of the graph of f is also called a **turning point** of the graph. In calculus it is shown that the number of turning points of the graph of a polynomial function of degree n is either $n - 1$ or is less than $n - 1$ by an even positive integer. This fact can be used as an aid in determining the shape of the graph of a polynomial function. For example, using this fact we know that $f(x) = x^3 - 2x^2 + 1$ has either 2 or 0 turning points. As another example, we know that $f(x) = x^6 - x^3 + x^2 + 10$ has either 5, 3, or 1 turning points.

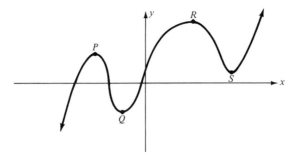

Figure 5.6

EXAMPLE 2

Graph $f(x) = 2x^3 - 3x^2 - 12x + 1$.

Solution   We begin by setting up a table of corresponding values of x and $f(x)$:

x	-3	-2	-1	0	1	2	3	4
$f(x)$	-44	-3	8	1	-12	-19	-8	33

Plotting the ordered pairs determined in the previous table as points on a coordinate plane, we obtain the curve shown in Figure 5.7 as the graph of $f(x) = 2x^3 - 3x^2 - 12x + 1$. For this function f, we see that the graph of f has 2 (rather than 0) turning points. Note that we have used *different* unit lengths for the two coordinate axes since the $f(x)$ values change so rapidly.   ∎

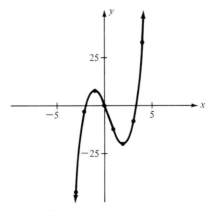

Figure 5.7

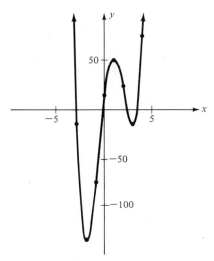

Figure 5.8

EXAMPLE 3

Graph $f(x) = 3x^4 - 8x^3 - 30x^2 + 72x + 15$.

Solution We begin by setting up a table of corresponding values of x and $f(x)$:

x	-4	-3	-2	-1	0	1	2	3	4
$f(x)$	527	-12	-137	-76	15	52	23	-12	79

Plotting the ordered pairs determined by the previous table as points of a coordinate plane, we obtain the curve shown in Figure 5.8 as the graph of the given function f. For our function f, we note that the graph of f has 3 (rather than 1) turning points. As in Example 2, we have used different unit lengths for the two coordinate axes since the $f(x)$ values vary so greatly.   ∎

Problems 5.2

In problems 1–12, graph the given polynomial function.

1. $f(x) = 5$ **2.** $f(x) = -3$ **3.** $f(x) = -\frac{1}{2}$
4. $f(x) = x - 5$ **5.** $f(x) = 2x + 1$ **6.** $f(x) = 3x - 2$
7. $f(x) = x^2 - 4x - 5$ **8.** $f(x) = x^2 - 2x - 3$ **9.** $f(x) = x^2 - x - 6$
10. $f(x) = -x^2 - 2x$ **11.** $f(x) = -x^2 + 4$ **12.** $f(x) = -2x^2 - 5x - 3$

In problems 13–24, graph the given polynomial functions by plotting the points which have the given x-values.

13. $f(x) = x^3$, x-values: $-3, -2, -1, 0, 1, 2, 3$

14. $f(x) = x^3 - 12x$, x-values: $-3, -2, -1, 0, 1, 2, 3$

15. $f(x) = -x^3 - x$, x-values: $-3, -2, -1, 0, 1, 2, 3$

16. $f(x) = x^3 - 12x + 2$, x-values: $-4, -3, -2, -1, 0, 1, 2, 3, 4$

17. $f(x) = x^3 - 3x^2 - 9x + 6$, x-values: $-3, -2, -1, 0, 1, 2, 3, 4, 5$

18. $f(x) = x^3 - 3x + 5$, x-values: $-3, -2, -1, 0, 1, 2, 3$

19. $f(x) = x^4$, x-values: $-3, -2, -1, 0, 1, 2, 3$

20. $f(x) = -x^4 - x^2$, x-values: $-3, -2, -1, 0, 1, 2, 3$

21. $f(x) = x^4 - 4x^3 - 10x^2 + 3$, x-values: $-3, -2, -1, 0, 1, 2, 3, 4, 5, 6$

22. $f(x) = x^4 - 4x^3 - 2x^2 + 12x - 2$, x-values: $-2, -1, 0, 1, 2, 3, 4$

23. $f(x) = x^4 - 2x^3 - 7x^2 + 10x - 15$, x-values: $-3, -2, -1, 0, 1, 2, 3, 4$

24. $f(x) = x^4 - 2x^3 - 13x^2 - 2x + 4$, x-values: $-3, -2, -1, 0, 1, 2, 3, 4, 5$

Answers 5.2

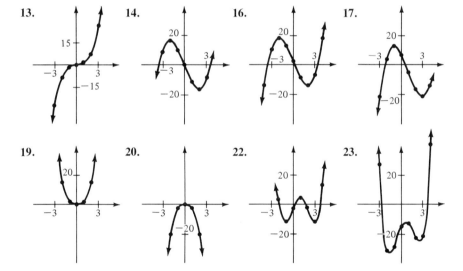

5.3 Rational Functions

We now consider the graphs of rational functions.

Definition 5.3 A function f defined by an equation of the form

$$f(x) = \frac{F(x)}{G(x)},$$

where F and G are polynomial functions, with G not the zero function, is called a **rational function.**

Note that the domain of the rational function $f(x) = 1/x$ is undefined for $x = 0$. Hence the graph of $f(x) = 1/x$ contains no ordered pair (x, y) having an x-coordinate of 0. Since x can equal any real number except 0, we can consider the graph of $f(x) = 1/x$ for values of x as close to 0 as we please. Observe that as x gets closer and closer to 0 from the right (i.e., as x becomes a smaller and smaller positive number), the value of $f(x)$ becomes very large in the positive sense. Also, note that as x gets closer and closer to 0 from the left, the value of $f(x)$ becomes very large in the negative sense. In Figure 5.9, note that the graph of $f(x) = 1/x$ approaches, but does not touch, the vertical line $x = 0$. In situations of this kind, the *vertical line* that the curve approaches is called a **vertical asymptote.**

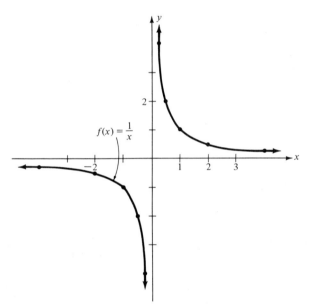

Figure 5.9

The following theorem, which we state without proof, can be used to determine the vertical asymptotes of the graph of a rational function.

Theorem 5.1   If the rational function f is defined by

$$f(x) = \frac{F(x)}{G(x)},$$

and if $G(a) = 0$ and $F(a) \neq 0$, then the line $x = a$ is a vertical asymptote of the graph of f.

EXAMPLE 1

Determine the vertical asymptotes of the graph of $f(x) = x/[(x + 1)(x - 4)]$.

Solution According to Theorem 5.1, the lines $x = -1$ and $x = 4$ are vertical asymptotes of the graph of f. ∎

EXERCISE 1

What are the vertical asymptotes for the graph of each function?
(a) $f(x) = -1/[(x - 2)(x + 3)]$.   (b) $f(x) = 3/(x^3 - 4x)$.

Answer (a) $x = 2$, $x = -3$ (b) $x = 0$, $x = 2$, $x = -2$

We now return to the graph of the rational function $f(x) = 1/x$ in Figure 5.9. Note that as x increases indefinitely in the positive direction, $f(x) = 1/x$ becomes closer and closer to 0. Similarly, we note that as x increases indefinitely in the negative direction, $f(x) = 1/x$ becomes closer and closer to 0. Thus the graph of $f(x) = 1/x$ approaches, but does not touch, the horizontal line $y = 0$. In situations of this kind, the *horizontal line* that the curve approaches is called a **horizontal asymptote.**

The following theorem can be used to determine the horizontal asymptote of the graph of a rational function.

Theorem 5.2 If the rational function f is defined by

$$f(x) = \frac{a_0 x^n + a_1 x^{n-1} + \cdots + a_n}{b_0 x^m + b_1 x^{m-1} + \cdots + b_m},$$

where $a_0 \neq 0$, $b_0 \neq 0$, and n and m are nonnegative integers, then the graph of the function f has

(a) The line $y = 0$ as a horizontal asymptote if $n < m$.
(b) The line $y = a_0/b_0$ as a horizontal asymptote if $n = m$.
(c) No horizontal asymptote if $n > m$.

Proof of (a) Dividing both the numerator and the denominator of $f(x)$ by x^m, we get

$$f(x) = \frac{(a_0/x^{m-n}) + (a_1/x^{m-n+1}) + \cdots + (a_n/x^m)}{b_0 + (b_1/x) + \cdots + (b_m/x^m)}. \qquad (5-1)$$

If $n < m$, then as x increases (or decreases) indefinitely, the numerator of $f(x)$ in Eq. (5–1) becomes closer and closer to 0 and the denominator becomes closer and closer to b_0, where $b_0 \neq 0$. Hence $f(x)$ approaches $0/b_0$ as x increases (or decreases) indefinitely. Therefore, $y = 0$ is a horizontal asymptote of the graph of f.

The proofs of (b) and (c) are similar. ∎

EXAMPLE 2

Determine the horizontal asymptotes, if any, of the graph of $f(x) = (2x^2 - 1)/(x^2 - 2x - 3)$.

Solution In this case, $n = m$. Therefore, according to Theorem 5.2, the line $y = \frac{2}{1} = 2$ is the horizontal asymptote of the graph of f. ∎

EXERCISE 2

What is the horizontal asymptote, if any, for the graph of each function?
(a) $f(x) = x/[(x-3)(x+1)]$.   (b) $f(x) = [3x(x-1)]/[(x-3)(x+1)]$.

Answer (a) $y = 0$ (b) $y = 3$

It follows from the proof of Theorem 5.2 that a rational function f can have no more than one horizontal asymptote. In addition to vertical and horizontal asymptotes, the graph of a rational function can also have *slant asymptotes*. However, in this book we shall consider only those rational functions whose graphs have only vertical and horizontal asymptotes.

The next two examples show how asymptotes and intercepts can be used as an effective aid in the graphing of rational functions.

EXAMPLE 3

Graph $f(x) = (2x - 1)/(x + 1)$.

Solution Setting $f(x) = 0$, we obtain $\frac{1}{2}$ as the only x-intercept. Setting $x = 0$, we obtain -1 as the y-intercept. Using Theorem 5.1, we find that $x = -1$ is the only vertical asymptote. Using Theorem 5.2, we find that $y = \frac{2}{1} = 2$ is the horizontal asymptote. These asymptotes are indicated in Figure 5.10 as dashed lines. Since $x = -1$ is a vertical asymptote, the graph of f approaches $x = -1$ as x gets closer and closer to -1. Since $y = 2$ is a horizontal asymptote, the graph of f approaches $y = 2$ as $|x|$ increases indefinitely. Since $(2x - 1)/(x + 1)$ is positive when $x > \frac{1}{2}$ and when $x < -1$, the graph of f is *above* the x-axis for these values of x. Since $(2x - 1)/(x + 1)$ is negative when $-1 < x < \frac{1}{2}$, the graph of f is *below* the x-axis for these values of x. Using this information, the graph of f has been sketched in Figure 5.10. ∎

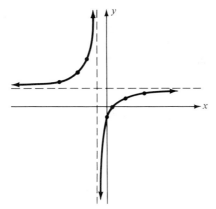

Figure 5.10

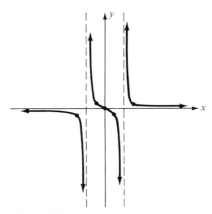

Figure 5.11

EXAMPLE 4

Graph $f(x) = x/(x^2 - 4)$.

Solution   Setting $f(x) = 0$, we obtain 0 as the only x-intercept. Setting $x = 0$, we obtain 0 as the y-intercept. Using Theorem 5.1, we find that $x = 2$ and $x = -2$ are vertical asymptotes. Using Theorem 5.2, we find that $y = 0$ is the horizontal asymptote. These asymptotes are indicated in Figure 5.11 as dashed lines. Since $x = 2$ and $x = -2$ are vertical asymptotes, the graph of f approaches $x = 2$ as x gets closer and closer to 2 and the graph of f approaches $x = -2$ as x gets closer and closer to -2. Since $y = 0$ is the horizontal asymptote, the graph of f approaches $y = 0$ as $|x|$ increases indefinitely. Since

$$\frac{x}{x^2 - 4} = \frac{x}{(x-2)(x+2)}$$

is positive when $x > 2$ and when $-2 < x < 0$, the graph of f is *above* the x-axis for these values of x. On the other hand, the graph of f is *below* the x-axis when $0 < x < 2$ and when $x < -2$. Using the previous information, the graph of f has been sketched in Figure 5.11. ∎

Problems 5.3

In problems 1–12, determine the vertical and horizontal asymptotes of the graph of the given rational function.

1. $f(x) = \dfrac{1}{x+1}$

2. $f(x) = \dfrac{1}{x-2}$

3. $f(x) = \dfrac{1}{x-5}$

4. $f(x) = \dfrac{x+2}{(x-2)^2}$

5. $f(x) = \dfrac{3x-1}{(x+3)^2}$

6. $f(x) = \dfrac{2x+5}{(x-5)^2}$

7. $f(x) = \dfrac{(2x-1)(x-3)}{(x+1)(x-2)}$

8. $f(x) = \dfrac{(2x+1)(x-4)}{x(x-2)}$

9. $f(x) = \dfrac{-3x(x-1)}{(x+2)(x-3)}$

10. $f(x) = \dfrac{4x^2-9}{x^2+2x-3}$

11. $f(x) = \dfrac{x^2-25}{x^2+x-6}$

12. $f(x) = \dfrac{3x^2-27}{x^2+3x-4}$

In problems 13–30, determine the intercepts and asymptotes of the graph of the given function. Then use this information to sketch the graph of the function.

13. $f(x) = \dfrac{1}{x-3}$

14. $f(x) = \dfrac{4}{x+1}$

15. $f(x) = \dfrac{-1}{x+4}$

16. $f(x) = \dfrac{2}{(x+1)^2}$

17. $f(x) = \dfrac{-1}{(x-3)^2}$

18. $f(x) = \dfrac{1}{(x-2)^2}$

19. $f(x) = \dfrac{3x-2}{x+1}$

20. $f(x) = \dfrac{-x+3}{x-2}$

21. $f(x) = \dfrac{2x-1}{x-3}$

22. $f(x) = \dfrac{2x-3}{(x+1)x}$

23. $f(x) = \dfrac{x+5}{(x-1)(x+3)}$

24. $f(x) = \dfrac{3x-2}{(x+1)(x-2)}$

25. $f(x) = \dfrac{(x-1)(x+2)}{(x+1)^2}$

26. $f(x) = \dfrac{2x(x-3)}{(x+2)^2}$

27. $f(x) = \dfrac{x(x-2)}{(x-3)^2}$

28. $f(x) = \dfrac{x^2-5x+4}{x^2-x-2}$

29. $f(x) = \dfrac{x^2-x-6}{x^2-2x}$

30. $f(x) = \dfrac{x^2-2x}{x^2-x-6}$

31. Determine the intercepts and asymptotes for the graph of $f(x) = (x+1)/x(x+1)$ and use this information to sketch the graph of the function. Explain why $x=-1$ is *not* a vertical asymptote for the graph of f.
32. Determine the intercepts and asymptotes for the graph of $f(x) = (x-1)(x+2)/(x+1)(x+2)$ and use this information to sketch the graph of the function. Explain why $x=-2$ is *not* a vertical asymptote for the graph of f.

Answers 5.3

1. $x=-1$, $y=0$

2. $x=2$, $y=0$

4. $x=2$, $y=0$

5. $x=-3$, $y=0$

7. $x=-1$, $x=2$, $y=2$

8. $x=0$, $x=2$, $y=2$

10. $x=1$, $x=-3$, $y=4$

11. $x=2$, $x=-3$, $y=1$

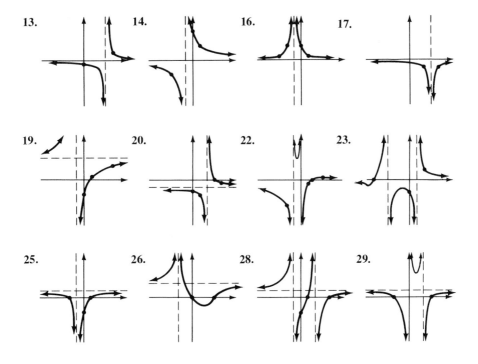

5.4 Square Root Functions

Recall that the graph of the relation $y^2 = x$ is a parabola opening to the right with vertex $(0, 0)$. See Figure 5.12. By taking square roots of both sides of the equation

$$y^2 = x,$$

we get

$$y = \pm\sqrt{x}.$$

Hence it follows that the graphs of $y = \sqrt{x}$ and $y = -\sqrt{x}$ combine to give the graph of $y = \pm\sqrt{x}$ and hence of $y^2 = x$. Since $\sqrt{x}$ represents the nonnegative square root of x, the graph of $y = \sqrt{x}$ is the upper half of the parabola in Figure 5.12. Similarly, the graph of $y = -\sqrt{x}$ is the lower half of the same parabola.

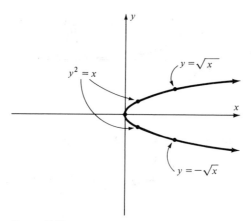

Figure 5.12

EXAMPLE 1

Graph the function defined by $y = \sqrt{4 - x^2}$.

Solution   Since $y = \sqrt{4 - x^2}$ is one of the two equations, $y = \sqrt{4 - x^2}$ and $y = -\sqrt{4 - x^2}$, which combine to give

$$y = \pm\sqrt{4 - x^2},$$
$$y^2 = 4 - x^2,$$

and hence

$$x^2 + y^2 = 4,$$

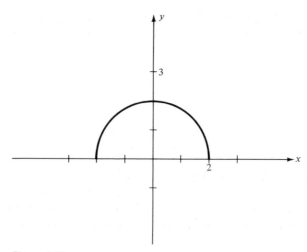

Figure 5.13

it follows that the graph of $y = \sqrt{4 - x^2}$ (see Figure 5.13) is the upper half of the graph of the circle $x^2 + y^2 = 4$.   ∎

EXAMPLE 2

Graph the function defined by $y = -\sqrt{4 + x^2}$.

Solution   Since $y = -\sqrt{4 + x^2}$ is one of the two equations, $y = \sqrt{4 + x^2}$ and $y = -\sqrt{4 + x^2}$, which combine to give

$$y = \pm\sqrt{4 + x^2},$$
$$y^2 = 4 + x^2,$$

and hence

$$y^2 - x^2 = 4,$$

it follows that the graph of $y = -\sqrt{4 + x^2}$ (see Figure 5.14) is the lower half of the graph of the hyperbola $y^2 - x^2 = 4$.   ∎

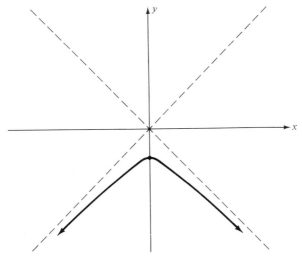

Figure 5.14

EXAMPLE 3

Graph $y = 1 + \sqrt{2 - x}$.

Solution   Since $y = 1 + \sqrt{2 - x}$ is one of the two equations, $y - 1 = \sqrt{2 - x}$ and $y - 1 = -\sqrt{2 - x}$, which combine to give

$$y - 1 = \pm\sqrt{2 - x},$$
$$(y - 1)^2 = 2 - x,$$

and

$$(y-1)^2 = -(x-2),$$

it follows that the graph of $y = 1 + \sqrt{2-x}$ (see Figure 5.15) is the upper half of the graph of the parabola $(y-1)^2 = -(x-2)$ which opens to the left and has a vertex of (2, 1).   ∎

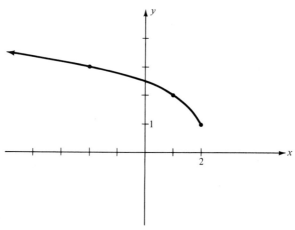

Figure 5.15

Problems 5.4

In problems 1–24, graph the function defined by the given equation.

1. $y = -\sqrt{x}$ 2. $y = \sqrt{-x}$ 3. $y = -\sqrt{-x}$
4. $y = -\sqrt{x-1}$ 5. $y = \sqrt{x+2}$ 6. $y = \sqrt{4-x}$
7. $y = -\sqrt{1-x^2}$ 8. $y = \sqrt{9-x^2}$ 9. $y = -\sqrt{25-x^2}$
10. $y = \sqrt{4x-x^2}$ 11. $y = 2 - \sqrt{4-x^2}$ 12. $y = 1 + \sqrt{1-x^2}$
13. $y = -3 + \sqrt{9-x^2}$ 14. $y = \sqrt{-x^2-2x}$ 15. $y = \sqrt{6x-x^2}$
16. $y = -2\sqrt{1-x^2}$ 17. $y = 4\sqrt{1-x^2}$ 18. $y = -3\sqrt{1-x^2}$
19. $y = \sqrt{4+x^2}$ 20. $y = -\sqrt{x^2-9}$ 21. $y = \sqrt{x^2-16}$
22. $y = 2\sqrt{x^2-1}$ 23. $y = -3\sqrt{x^2+1}$ 24. $y = 2\sqrt{x^2+1}$

Answers 5.4

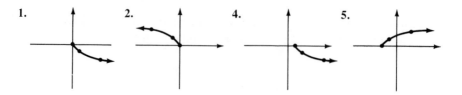

1.   2.   4.   5.

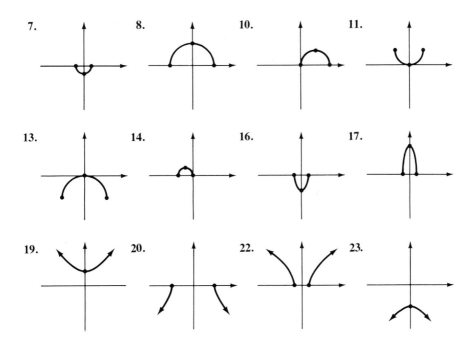

7.   8.   10.   11.

13.   14.   16.   17.

19.   20.   22.   23.

5.5 Special Functions

In this section, we consider two additional kinds of functions that are particularly useful in more advanced mathematics courses.

Absolute Value Functions

Recall that $|x|$ is defined as

$$|x| = \begin{cases} x & \text{if } x \geq 0, \\ -x & \text{if } x < 0. \end{cases}$$

Thus to graph the function defined by

$$y = |x|.$$

we graph the equivalent function

$$y = \begin{cases} x & \text{if } x \geq 0, \\ -x & \text{if } x < 0. \end{cases}$$

That is, we graph $y = x$ when $x \geq 0$, and we graph $y = -x$ when $x < 0$. Doing this, we obtain the graph shown in Figure 5.16.

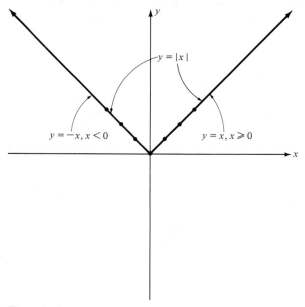

Figure 5.16

EXAMPLE 1

Graph the function defined by $y = |x - 1| - 2$.

Solution Since

$$|x-1| = \begin{cases} x-1 & \text{when } x-1 \geq 0 \quad \text{(i.e., when } x \geq 1\text{),} \\ -(x-1) & \text{when } x-1 < 0 \quad \text{(i.e., when } x < 1\text{),} \end{cases}$$

the equation $y = |x - 1| - 2$ is equivalent to

$$y = \begin{cases} (x-1)-2 & \text{when } x \geq 1, \\ -(x-1)-2 & \text{when } x < 1 \end{cases}$$

and hence to

$$y = \begin{cases} x-3 & \text{when } x \geq 1, \\ -x-1 & \text{when } x < 1. \end{cases}$$

Consequently, to graph $y = |x - 1| - 2$, we graph $y = x - 3$ when $x \geq 1$, and we graph $y = -x - 1$ when $x < 1$. Doing this, we obtain the graph shown in Figure 5.17.

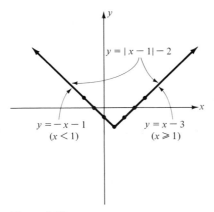

Figure 5.17

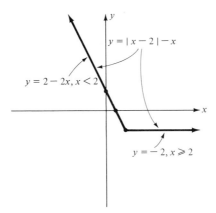

Figure 5.18

EXAMPLE 2

Graph the function defined by $y = |x - 2| - x$.

Solution   Since

$$|x-2| = \begin{cases} x-2 & \text{when } x-2 \geq 0 \quad \text{(i.e., when } x \geq 2), \\ -(x-2) & \text{when } x-2 < 0 \quad \text{(i.e., when } x < 2), \end{cases}$$

the equation $y = |x - 2| - x$ is equivalent to

$$y = \begin{cases} (x-2)-x & \text{when } x \geq 2, \\ -(x-2)-x & \text{when } x < 2, \end{cases}$$

and hence to

$$y = \begin{cases} -2 & \text{when } x \geq 2, \\ 2-2x & \text{when } x < 2. \end{cases}$$

Consequently, to graph $y = |x - 2| - x$, we graph $y = -2$ when $x \geq 2$, and we graph $y = 2 - 2x$ when $x < 2$. Doing this, we get the graph shown in Figure 5.18. ∎

Bracket Functions

We define the symbol $[\![x]\!]$, read "bracket x," as the greatest integer that is less than or equal to x. For example,

$$[\![\pi]\!] = 3, \quad [\![2.9]\!] = 2, \quad [\![-1]\!] = -1, \quad \text{and} \quad [\![-1.7]\!] = -2.$$

From the definition of $[\![x]\!]$, we observe that

$$
\begin{array}{ll}
[\![x]\!] = -2 & \text{when } -2 \leq x < -1, \\
[\![x]\!] = -1 & \text{when } -1 \leq x < 0, \\
[\![x]\!] = 0 & \text{when } 0 \leq x < 1, \\
[\![x]\!] = 1 & \text{when } 1 \leq x < 2, \\
[\![x]\!] = 2 & \text{when } 2 \leq x < 3,
\end{array}
$$

and so on. Thus we are led to the graph of the function

$$y = [\![x]\!]$$

shown in Figure 5.19.

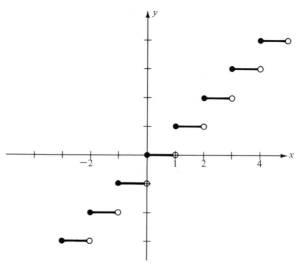

Figure 5.19

EXAMPLE 3

Graph the function defined by $y = x - [\![x]\!]$ for $-3 \leq x < 3$.

Solution   Using the definition of $[\![x]\!]$, we see that the given equation is equivalent to

$$
\begin{array}{ll}
y = x - (-3) & \text{when } -3 \leq x < -2, \\
y = x - (-2) & \text{when } -2 \leq x < -1, \\
y = x - (-1) & \text{when } -1 \leq x < 0, \\
y = x - 0 & \text{when } 0 \leq x < 1, \\
y = x - 1 & \text{when } 1 \leq x < 2,
\end{array}
$$

and

$$ y = x - 2 \qquad \text{when } 2 \leq x < 3. $$

Graphing each of the above six functions on the given interval, we get the graph of $y = x - [\![x]\!]$, $-3 \leq x < 3$, shown in Figure 5.20. ∎

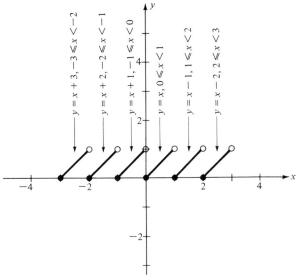

Figure 5.20

Problems 5.5

In problems 1 – 18, graph the absolute value function defined by the given equation.

1. $y = |x| + 1$ 2. $y = |x| - 3$ 3. $y = |x| - 2$
4. $y = -|x|$ 5. $y = -|x| + 2$ 6. $y = -|x| - 1$
7. $y = |x + 1|$ 8. $y = |x + 3|$ 9. $y = |x - 2|$

10. $y = |x-2| + 2$ **11.** $y = |x+1| - 2$ **12.** $y = |x-3| - 1$

13. $y = |x-2| + x$ **14.** $y = |x+1| - x$ **15.** $y = |x-1| + 2x$

16. $y = |x-2| + |x|$ **17.** $y = |x-2| - |x|$ **18.** $y = |x^2 - 2x|$

In problems 19–30, graph the bracket function defined by the given equation for $-3 \le x < 3$.

19. $y = [\![2x]\!]$ **20.** $y = [\![x/2]\!]$ **21.** $y = -[\![x]\!]$

22. $y = [\![x-1]\!]$ **23.** $y = [\![x]\!] - 1$ **24.** $y = [\![x^2]\!]$

25. $y = x + [\![x]\!]$ **26.** $y = x[\![x]\!]$ **27.** $y = x/[\![x]\!]$

28. $y = |[\![x]\!]|$ **29.** $y = [\![|x|]\!]$ **30.** $y = |x| - [\![x]\!]$

Answers 5.5

1.   **2.**   **4.**   **5.**

7. 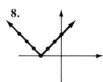   **8.**   **10.**   **11.**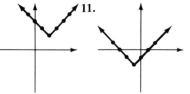

13. 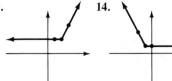   **14.**   **16.**   **17.**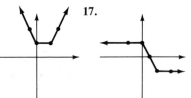

19. 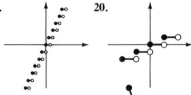   **20.**   **22.**   **23.**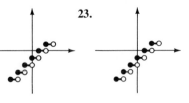

25. 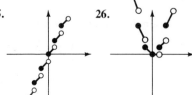   **26.**   **28.**   **29.**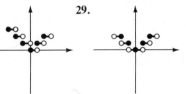

5.6 Variation As a Functional Relationship

In many scientific laws the relationships that exist between the physical quantities involved are defined by means of a functional relationship known as *variation* or *proportion*. We shall now describe the terminology that is used in discussing the three basic kinds of variation.

Definition 5.4 If two variables x and y and a nonzero constant k are related so that

$$y = kx$$

for all values of x, we say that

y varies directly as x, or
y varies as x, or
y is directly proportional to x, or
y is proportional to x.

The nonzero constant k is called the *constant of variation* or the *constant of proportionality*.

EXAMPLE 1

The equation

$$C = 2\pi r$$

from plane geometry states that the circumference C of a circle varies directly as its radius r. In this case the constant of proportionality is 2π.

Definition 5.5 If three variables x, y, and z and a nonzero constant of variation k are related so that

$$z = kxy$$

for all values of x and y, we say that

z varies jointly as x and y, or
z varies directly as x and directly as y, or
z varies directly as the product of x and y.

EXAMPLE 2

The equation

$$A = \tfrac{1}{2}bh$$

from plane geometry states that the area A of a triangle varies jointly as its base b and its altitude h. Here the constant of variation is $\tfrac{1}{2}$.

Definition 5.6 If two variables x and y and a nonzero constant of variation k are related so that

$$y = \frac{k}{x}$$

for all nonzero values of x, we say that

y varies inversely as x, or
y is inversely proportional to x.

EXAMPLE 3

Boyle's law,

$$V = \frac{k}{P},$$

from chemistry and physics states that, at a fixed temperature, the volume V of a given mass of gas varies inversely as the pressure P applied to the gas.

EXERCISE 1

Express the given statement as an equation.
(a) The volume V of a sphere varies directly as the cube of the radius r.
(b) The kinetic energy K varies jointly as the mass m and the square of the velocity v.
(c) The intensity I of light varies inversely as the square of the distance d from the source of the light.

Answer (a) $V = kr^3$ (b) $K = kmv^2$ (c) $I = k/d^2$

The different kinds of variation often occur simultaneously in problems.

EXAMPLE 4

If T varies directly as the cube of x and inversely as the square root of y, and if $T = 5$ when $x = 2$ and $y = 16$, determine T when $x = 3$ and $y = 25$.

Solution The equation of variation is

$$T = \frac{kx^3}{\sqrt{y}}.$$

Since we are given that $T = 5$ when $x = 2$ and $y = 16$, it follows that

$$5 = \frac{k(2)^3}{\sqrt{16}}.$$

Solving the previous equation for the constant of proportionality k, we get $k = \frac{5}{2}$. Since k is a constant, the equation of variation is

$$T = \frac{5x^3}{2\sqrt{y}}.$$

Therefore, when $x = 3$ and $y = 25$, it follows that

$$T = \frac{5(3)^3}{2\sqrt{25}} = \frac{27}{2}.$$ ∎

Problems 5.6

In problems 1–12, express the given statement as an equation.

1. P varies jointly as x, y, and the square of z.
2. Q varies jointly as x and y and inversely as z.
3. R varies directly as the square of x and inversely as the square root of y.
4. Q varies directly as the square root of x and inversely as the cube of y.
5. R varies inversely as x and inversely as the square root of y.
6. T varies jointly as x and the square of y and inversely as the cube of z.
7. The surface area S of a sphere varies directly as the square of its radius r. Insert the correct constant of variation.
8. The volume V of a right circular cylinder varies jointly as its altitude h and the square of its radius r. Insert the correct constant of variation.
9. The volume V of a right circular cone varies jointly as its altitude h and the square of its radius r. Insert the correct constant of variation.
10. The force F of attraction between two spheres varies jointly as their masses m_1 and m_2 and inversely as the square of the distance d between their centers.
11. The resistance R of a wire varies directly as its length l and the square of its radius r.
12. The current I in a wire varies directly as the electromotive force E and inversely as the resistance R.
13. Referring to problem 7, determine how the surface area of a sphere is affected when we double its radius.
14. Referring to problem 8, determine how the volume of a right circular cylinder is affected if we double its radius and reduce its altitude by one third.
15. Referring to problem 9, determine how the volume of a right circular cone is affected if we increase both its radius and its altitude by 25 percent.
16. If K varies directly as the square of x and inversely as y, and if $K = 8$ when $x = 2$ and $y = 3$, determine K when $x = 3$ and $y = 2$.
17. If T varies jointly as x and the square root of y, and if $T = 16$ when $x = 2$ and $y = 4$, determine T when $x = 3$ and $y = 9$.
18. If Q varies directly as the square root of x and inversely as the square of y, and if $Q = 9$ when $x = 4$ and $y = 2$, determine Q when $x = 25$ and $y = 3$.

19. Boyle's law states that, at a fixed temperature, the volume of a given mass of gas varies inversely as the pressure applied to the gas. If a certain mass of gas has a volume of 40 cubic inches when the pressure is 22 pounds, what is the volume of the gas when the pressure is 30 pounds?

20. The weight of a body above the surface of the earth varies inversely as the square of the distance of the body from the center of the earth. If a man weighs 200 pounds on the surface of the earth, how much would he weigh 200 miles above the surface? Assume that the radius of the earth is 4000 miles.

21. The distance a body falls, in a vacuum near the earth's surface, is directly proportional to the square of the length of time it falls. If a body falls 144 feet in 3 seconds, how far will it fall in 5 seconds?

22. The maximum safe load for a horizontal beam, which is supported at both ends, varies jointly as the width and the square of its depth and inversely as the length. If a 6- by 8-inch horizontal beam which is 12 feet long supports 1800 pounds when lying on its 8-inch side, how many pounds will it support when lying on its 6-inch side?

23. Hooke's law states that the extension of a spring beyond its natural length varies directly as the force applied. If a force of 4 pounds causes a spring, whose natural length is 12 inches, to stretch from 12 inches to 12.5 inches, use Hooke's law to determine the force that is required to stretch the spring from 12 inches to 15 inches.

24. If 2 men, each working at the same rate, can assemble 6 machines in 9 hours, how long will it take 6 men, each working at the same rate as the first two men, to assemble 12 machines?

Answers 5.6

1. $P = kxyz^2$	2. $Q = kxy/z$	4. $Q = k\sqrt{x}/y^3$	5. $R = k/x\sqrt{y}$
7. $S = 4\pi r^2$	8. $V = \pi r^2 h$	10. $F = km_1 m_2/d^2$	11. $R = klr^2$
13. multiplied by 4	14. multiplied by $\frac{8}{3}$	16. 27	17. 36
19. $29\frac{1}{3}$ in³	20. 181.4 lb	22. 2400 lb	23. 24 lb

chapter 5 review problems

1. Define a function from X to Y. Define a real-valued function.
2. Explain the difference between a relation on R and a real-valued function. Given the graph of a relation on R, how can we tell whether or not the relation is a function?
3. Explain why the given relation is (or is not) a function.
   (a) $\{(1, 2), (1, 5), (2, 7)\}$ (b) $y^2 = x$ (c) $y = [\![x - 2]\!]$
4. Graph each of the following functions and determine its domain and its range.
   (a) $y = \sqrt{x - 3}$ (b) $y = |x - 3|$ (c) $y = [\![x]\!]$

5. If $f(x) = x^2 - 4x$, determine $f(3)$, $f(a - 1)$, and $f[f(-1)]$.
6. Graph the following polynomial functions.
   (a) $y = -2$ (b) $y = -x + 3$
   (c) $y = x^2 + 2x - 1$ (d) $y = x^3 - 3x + 1$
7. Graph the following rational functions.
   (a) $y = 1/(x - 2)$ (b) $y = x/(x - 2)$ (c) $y = x/[(x + 1)(x - 2)]$
8. Graph the following square-root functions.
   (a) $y = \sqrt{2 - x}$ (b) $y = -\sqrt{4 - x^2}$ (c) $y = \sqrt{x^2 - 4}$
9. Graph the following absolute value functions.
   (a) $y = -|x| + 1$ (b) $y = |x - 1|$ (c) $y = |x - 1| + x$
10. If T varies jointly as x and the square of y and inversely as the square root of z, what change occurs in T when x, y, and z are each doubled?
11. The resistance of a wire varies directly as its length l and the square of its radius r. If $R = 64$ ohms for a 16-foot piece of wire whose radius is .01 inch, determine the resistance in a piece of the same kind of wire which has a length of 100 feet and a radius of .005 inch.

Answers

3. (a) is not   (b) is not   (c) is

4. (a)   (b)   (c)

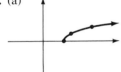
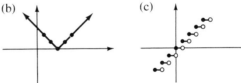

5. $f(3) = -3$, $f(a - 1) = a^2 - 6a + 5$, $f[f(-1)] = 5$

6. (a)   (b)   (c)   (d)

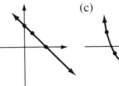
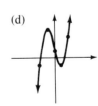

7. (a)   (b)   (c)

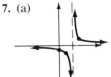

8. (a) (b) (c)

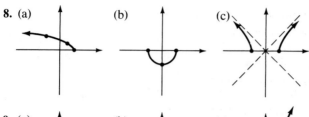

9. (a) (b) (c)

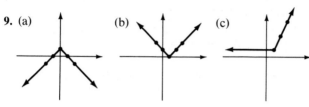

10. T is multiplied by $4\sqrt{2}$.

11. 100 ohms

6

exponential and logarithmic functions

6.1 Inverse Functions

Recall that no two ordered pairs of a function have the same first element. In general, however, a function does not have the property that no two ordered pairs of the function have the same second elements. But, we shall find that many important functions do possess this additional property. Such functions are called one-to-one functions.

Definition 6.1 The function $f: X \to Y$ is said to be a **one-to-one function** if no two different ordered pairs of f have the same second element.

For real-valued functions, we can restate Definition 6.1 in the following way. A real-valued function is a one-to-one function if each real number y in the range of the function corresponds with *one and only one* real number x in the domain of the function.

EXAMPLE 1

The function $\{(1, 2), (2, 3), (3, 1)\}$ is a one-to-one function, since no two different ordered pairs of the function have the same second element. On the other hand, the function $\{(1, 7), (2, 7), (3, 0)\}$ is not a one-to-one function, since two different ordered pairs, namely $(1, 7)$ and $(2, 7)$ have the same second element.

201

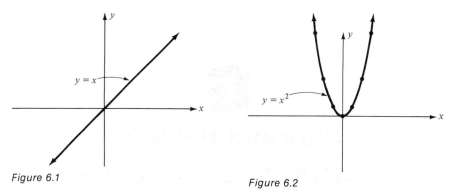

Figure 6.1   *Figure 6.2*

EXAMPLE 2

The function $f = \{(x, y)\,|\,y = x\}$ is a one-to-one function, since each element y in the range of the function corresponds with *exactly one* element x in the domain of the function. The fact that f is a one-to-one function can also be seen from the graph of $y = x$ in Figure 6.1, since no two different points of the graph have the same second element.

EXAMPLE 3

The function $f = \{(x, y)\,|\,y = x^2\}$ is not a one-to-one function, since each nonzero element y in the range of the function corresponds with more than one element x in the domain of the function. The fact that f fails to be a one-to-one function can also be seen from the graph of $y = x^2$ in Figure 6.2, since there are numerous examples of different points of the graph [for example, $(1, 1)$ and $(-1, 1)$] having the same second element.

Using Definitions 4.3, 5.1, and 6.1, we obtain the following rule for deciding whether or not a real-valued function is a one-to-one function.

Horizontal-Line Rule

A real-valued function is a one-to-one function if and only if no horizontal line crosses the graph of the function more than once.

EXERCISE 1

Determine whether or not the given function is a one-to-one function by applying the horizontal-line rule to its graph.

(a) $y = x^3$.   (b) $y = |x|$.   (c) $y = [\![x]\!]$.

Answer   (a) defines a one-to-one function, (b) and (c) do not.

Inverse Functions

If we interchange the first and second elements of each ordered pair of a one-to-one function f, we obtain another collection of ordered pairs (i.e., a relation), which we denote by the symbol f^{-1}. Thus

$$(x, y) \in f^{-1} \quad \text{if and only if} \quad (y, x) \in f. \qquad (6-1)$$

Since no two different ordered pairs of f have the same second elements, it follows that no two different ordered pairs of f^{-1} have the same first element. Therefore, f^{-1} is also a function. The function f^{-1} is called the inverse function of f. Expressing $(6-1)$ in functional notation, we obtain the following definition.

Definition 6.2 If f is a one-to-one function, the **inverse function of f,** denoted by f^{-1}, is the function defined by

$$y = f^{-1}(x) \quad \text{if and only if} \quad x = f(y). \qquad (6-2)$$

The two functions f and f^{-1} are said to be inverses of each other.

Since the ordered pairs of f^{-1} are obtained from those of f by interchanging the first and second elements in each ordered pair of f, it follows that the domain of f becomes the range of f^{-1} and the range of f becomes the domain of f^{-1}. That is,

$$D_{f^{-1}} = R_f \quad \text{and} \quad R_{f^{-1}} = D_f.$$

When f is a one-to-one function, we can express Eq. $(6-2)$ in set notation as follows:

$$f^{-1} = \{(x, y) \mid x = f(y)\}. \qquad (6-3)$$

Note that Eq. $(6-3)$ states that we obtain the equation that defines f^{-1} by interchanging the variables x and y in the equation that defines f. In other words, if the one-to-one function f is defined by $y = f(x)$, then the inverse function f^{-1} is defined by $x = f(y)$.

EXAMPLE 4

If the one-to-one function f is defined by

$$y = 2x,$$

then the equation which defines f^{-1} is obtained from the previous equation by interchanging the x and y variables. Thus f^{-1} is defined by

$$x = 2y \quad \text{or} \quad y = \tfrac{1}{2}x.$$

The graphs of f and f^{-1} are shown in Figure 6.3.

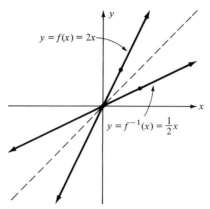

Figure 6.3

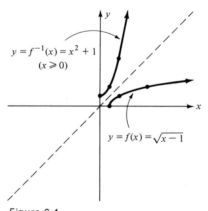

Figure 6.4

EXAMPLE 5

If the one-to-one function f is defined by

$$y = \sqrt{x - 1},$$

then f^{-1} is defined by

$$x = \sqrt{y - 1}.$$

After observing that the last equation always has nonnegative values of x, we can rewrite it as

$$x^2 = y - 1 \qquad (x \geq 0)$$

and hence as

$$y = x^2 + 1 \qquad (x \geq 0).$$

The graphs of f and f^{-1} are shown in Figure 6.4.

As you may have noticed in Figures 6.3 and 6.4, there is an interesting relationship between the graph of a one-to-one function f and the graph of its inverse f^{-1}. Note that the graph of f^{-1} appears as a mirror image to the graph of f with respect to the dashed line $y = x$. This is true because (x, y) is a point of the graph of f^{-1} if and only if (y, x) is a point of the graph of f. Thus we can always obtain the graph of f^{-1} from the graph of a one-to-one function f by reflecting the graph of f across the line $y = x$.

EXERCISE 2

Determine the equation that defines f^{-1} if the one-to-one function f is defined by the given equation. Then graph f and f^{-1} and note that the graphs are reflections of one another with respect to the line $y = x$.
(a) $y = 3x - 1$.　　(b) $y = \sqrt{x - 3}$.

Answer　(a) $y = \frac{1}{3}x + \frac{1}{3}$　　(b) $y = x^2 + 3$, $x \geq 0$

We now state a useful theorem that exhibits an important algebraic relationship between a one-to-one function and its inverse.

Theorem 6.1　If f is a one-to-one function, then
(a) $f[f^{-1}(x)] = x$ for all $x \in D_{f^{-1}}$.　　　　　　　　　　(6–4)
(b) $f^{-1}[f(x)] = x$ for all $x \in D_f$.　　　　　　　　　　　　(6–5)

Proof of (a)　If $x \in D_{f^{-1}}$, then it follows from Definition 6.2 that

$$f[f^{-1}(x)] = f[y] = x.$$

The proof of (b) is similar.　　　　　　　　　　　　　　　　　■
The previous theorem can also be used to determine the equation that defines the inverse f^{-1} of a given one-to-one function f.

EXAMPLE 6

If $f(x) = x/2 - 1/2$, determine $f^{-1}(x)$.

Solution It is clear from the graph of f in Figure 6.5 that f is a one-to-one function. Note that $D_{f^{-1}} = R_f = \{x|x \in R\}$. Since

$$f[f^{-1}(x)] = \frac{f^{-1}(x)}{2} - \frac{1}{2},$$

it follows from Equation (6–4) that

$$\frac{f^{-1}(x)}{2} - \frac{1}{2} = x \qquad \text{for all } x \in D_{f^{-1}} = \{x|x \in R\}.$$

Solving for $f^{-1}(x)$, we get

$$f^{-1}(x) = 2x + 1. \qquad \blacksquare$$

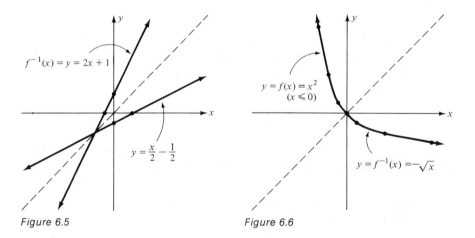

Figure 6.5   Figure 6.6

Even though a function is not a one-to-one function, it may be possible to restrict its domain so that the restricted function is a one-to-one function that has an inverse. For example, we can observe from the graph of $f(x) = x^2$ in Figure 6.2 that f is *not* a one-to-one function. However, by restricting the domain of $f(x) = x^2$ to $x \le 0$ (or to $x \ge 0$), the restricted function (see Figure 6.6) *does have* an inverse.

EXAMPLE 7

If $f(x) = x^2$ for $x \le 0$, determine $f^{-1}(x)$.

Solution   It is clear from the graph of f in Figure 6.6 that f is a one-to-one function. Note that $D_{f^{-1}} = R_f = \{x \mid x \geq 0\}$. Since

$$f[f^{-1}(x)] = [f^{-1}(x)]^2,$$

it follows from Eq. (6–4) that

$$[f^{-1}(x)]^2 = x \qquad \text{for all } x \in D_{f^{-1}} = \{x \mid x \geq 0\}.$$

Hence

$$f^{-1}(x) = -\sqrt{x} \qquad \text{for } x \geq 0,$$

since $R_{f^{-1}} = D_f = \{x \mid x \leq 0\}$.   ∎

Problems 6.1

In problems 1–24, examine the graph of the function f defined by the given equation to determine if f is a one-to-one function. Then determine $f^{-1}(x)$, if it exists, and graph f^{-1} on the same coordinate plane with f.

1. $y = 4x + 3$	**2.** $y = 2x - 1$
3. $y = 5 - 3x$	**4.** $y = \sqrt{x}$
5. $y = \sqrt{3 - x}$	**6.** $y = \sqrt{x + 5}$
7. $y = -\sqrt{x - 2}$	**8.** $y = -\sqrt{x + 1}$
9. $y = -\sqrt{1 - x}$	**10.** $y = x^2 + 1$
11. $y = x^2 + 1,\ x \geq 0$	**12.** $y = x^2 + 1,\ x \leq 0$
13. $y = x^2 - 2x,\ x \geq 1$	**14.** $y = x^2 - 2x,\ x \leq 1$
15. $y = |x - 2|$	**16.** $y = 1/x$
17. $y = 1/x^2$	**18.** $y = 1/x^2,\ x > 0$
19. $y = \sqrt{1 - x^2},\ 0 \leq x \leq 1$	**20.** $y = x^2 + 2x + 1,\ x \leq -1$
21. $y = x^2 + 2x + 1,\ x \geq -1$	**22.** $y = x^3$
23. $y = \sqrt{x^2 - 1},\ x \geq 1$	**24.** $y = -\sqrt{x^2 - 1},\ x \leq -1$

25. Prove Theorem 6.1(b).

26. A real-valued function f is said to be an **increasing function** if

$$f(x_1) < f(x_2) \qquad \text{when } x_1 < x_2 \text{ and } x_1, x_2 \in D_f.$$

Give three examples of increasing functions.

27. Prove that every increasing function f has an inverse.

28. A real-valued function f is said to be a **decreasing function** if

$$f(x_1) > f(x_2) \qquad \text{when } x_1 < x_2 \text{ and } x_1, x_2 \in D_f.$$

Give three examples of decreasing functions.

29. Prove that every decreasing function f has an inverse.

Answers 6.1

1. $f^{-1}(x)=\frac{1}{4}x-\frac{3}{4}$ **2.** $f^{-1}(x)=\frac{1}{2}x+\frac{1}{2}$

4. $f^{-1}(x)=x^2,\ x\geq 0$ **5.** $f^{-1}(x)=3-x^2,\ x\geq 0$

7. $f^{-1}(x)=x^2+2,\ x\leq 0$ **8.** $f^{-1}(x)=x^2-1,\ x\leq 0$

10. f^{-1} does not exist   **11.** $f^{-1}(x)=\sqrt{x-1}$

13. $f^{-1}(x)=1+\sqrt{x+1}$ **14.** $f^{-1}(x)=1-\sqrt{x+1}$

16. $f^{-1}(x)=1/x$ **17.** f^{-1} does not exist

19. $f^{-1}(x)=\sqrt{1-x^2},\ 0\leq x\leq 1$ **20.** $f^{-1}(x)=-1-\sqrt{x}$

22. $f^{-1}(x)=\sqrt[3]{x}$ **23.** $f^{-1}(x)=\sqrt{x^2+1},\ x\geq 0$

6.2 Exponential Functions

If b is a positive number and x is a rational number, we have previously defined the number b^x in Chapter 2. It is also possible to define the number b^x when b is a positive number and x is an irrational number. Although we shall not give a rigorous definition of the number b^x when x is an irrational number, it is still possible to obtain an intuitive understanding of such numbers. As an example of how we can do this, we consider the particular number $3^{\sqrt{2}}$. By continuing to add one additional decimal place to the decimal expansion of $\sqrt{2}$ to obtain successive decimal approximations of $\sqrt{2}$, it seems plausible to expect the successive numbers, $3^1,\ 3^{1.4},\ 3^{1.41},\ 3^{1.4142},\ \ldots$, to be better and better approximations of the number we wish to define as $3^{\sqrt{2}}$. The formal definition of b^x for $b>0$ and x irrational, which must wait for more advanced courses, involves the same basic approximation procedure for defining b^x.

With the above intuitive understanding of the number b^x, we define exponential functions as follows.

Definition 6.3 If $b>0$, the function f defined by the equation

$$f(x)=b^x$$

is called the **exponential function with base b.** The domain of f is the set of real numbers and the range of f is the set of positive real numbers.

EXAMPLE 1

Graph $f(x)=2^x$.

Solution   We begin by setting up a table of corresponding values of x and $f(x)$:

x	-3	-2	-1	0	1	2	3
$f(x)$	1/8	1/4	1/2	1	2	4	8

Using the points determined by the previous table, we obtain the exponential curve shown in Figure 6.7 as the graph of $f(x) = 2^x$. Since $2^x = 1/2^{-x}$ approaches 0 as x becomes increasingly larger in the negative sense, we observe that the graph of $f(x) = 2^x$ approaches the x-axis as x increases indefinitely in the negative direction. In other words, the x-axis is a horizontal asymptote of the graph of f.   ∎

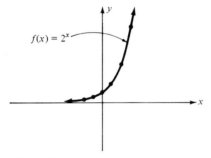

Figure 6.7   Figure 6.8

EXAMPLE 2
Graph $f(x) = \frac{1}{2}^x$.

Solution   We begin by setting up a table of corresponding values of x and $f(x)$:

x	-3	-2	-1	0	1	2	3
$f(x)$	8	4	2	1	1/2	1/4	1/8

Using the points determined by the previous table, we obtain the exponential curve shown in Figure 6.8 as the graph of $f(x) = \frac{1}{2}^x$. Observe that the graph of $f(x) = \frac{1}{2}^x$ approaches the x-axis as x increases indefinitely in the positive direction.   ∎

It is interesting to note that the graphs of $f(x) = b^x$ and $f(x) = (1/b)^x = b^{-x}$ are mirror images of one another with respect to the y-axis. This symmetry can be seen be comparing the graphs in Figures 6.7 and 6.8. Other properties of the exponential function $f(x) = b^x$, where $b > 0$, which are illustrated by the graphs in Figures 6.7 and 6.8 are as follows:

1. For any real number x, the value of $f(x) = b^x$ is positive (i.e., the graph of f lies above the x-axis).
2. When $b \neq 1$, $f(x) = b^x$ is a one-to-one function.
3. If $b > 1$, $f(x) = b^x$ is an increasing function (i.e., its graph rises as x increases).
4. If $b < 1$, $f(x) = b^x$ is a decreasing function (i.e., the graph falls as x increases).
5. When $b \neq 1$, the x-axis is a horizontal asymptote of the graph of $f(x) = b^x$.

Problems 6.2

In problems 1–6, use the laws of exponents to write the given expression in the form b^x.

  1. $3^x/2^x$ **2.** $3^{3x}/3^{5x}$ **3.** $(2^x)^3$
  4. $(a^x)^2(a^{3x})$ **5.** $b^{3x}c^{2x}$ **6.** b^{2x}/c^x

In problems 7–12, solve the given equation for x.

  7. $8^x = 4$ **8.** $(27)^x = \frac{1}{9}$ **9.** $(64)^x = \frac{1}{32}$
10. $2^x 4^{2x-1} = \frac{1}{8}$ **11.** $5^x/(25)^{x-1} = (125)^{-x}$ **12.** $3^{x+1}(27)^{3x+1} = 9$

In problems 13–18, graph the given exponential function by plotting at least five points of the graph.

13. $f(x) = 3^x$ **14.** $f(x) = \frac{3}{2}^x$ **15.** $f(x) = \frac{1}{3}^x$
16. $f(x) = \frac{2}{3}^x$ **17.** $f(x) = (1/\pi)^x$ **18.** $f(x) = (\sqrt{2})^x$

In problems 19–24, graph the given function by plotting as many points of the graph as necessary.

19. $f(x) = 2^{2-x}$ **20.** $f(x) = -2^{x+1}$ **21.** $f(x) = 2^{-x^2}$
22. $f(x) = 2^{|x|}$ **23.** $f(x) = 2^x + 2^{-x}$ **24.** $f(x) = 2^x - 2^{-x}$
25. Graph $f(x) = 1^x$. Is this an exponential function? Give another name for this function.
26. Graph $f(x) = 3^x$ and $g(x) = 3^{-x}$ on the same coordinate plane. How do the graphs of f and g compare?
27. Graph $f(x) = 2^{(3^x)}$.
28. Graph $f(x) = (2^3)^x$.
29. Explain why $f(x) = 2^{3^x}$ does (or does not) define a function. (*Hint:* See problems 27 and 28.)

Answers 6.2

1. $\frac{3}{2}x$ 2. $\frac{1}{9}x$ 4. $(a^5)^x$ 5. $(b^3c^2)^x$

7. $\frac{2}{3}$ 8. $-\frac{2}{3}$ 10. $-\frac{1}{5}$ 11. -1

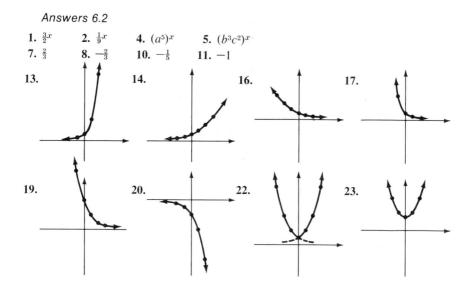

13.   14.   16.   17.

19.   20.   22.   23.

6.3 Logarithmic Functions

Since the exponential function $f(x) = b^x$, $b \neq 1$, is a one-to-one function, it has an inverse function f^{-1} associated with it. The equation that defines this inverse is obtained by interchanging the variables in the equation that defines f. Thus f^{-1} is defined by $x = b^y$ when $b \neq 1$, since f is defined by $y = b^x$ when $b \neq 1$. Since we do not know how to algebraically solve the equation $x = b^y$ for y in terms of x, we give the inverse of the exponential function its own name, the logarithmic function.

Definition 6.4   If $b > 0$ with $b \neq 1$, the **logarithmic function with base b,**

$$f^{-1}(x) = \log_b x,$$

is defined as the inverse of the exponential function $f(x) = b^x$.

Recall that the domain of the exponential function f defined by $f(x) = b^x$ is the set of real numbers, and that the range of f is the set of positive real numbers. Thus, since the logarithmic function defined by $f^{-1}(x) = \log_b x$ is the *inverse* of the exponential function f defined by $f(x) = b^x$, it follows that the domain of f^{-1} is the set of positive real numbers and that the range of f^{-1} is the set of real numbers.

Since the functions $f(x) = b^x$ and $f^{-1}(x) = \log_b x$ are inverses of each other, it follows from Eq. (6–2) that

$$y = \log_b x \quad \text{if and only if} \quad x = b^y, \tag{6-6}$$

when $b \neq 1$. In words, Eq. (6–6) states that *the logarithm of a number x to the base b is that exponent which must be placed on b to give x.* For example, $\log_2 8$ is that exponent which must be placed on 2 to give 8. That is, $\log_2 8 = 3$, since $2^3 = 8$.

It is important to be able to use Eq. (6–6) to convert the *logarithmic equation* $y = \log_b x$ into its equivalent *exponential equation* $x = b^y$, and vice versa.

EXAMPLE 1

(a) $\log_5 25 = 2$ is equivalent to $5^2 = 25.$
(b) $\log_3 1 = 0$ is equivalent to $3^0 = 1.$
(c) $\log_2 \frac{1}{16} = -4$ is equivalent to $2^{-4} = \frac{1}{16}.$
(d) $\log_4 8 = \frac{3}{2}$ is equivalent to $4^{3/2} = 8.$

EXERCISE 1

Express the given equation as a logarithmic equation.
(a) $3^{-3} = \frac{1}{27}.$ (b) $8^{4/3} = 16.$

Answer (a) $\log_3 \frac{1}{27} = -3$ (b) $\log_8 16 = \frac{4}{3}$

EXERCISE 2

Express the given equation as an exponential equation.
(a) $\log_5 125 = 3.$ (b) $\log_{16} 32 = \frac{5}{4}.$

Answer (a) $5^3 = 125$ (b) $16^{5/4} = 32$

EXERCISE 3

Convert the given logarithmic equation into an equivalent exponential equation and solve the resulting equation for the variable x, b, or y.
(a) $\log_3 81 = y.$ (b) $\log_5 x = 0.$ (c) $\log_b 3 = 2.$ (d) $\log_{27} 9 = y.$

Answer (a) 4   (b) 1   (c) $\sqrt{3}$ (d) $\frac{2}{3}$
Using Eq. (6–6), we can graph logarithmic functions.

EXAMPLE 2

Graph $f(x) = \log_2 x.$

Solution Since $x = 2^y$ is equivalent to $y = \log_2 x$, the graph of f consists of those ordered pairs (x, y) which satisfy the equation $x = 2^y$. The following is a table of corresponding values of x and y for the equation $x = 2^y$:

x	1/8	1/4	1/2	1	2	4	8
$f(x)$	-3	-2	-1	0	1	2	3

Using the points determined by the previous table, we obtain the logarithmic curve shown in Figure 6.9 as the graph of $f(x) = \log_2 x$. Compare the graph of $f(x) = \log_2 x$ in Figure 6.9 with the graph of $f(x) = 2^x$ in Figure 6.7, and recall that the graph of a one-to-one function and its inverse are mirror images of each other with respect to the line $y = x$. Thus it follows that the y-axis is a vertical asymptote of $f(x) = \log_2 x$, since the x-axis is a horizontal asymptote of $f(x) = 2^x$. ∎

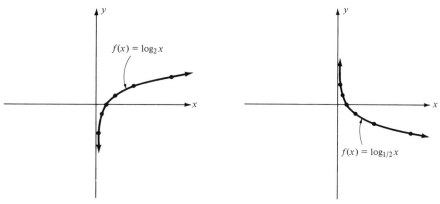

Figure 6.9   Figure 6.10

EXAMPLE 3

Graph $f(x) = \log_{(1/2)} x$.

Solution Since $x = \frac{1}{2}^y$ is equivalent to $y = \log_{(1/2)} x$, the graph of f consists of those ordered pairs (x, y) which satisfy the equation $x = \frac{1}{2}^y$. The following is a table of corresponding values of x and y for the equation $x = \frac{1}{2}^y$:

x	8	4	2	1	1/2	1/4	1/8
$f(x)$	-3	-2	-1	0	1	2	3

Using the points determined by the previous table, we obtain the logarithmic curve shown in Figure 6.10 as the graph of $f(x) = \log_{(1/2)} x$. Compare this graph with the graph in Figure 6.8. ∎

It is interesting to note that the graphs of $f(x) = \log_b x$ and $f(x) = \log_{(1/b)} x$ are mirror images of one another with respect to the x-axis. This symmetry can be seen in Figures 6.9 and 6.10. Other properties of the logarithmic function $f(x) = \log_b x$, where $b > 0$ and $b \neq 1$, which are illustrated by the graphs in Figures 6.9 and 6.10 are as follows:

1. If $b > 1$, $f(x) = \log_b x$ is an increasing function.
2. If $b < 1$, $f(x) = \log_b x$ is a decreasing function.
3. If $b \neq 1$, the y-axis is a vertical asymptote of the graph of $f(x) = \log_b x$.

We now examine some important properties of logarithmic functions. These properties are frequently called the *laws of logarithms*.

Theorem 6.2   Let $b > 0$ with $b \neq 1$. If x and y are positive numbers, then
(a) $\log_b(xy) = \log_b x + \log_b y$.
(b) $\log_b(x/y) = \log_b x - \log_b y$.
(c) $\log_b(x^k) = k \log_b x$ $(k \in R)$.

Proof of (a)   Let $\log_b x = s$ and $\log_b y = t$. Using $(6-6)$, it follows that

$$\log_b x = s \quad \text{and} \quad \log_b y = t$$

if and only if

$$b^s = x \quad \text{and} \quad b^t = y.$$

Hence

$$xy = b^s b^t = b^{s+t},$$

which is equivalent to

$$\log_b(xy) = s + t = \log_b x + \log_b y$$

according to $(6-6)$.
    The proofs of (b) and (c) are left as problems.   ∎

EXAMPLE 4

Express $\log_5 x - \frac{1}{2} \log_5 \pi - \log_5 y$ as a single logarithm.

Solution　Using Theorem 6.2, we get

$$\log_5 x - \tfrac{1}{2}\log_5 \pi - \log_5 y$$
$$= \log_5 x - \log_5 \sqrt{\pi} - \log_5 y$$
$$= \log_5 x - (\log_5 \sqrt{\pi} + \log_5 y)$$
$$= \log_5 x - \log_5 (\sqrt{\pi} y)$$
$$= \log_5 \frac{x}{(\sqrt{\pi} y)}. \qquad ■$$

EXAMPLE 5

Express $\log_2(xy^3/\sqrt{z})$ in terms of logarithms of x, y, and z.

Solution　Using Theorem 6.2, we get

$$\log_2 \frac{xy^3}{\sqrt{z}}$$
$$= \log_2 xy^3 - \log_2 \sqrt{z}$$
$$= \log_2 x + \log_2 y^3 - \log_2 \sqrt{z}$$
$$= \log_2 x + 3 \log_2 y - \tfrac{1}{2}\log_2 z. \qquad ■$$

Applying Theorem 6.1 to the function $f(x) = b^x$ and its inverse $f^{-1}(x) = \log_b x$, we get the following additional properties of logarithmic functions.

Theorem 6.3　Let $b > 0$ with $b \neq 1$. If x is a positive number, then
(a) $b^{\log_b x} = x$
(b) $\log_b b^x = x$

EXAMPLE 6

Evaluate $9^{\log_3 5}$.

Solution　Using Theorems 6.2 and 6.3, it follows that

$$9^{\log_3 5} = (3^2)^{\log_3 5} = 3^{2\,\log_3 5} = 3^{\log_3 5^2} = 3^{\log_3 25} = 25. \qquad ■$$

Problems 6.3

In problems 1–6, express the given equation as an equivalent logarithmic equation.

1. $2^3 = 8$　　　　**2.** $5^0 = 1$　　　　**3.** $2^{-3} = \tfrac{1}{8}$
4. $32^{-1/5} = \tfrac{1}{2}$　　**5.** $16^{3/4} = 8$　　**6.** $\tfrac{1}{2}^{-2} = 4$

In problems 7–12, express the given equation as an equivalent exponential equation.

7. $\log_{16} 2 = \tfrac{1}{4}$　　**8.** $\log_{1/3} 9 = -2$　　**9.** $\log_3 81 = 4$
10. $\log_8 1 = 0$　　　**11.** $\log_{32} 4 = \tfrac{2}{5}$　　**12.** $\log_8 \tfrac{1}{2} = -\tfrac{1}{3}$

In problems 13–24, convert the given logarithmic equation into an equivalent exponential equation and solve for the variable x, b, or y.

13. $\log_8 16 = y$ **14.** $\log_{32} 4 = y$ **15.** $\log_{27} 243 = y$
16. $\log_b 125 = -3$ **17.** $\log_b 27 = -3$ **18.** $\log_{1/6} x = -2$
19. $\log_9 x = -\frac{3}{2}$ **20.** $\log_8 x = -\frac{2}{3}$ **21.** $\log_b \frac{1}{25} = -\frac{2}{3}$
22. $\log_b \frac{3}{4} = -\frac{1}{2}$ **23.** $\log_b 2 = 3$ **24.** $\log_b \frac{2}{3} = -\frac{1}{3}$

In problems 25–30, express the given logarithm in terms of logarithms of x, y, and z.

25. $\log_6(\sqrt{x}/y)$ **26.** $\log_2(y/\sqrt{z})$ **27.** $\log_{10}\sqrt{xy}$
28. $\log_3(x^2 y/z^4)$ **29.** $\log_5(x^3/(yz^3))$ **30.** $\log_4((x^5 y)/z^3)$

In problems 31–36, express the given expression as a single logarithm.

31. $2\log_{10} x - \frac{1}{3}\log_{10} y$ **32.** $3\log_6 x - \frac{1}{6}\log_6 y^3$
33. $2\log_7 x - \frac{1}{5}\log_7 3$ **34.** $3\log_4 x - 2\log_4 y - \log_4 7$
35. $5\log_3 x - \log_3 y - 2\log_3 5$ **36.** $\log_5 x - 2\log_5 y - 3\log_5 2$

In problems 37–45, evaluate the given expression.

37. $3^{\log_3 7}$ **38.** $5^{-\log_5 k}$ **39.** $7^{\log_7 x}$
40. $27^{\log_3 2}$ **41.** $3^{\log_9 5}$ **42.** $2^{-\log_{16} 2}$
43. $\log_3 3^x$ **44.** $\log_7 7^y$ **45.** $\log_4 4^k$

In problems 46–51, graph the given logarithmic function by plotting at least five points of the graph.

46. $f(x) = \log_3 x$ **47.** $f(x) = \log_4 x$ **48.** $f(x) = \log_{(1/3)} x$
49. $f(x) = \log_{(2/3)} x$ **50.** $f(x) = \log_{\sqrt{2}} x$ **51.** $f(x) = \log_\pi x$
52. Prove that $\log_b 1 = 0$ when $b > 0$ and $b \ne 1$.
53. Prove that $\log_b b = 1$ when $b > 0$ and $b \ne 1$.
54. Does $y = \log_x x$, $x > 1$, define a function? If so, what is its domain? What is its range? Graph the function.
55. Prove Theorem 6.2(b).   **56.** Prove Theorem 6.2(c).

Answers 6.3

1. $\log_2 8 = 3$ **2.** $\log_5 1 = 0$ **4.** $\log_{32} \frac{1}{2} = -\frac{1}{5}$ **5.** $\log_{16} 8 = \frac{3}{4}$
7. $16^{1/4} = 2$ **8.** $\frac{1}{3}^{-2} = 9$ **10.** $8^0 = 1$ **11.** $32^{2/5} = 4$
13. $\frac{4}{3}$ **14.** $\frac{2}{5}$ **16.** $\frac{1}{5}$ **17.** $\frac{1}{3}$
19. $\frac{1}{27}$ **20.** $\frac{1}{4}$ **22.** $\frac{16}{9}$ **23.** $\sqrt[3]{2}$
25. $\frac{1}{2}\log_6 x - \log_6 y$ **26.** $\log_2 y - \frac{1}{2}\log_2 z$
28. $2\log_3 x + \log_3 y - 4\log_3 z$ **29.** $3\log_5 x - \log_5 y - 3\log_5 z$
31. $\log_{10}(x^2/\sqrt[3]{y})$ **32.** $\log_6(x^3/\sqrt{y})$ **34.** $\log_4(x^3/7y^2)$ **35.** $\log_3(x^5/25y)$
37. 7   **38.** $1/k$ **40.** 8   **41.** $\sqrt{5}$ **43.** x **44.** y

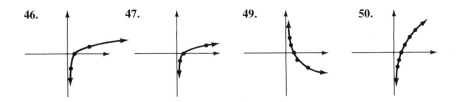

46.   **47.**   **49.**   **50.**

6.4 Common Logarithms

In this section, we confine our attention to the logarithmic function with base 10, which is defined by

$$f(x) = \log_{10} x.$$

Numbers of the form $\log_{10} x$ are called **common logarithms** or **logarithms to the base 10.** As a matter of convenience, the common logarithm $\log_{10} x$ is usually written as $\log x$. That is,

$$\log_{10} x = \log x.$$

Certain numbers of the form $\log_{10} x$ can be evaluated by Eq. (6–6). For example,

$$\log_{10} 100 = 2 \quad \text{since} \quad 10^2 = 100,$$

and

$$\log_{10} \tfrac{1}{10} = -1 \quad \text{since} \quad 10^{-1} = \tfrac{1}{10}.$$

On the other hand, Eq. (6–6) cannot be used to evaluate all numbers of the form $\log_{10} x$. For example, we cannot evaluate $y = \log_{10} 3$ using Eq. (6–6) since we cannot algebraically solve the equivalent exponential equation $10^y = 3$ for y. However, we can use a table of common logarithms, such as Table A at the end of this book, to find a decimal approximation for $\log_{10} 3$. In Table A, the common logarithm of each number between 1.00 and 9.99 at intervals of .01 has been listed correctly to four decimal places. Consider

			log x							
x	0	1	2	3	4	5	6	7	8	9
2.8	.4472	.4487	.4502	.4518	.4533	.4548	.4564	.4579	.4594	.4609
2.9	.4624	.4639	.4654	.4669	.4683	.4698	.4713	.4728	.4742	.4757
3.0	.4771	.4786	.4800	.4814	.4829	.4843	.4857	.4871	.4886	.4900
3.1	.4914	.4928	.4942	.4955	.4969	.4983	.4997	.5011	.5024	.5038
3.2	.5051	.5065	.5079	.5092	.5105	.5119	.5132	.5145	.5159	.5172

Figure 6.11

the excerpt from Table A, which is shown in Figure 6.11. The numbers in the vertical column that is headed x represent the first two digits of the number x, and the numbers in the horizontal row that contains x represent the third digit of the number x. The value of log x is located at the intersection of the row in which the first two digits of x appear and the column in which the third digit of x appears. For example, using the excerpt from Table A that appears in Figure 6.11, we find that

$$\log 2.85 = .4548, \quad \log 3.07 = .4871, \quad \text{and} \quad \log 3.22 = .5079.$$

Strictly speaking, we should write

$$\log 2.85 \doteq .4548$$

(the symbol "$\doteq$" is read "is approximately equal to"), since .4548 is a four-decimal approximation of log 2.85. However, we shall write

$$\log 2.85 = .4548$$

with the understanding that .4548 is a four-decimal approximation of log 2.85 rather than the exact value of log 2.85.

EXERCISE 1

Use the table in Figure 6.11 to evaluate the following.
(a) log 2.92   (b) log 3.18   (c) log 3.25

Answer (a) .4654   (b) .5024   (c) .5119

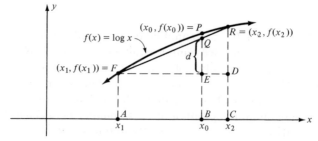

Figure 6.12

It is frequently necessary to determine the approximate value of log x for a number between two consecutive values of x in Table A. To do this, we use a procedure known as **linear interpolation,** (or **interpolation,** for short). That is, we assume that the graph of $f(x) = \log x$ between x_1 and x_2 is closely approximated by the line segment joining $(x_1, f(x_1))$ and $(x_2, f(x_2))$, where x_1 and x_2 are two consecutive values of x in Table A. In this case we assume that line segment $\overline{FR}$ in Figure 6.12 is a good approximation for the graph of log x between x_1 and x_2. Dropping perpendiculars from each of the points F, P, and R to the x-axis and constructing line segment $\overline{FD}$ parallel to the x-axis, it then follows that

$$\log x_0 = f(x_0) = D(B, P) \doteq D(B, Q) = D(B, E) + D(E, Q) = D(F, A) + d = \log x_1 + d.$$

Since log x_1 is available in Table A, the approximate value of log x_0 will be known if we can calculate d. We do this by using the fact that the ratios of the lengths of the corresponding sides of similar triangles are equal. Since $\triangle FEQ$ is similar to $\triangle FDR$, we have

$$\frac{D(E, F)}{D(D, F)} = \frac{d}{D(R, D)},$$

and hence

$$\frac{x_0 - x_1}{x_2 - x_1} = \frac{d}{\log x_2 - \log x_1}. \qquad (6-7)$$

The proportions involved in Eq. (6-7) can easily be seen by arranging the data in the tabular form, which is shown in the following example.

EXAMPLE 1

Use Table A to approximate log 6.837.

Solution   Using Table A, we get log $6.83 = .8344$ and log $6.84 = .8351$. The proportion involved in Eq. (6-7) can easily be seen if arrange our data as follows:

$$.010\left\{.007\left\{\begin{matrix}\log 6.830 = .8344 \\ \log 6.837 = ? \\ \log 6.840 = .8351.\end{matrix}\right\}d\right\}.0007.$$

Consequently, we get the proportion

$$\frac{.007}{.010}=\frac{d}{.0007},$$

from which it follows that $d = .0005$, correct to four decimal places. Since it would be wrong to expect greater accuracy in our interpolated result than exists in the values of Table A, we have rounded off d correct to four decimal places, since the values in Table A are each correct to exactly four decimal places. Therefore, $\log 6.837 = \log 6.830 + d = .8344 + .0005 = .8349.$ ∎

We can also use Table A to determine an approximation for x if $\log x$ is known.

EXAMPLE 2

Use Table A to approximate x if $\log x = .5748$.

Solution Using Table A, we find that $\log 3.75 = .5740$ and $\log 3.76 = .5752$. Once again the proportion involved can easily be seen by arranging our data as follows:

$$.010\left\{d\begin{cases}\log 3.750=.5740\\ \log x \quad\ \ =.5748\\ \log 3.760=.5752.\end{cases}\bigg\}.0008\right\}.0012.$$

Consequently, we get the proportion

$$\frac{d}{.010}=\frac{.0008}{.0012},$$

and hence $d = .007$. Thus $x = 3.750 + .007 = 3.757$.   ∎

We now consider the problem of determining $\log x$ when $x \geq 10$ or $0 < x < 1$. If x is any positive number, then x can be expressed in the form $x = k \cdot 10^n$ (called **scientific notation**) where $1 \leq k < 10$ and $n \in I$. Expressing x in scientific notation as $k \cdot 10^n$, it follows that

$$\log x=\log (k \cdot 10^n)=\log k+\log 10^n$$
$$=\log k+n \log 10=\log k+n.$$

Since $1 \leq k < 10$, a four-decimal approximation of $\log k$ can be obtained from Table A. Therefore, if a real number x is expressed in the scientific notation $k \cdot 10^n$, $\log x$ can be calculated by using the equation

$$\log x=\log k+n. \tag{6-8}$$

The real number $\log k$ is called the **mantissa** of $\log x$, and the integer n is called the **characteristic** of $\log x$. The form $\log k + n$ is called the **standard form** of $\log x$.

EXAMPLE 3

Use Table A and Eq. (6–8) to approximate log 37,100.

Solution Since $37,100 = (3.71)(10^4)$, it follows by Eq. (6–8) that

$$\log 37,100 = \log[(3.71)(10^4)] = \log 3.71 + (4).$$

Using Table A, we get log 3.71 = .5694. Hence

$$\log 37,100 = .5694 + 4 = 4.5694. \qquad \blacksquare$$

EXAMPLE 4

Use Table A and Eq. (6–8) to approximate log .0006363.

Solution Since $.0006363 = (6.363)(10^{-4})$, it follows by Eq. (6–8) that

$$\log .0006363 = \log[(6.363)(10^{-4})] = \log 6.363 + (-4).$$

Using Table A and interpolating, we find that

$$.010\left\{.003\begin{cases}\log 6.360 = .8035 \\ \log 6.363 = ?\end{cases}d\\ \log 6.370 = .8041.\end{cases}\right\}.0006.$$

Consequently, $.003/.010 = d/.0006$, and hence $d = .0002$. Thus log 6.363 = log 6.360 + d = .8035 + .0002 = .8037. Therefore, log .0006363 = $\log[(6.363)(10^{-4})] = \log 6.363 + (-4) = ,8037 + (-4) = -3.1963.$ $\blacksquare$

You have probably noticed by now that *the mantissa of log x is always a number between 0 and 1.* We can prove this as follows. Let $x = k \cdot 10^n$, where $1 \le k < 10$. Since $f(x) = \log x$ is an increasing function and since $1 \le k < 10$, it follows that $0 = \log 1 \le \log k < \log 10 = 1$. Hence log k (the mantissa of log x) is a number between 0 and 1.

EXAMPLE 5

Approximate x if log $x = 3.7642$.

Solution Expressing log x in standard form, we get

$$\log x = .7642 + (3).$$

Thus log $k = .7642$ and $n = 3$. Using Table A, we find that log 5.81 = .7642 and hence $k = 5.81$. Consequently, $x = k \cdot 10^n = (5.81)(10^3) = 5810.$ $\blacksquare$

EXAMPLE 6

Approximate x if log $x = -1.4001$.

Solution   A *common mistake* that is made in a problem of this kind is to conclude that the mantissa of log x is .4001 and the characteristic is -1. This is *incorrect*, because $-1.4001 \neq .4001 + (-1)$. Recall that the mantissa of a logarithm is always a number between 0 and 1. To obtain the *correct* mantissa and characteristic of log x, we express log x in standard form by adding and subtracting the smallest positive integer that is larger than log x. Thus

$$\log x = -1.4001 = 2 + (-1.4001) - 2$$
$$= (2 - 1.4001) + (-2) = .5999 + (-2).$$

Thus log $k = .5999$ and $n = -2$. Using Table A, we find that log $3.98 = .5999$ and hence $k = 3.98$. Consequently, $x = k \cdot 10^n = (3.98)(10^{-2}) = .0398.$∎

EXAMPLE 7

Approximate x if log $x = 1.9869$.

Solution   Expressing log x in standard form, we get

$$\log x = .9869 + (1).$$

Thus log $k = .9869$ and $n = 1$. Using Table A and interpolating, we get

$$.010 \left\{ d \left\{ \begin{matrix} \log 9.700 = .9868 \\ \log k \quad\; = .9869 \\ \log 9.710 = .9872. \end{matrix} \right\} .0001 \right\} .0004.$$

Consequently, $d/.010 = .0001/.0004$, and hence $d = .002$. Thus $k = 9.700 + .002 = 9.702$, and hence $x = k \cdot 10^n = (9.702)(10^1) = 97.02.$ ∎

Problems 6.4

In problems 1–9, use Table A and Eq. (6–8) to approximate the given logarithm.

1. log 325	**2.** log 4760	**3.** log 53.8
4. log .0421	**5.** log .00648	**6.** log .813
7. log 93,200	**8.** log 467,000	**9.** log 2,860,000

In problems 10–18, use Table A together with Eq. (6–8) and the method of linear interpolation to approximate the given logarithm.

10. log .02113	**11.** log .004271	**12.** log .1964
13. log 5264	**14.** log 243.1	**15.** log 26,840
16. log 456,200	**17.** log 76.13	**18.** log 97,160

In problems 19–27, use Table A and Eq. (6–8) to approximate x.

19. $\log x = 2.3139$	**20.** $\log x = 3.6618$	**21.** $\log x = 1.9020$
22. $\log x = .5276 - 1$	**23.** $\log x = .7910 - 2$	**24.** $\log x = .1367 - 3$
25. $\log x = -1.4342$	**26.** $\log x = -2.1203$	**27.** $\log x = -.6308$

In problems 28–36, use Table A together with Eq. (6–8) and the method of linear interpolation to approximate x.

28. $\log x = 2.8472$	**29.** $\log x = 1.4833$	**30.** $\log x = 3.9627$
31. $\log x = .9553 - 1$	**32.** $\log x = .3189 - 3$	**33.** $\log x = .6193 - 2$
34. $\log x = -1.3532$	**35.** $\log x = -.6119$	**36.** $\log x = -5.1092$

Answers 6.4

1. 2.5119	**2.** 3.6776	**4.** .6243 − 2	**5.** .8116 − 3
7. 4.9694	**8.** 5.6693	**10.** .3249 − 2	**11.** .6305 − 3
13. 3.7213	**14.** 2.3858	**16.** 5.6592	**17.** 1.8816
19. 206	**20.** 4590	**22.** .337	**23.** .0618
25. .0368	**26.** .00758	**28.** 703.4	**29.** 30.43
31. .9022	**32.** .002084	**34.** .04434	**35.** .2444

6.5 Using Logarithms to Make Numerical Calculations

Common logarithms can be used effectively to calculate products, quotients, powers, and roots of numbers. However, before demonstrating how to do this, we shall discuss the significant digits of a number.

Significant Digits

In making physical measurements, it is generally necessary to approximate the measurements, since it is usually impossible to obtain exact measurements. As an example, when we say that the height of a tree is 40 feet (ft), we probably mean that the height of the tree is closer to 40 ft than it is to 39 ft or 41 ft. However, we may also mean that the height of the tree is closer to 40 ft than it is to 30 ft or 50 ft. The first interpretation means that the exact height of the tree is somewhere between 39.5 ft and 40.5 ft, while the second interpretation means that the exact height of the tree is somewhere between 35 ft and 45 ft.

Frequently, we must make numerical calculations involving products, quotients, powers, and roots of approximate data. In such cases we must have some means of deciding how many digits in each approximate piece of data are actually significant. Thus we define **the number of significant digits in a number** as the number of digits obtained by counting the digits of the number from left to right, beginning with the first nonzero digit and ending with the digit farther to the right. For example, each of the numbers 213, 72.6, .159, .00375, and .0200 has three significant digits, whereas each of the numbers 1976, 20.25, .2320, .003000, and .0001234 has four significant digits. Referring to the first example of this section, you can see that the previous definition concerning the number of significant digits in a number leads to an ambigous situation when the number under consideration is an integer ending in one or more zeros. In such cases we shall assume that all zeros are significant unless we have information to the contrary. That is, to say that the height of a tree is approximately 40 ft means that the height of the tree is closer to 40 ft than it is to 39 ft or 41 ft. On the other hand, to say that the height of a tree is 40 ft to the nearest 10 ft means that the height of the tree is closer to 40 ft than it is to 30 ft or 50 ft.

In general, when numerical calculations are made, the results obtained will be no more accurate than the data used in the calculations. Thus, we shall round off all answers resulting from such numerical calculations so that each such answer will have the same number of significant digits as there are in the *least accurate* piece of given data. For example, when calculating

$$\frac{(725)(.023)}{223.5},$$

the answer should be determined correct to two significant digits, since .023 (which has two significant digits) is the least accurate piece of given data.

EXERCISE 1

How many significant digits does each of the following numbers have?
(a) 230   (b) 23.230   (c) 2323   (d) .00023

Answer (a) 3   (b) 5   (c) 4   (d) 2

EXERCISE 2

To how many significant digits should we obtain the answer in making each of the following calculations?
(a) (.234)(5678)   (b) $\sqrt[3]{.00234}(345.70)$ (c) 567,800/.023

Answer (a) 3   (b) 3   (c) 2

Numerical Calculations Using Logarithms

We are now ready to demonstrate how to use logarithms in making numerical calculations involving products, quotients, powers, and roots of numbers.

EXAMPLE 1

Use logarithms to calculate $(5.36)^3(.0721)/447$ correct to three significant digits.

Solution   Let $x = [(5.36)^3(.0721)]/447$. Then it follows by Theorem 6.2 and Table A that

$$
\begin{aligned}
\log x &= \log\left[\frac{(5.36)^3(.0721)}{447}\right] \\
&= 3 \log 5.36 + \log .0721 - \log 447 \\
&= 3(0.7292) + (.8579 - 2) - (2.6503) \\
&= 2.1876 + (.8579 - 2) - (2.6503) \\
&= (2.1876 + .8579 - 2.6503) + (-2) \\
&= .3952 + (-2).
\end{aligned}
$$

Hence using Table A, we find that $x = .0248$ correct to three significant digits when $\log x = .3952 - 2$. Thus

$$
\frac{(5.36)^3(.0721)}{447} = .0248. \qquad ∎
$$

EXAMPLE 2

Use logarithms to calculate $\sqrt[3]{.0882}$ correct to three significant digits.

Solution   Let $x = \sqrt[3]{.0882}$. Then it follows from Theorem 6.2 and Table A that

$$
\begin{aligned}
\log x &= \log \sqrt[3]{.0882} \\
&= \tfrac{1}{3} \log .0882 \\
&= \tfrac{1}{3}(.9455 - 2).
\end{aligned}
$$

Since we must divide $.9455 - 2$ by 3 and since the characteristic should always be an integer, we replace the characteristic -2 with $1 - 3$ so that the division of the characteristic by 3 will yield an integer. Thus we have

$$
\begin{aligned}
\log x &= \tfrac{1}{3}(.9455 - 2) \\
&= \tfrac{1}{3}(1.9455 - 3) \\
&= .6485 - 1.
\end{aligned}
$$

Hence using Table A, we find that $x = .445$ correct to three significant digits if $\log x = .6485 - 1$. Thus $\sqrt[3]{.0882} = .445$. ∎

EXAMPLE 3

Use logarithms to calculate $\sqrt[5]{7965}/81.73$, correct to four significant digits.

Solution   Let $x = \sqrt[5]{7965}/81.73$. Then it follows from Theorem 6.2 and Table A that

$$
\begin{aligned}
\log x &= \log \left(\frac{\sqrt[5]{7965}}{81.73} \right) \\
&= \tfrac{1}{5} \log 7965 - \log 81.73 \\
&= \tfrac{1}{5}(3.9012) - (1.9124) \\
&= 0.7802 - 1.9124 \\
&= -1.1322 \\
&= (2 - 1.1322) + (-2) \\
&= 0.8678 - 2.
\end{aligned}
$$

Hence using Table A, we find that $x = .07375$, correct to four significant digits when $\log x = .8678 - 2$. Thus $\sqrt[5]{7965}/81.73 = .07375$.   ∎

Problems 6.5

In problems 1–21, use logarithms to calculate the given expression correct to three significant digits.

1. $(.467)(6.24)$	**2.** $(26.1)(.00219)$	**3.** $(12.3)(86.1)$
4. $6280/.763$	**5.** $.0264/.924$	**6.** $241/67,600$
7. $(2.44)^9$	**8.** $(.421)^5$	**9.** $(.299)^6$
10. $\sqrt[4]{.944}$	**11.** $\sqrt[10]{76.8}$	**12.** $(26.1)\sqrt[3]{6.42}$
13. $\sqrt[4]{.601}\,(4.29)^4$	**14.** $\sqrt[3]{96.4}/939$	**15.** $(1.86)^3/\sqrt[3]{671}$
16. $(9.45/241)^4$	**17.** $(3.21)^3/(28.8)^2$	**18.** $\sqrt[5]{204}/[(.0741)(2.84)]$
19. $\sqrt[4]{(9.09)(.0621)}$	**20.** $\sqrt[5]{86.4}/.265$	**21.** $\sqrt[3]{(.414)^4/.261}$

In problems 22–30, use logarithms to compute the given expression correct to four significant digits.

22. $(8472)(.1212)$	**23.** $7661/84.94$	**24.** $(6.248)^3$
25. $\sqrt[3]{.6217}$	**26.** $\sqrt[8]{8.658}$	**27.** $3.842/\sqrt[3]{736.8}$
28. $(44.24)^3/\sqrt[4]{26.11}$	**29.** $\sqrt[5]{4262}/.4881$	**30.** $\sqrt[3]{686.3}/964.3$

Answers 6.5

1. 2.91	**2.** .0572	**4.** 8230	**5.** .0286
7. 3070	**8.** .0132	**10.** .986	**11.** 1.54
13. 298	**14.** .00488	**16.** .00000236	**17.** .0399
19. .867	**20.** 3.18	**22.** 1027	**23.** 90.19
25. .8535	**26.** 1.310	**28.** 38,300	**29.** 6.141

6.6 Natural Logarithms

There are two logarithmic functions of special importance in mathematics. One is the logarithmic function with base 10. The other is the logarithmic function with base e, which is defined by

$$f(x) = \log_e x,$$

where e is an irrational number approximately equal to 2.71828. Numbers of the form $\log_e x$ are called **natural logarithms** or **logarithms to the base e**. As a matter of convenience, the natural logarithm $\log_e x$ is usually written as $\ln x$. Thus

$$\log_e x = \ln x.$$

Tables of natural logarithms are available in many standard books of mathematical tables. It is also possible to calculate natural logarithms provided a table of common logarithms is available. This is done by using the following theorem.

Theorem 6.4   Let $a,b > 0$ with $a,b \neq 1$. If $x > 0$, then

$$\log_a x = \frac{\log_b x}{\log_b a}. \tag{6-9}$$

Proof   Let $s = \log_a x$. Then it follows by Eq. (6-6) that

$$a^s = x,$$

and hence

$$\log_b a^s = \log_b x$$

and

$$s \log_b a = \log_b x.$$

Therefore,

$$\log_a x = s = \frac{\log_b x}{\log_b a}. \qquad \blacksquare$$

EXAMPLE 1

Evaluate ln 154.

Solution   Using Eq. (6-9), we have

$$\ln 154 = \log_e 154 = \frac{\log_{10} 154}{\log_{10} e}.$$

Since $e \doteq 2.71828$, using Table A we find that $\log e = 0.4343$. $\blacksquare$

Therefore,

$$\ln 154 = \frac{\log 154}{\log e} = \frac{2.1875}{0.4343} = 5.0369.$$

EXAMPLE 2

Evaluate $\log_3 17$.

Solution   Using Eq. (6–9), we have

$$\log_3 17 = \frac{\log_{10} 17}{\log_{10} 3}.$$

Therefore,

$$\log_3 17 = \frac{\log 17}{\log 3} = \frac{1.2304}{.4771} = 2.5789. \qquad \blacksquare$$

Problems 6.6

In problems 1–21, evaluate the given logarithm.

1. $\log_9 70$
2. $\log_4 13$
3. $\log_7 60$
4. $\log_{12} 21$
5. $\log_{17} 71$
6. $\log_{14} 41$
7. $\log_5 55.5$
8. $\log_7 777$
9. $\log_3 3.33$
10. $\log_3 .0121$
11. $\log_5 .727$
12. $\log_6 .0275$
13. $\log_e 171$
14. $\log_e 4.38$
15. $\log_e 37.5$
16. $\ln .00231$
17. $\ln .0457$
18. $\ln .876$
19. $\ln 27.7$
20. $\ln 233$
21. $\ln 6.62$

In problems 22–30, given that $\log_a x = N$, use Theorem 6.4 to express the given logarithm in terms of N.

22. $\log_{1/a} x$
23. $\log_{(1/a^2)} x$
24. $\log_{(a^2)} x$
25. $\log_{(a^3)} x$
26. $\log_{\sqrt{a}} x$
27. $\log_{\sqrt[3]{a}} x$
28. $\log_{2a} x$
29. $\log_{a/2} x$
30. $\log_{(2a^2)} x$
31. Prove that $\log_a b = 1/\log_b a$ when $a,b > 0$ and $a,b \ne 1$.
32. Prove that $\log_a(1/b) = \log_{1/a} b$ when $a,b > 0$ and $a,b \ne 1$.

Answers 6.6

1. 1.9337
2. 1.8500
4. 1.2252
5. 1.5046
7. 2.4954
8. 3.4202
10. −4.0184
11. −0.1981
13. 5.1417
14. 1.4771
16. −6.0706
17. −3.0857
19. 3.3215
20. 5.4512
22. −N
23. −N/2
25. N/3
26. 2N
28. $N/(1 + \log_a 2)$
29. $N/(1 - \log_a 2)$

6.7 Exponential and Logarithmic Equations

An **exponential equation** is an equation in which the variable appears in one or more exponents. For example,

$$2^x = 3 \quad \text{and} \quad 5^{3x-1} = 2^{2x}$$

are exponential equations. The solutions of certain equations of this type can be determined by using logarithms.

EXAMPLE 1

Solve $5^{3x-1} = 2^{2x}$ for x.

Solution If we take the common logarithm of both sides of the given equation, we get

$$\log 5^{3x-1} = \log 2^{2x}.$$

Thus it follows by Theorem 6.2(c) that

$$(3x - 1) \log 5 = 2x \log 2.$$

Solving the previous linear equation for x, we get

$$x = \frac{\log 5}{3 \log 5 - 2 \log 2}. \qquad \blacksquare$$

If a decimal approximation for x is desired, we can use Table A to obtain

$$x = \frac{.6990}{3(.6990) - 2(.3010)} = \frac{.6990}{1.4950} = .4676.$$

A **logarithmic equation** is an equation in which the variable appears in one or more logarithms. For example,

$$\log x = 5 \quad \text{and} \quad \log_5 3x = \log_5(2x + 1) - 2$$

are logarithmic equations. The solutions of certain equations of this type can be determined by using logarithms.

EXAMPLE 2

Solve $\log_5 3x = \log_5(2x + 1) - 2$ for x.

Solution Combining the logarithms of the given equation into a single logarithm, we get

$$\log_5 3x - \log_5 (2x+1) = -2$$

and

$$\log_5\left(\frac{3x}{2x+1}\right) = -2.$$

Using Eq. (6–6), we obtain the equivalent equation,

$$\frac{3x}{2x+1} = 5^{-2}.$$

Solving this equation for x, we obtain $x = \frac{1}{73}$. ∎

Problems 6.7

In problems 1–27, solve the given equation for x.

1. $2^x = 4^{3x-2}$
2. $9^x = 3^{x+5}$
3. $9^x = 3^{x^2-3}$
4. $2^x = 30$
5. $5^x = 20$
6. $3^x = 18$
7. $(3.79)^x = .973$
8. $(5.21)^{x+1} = 12.5$
9. $(7.32)^{x-2} = 9.50$
10. $2^{3x-1} = 3^x$
11. $3^{4x+1} = 5^{x-3}$
12. $5^{7x-3} = 7^{x-1}$
13. $\log_3(2x-3) = 2$
14. $\log_2(1-5x) = 4$
15. $\log_5(7x-3) = 2$
16. $\log_4(x^2+3x+18) = 2$
17. $\log_3(2x^2-x+26) = 3$
18. $\log_2(3x^2+2x+1) = 1$
19. $\log (2x+3) = \log x + 2$
20. $\log x - \log (x+2) = 2$
21. $\log (3x-1) = \log x - 1$
22. $\log_6(5x+6) + \log_6 x = 3$
23. $\log_5(2x+1) + \log_5(3x-1) = 2$
24. $\log_7(x+16) = \log_7(x-2) + 1$
25. $\log \sqrt{x-1} = -1$
26. $\log x^2 = (\log x)^2$
27. $\log \sqrt{x} = \sqrt{\log x}$
28. Solve $y = 3(e^{5x-1})$ for x in terms of y.
29. Solve $y = \ln (x + \sqrt{x^2+1})$ for x in terms of y.
30. Solve $y = \ln (\sqrt{x^2+1} - x)$ for x in terms of y.

Answers 6.7

1. $\frac{4}{5}$
2. 5
4. 4.9073
5. 1.8612
7. −0.0206
8. .5303
10. .7067
11. −2.1284
13. 6
14. −3
16. −2, −1
17. −$\frac{1}{2}$, 1
19. $\frac{3}{98}$
20. −$\frac{200}{99}$
22. 6
23. 2
25. $\frac{101}{100}$
26. 1, 100
28. $x = \frac{1}{5}[1 + \ln(y/3)]$
29. $x = (e^y - e^{-y})/2$

6.8 Applications

In chemical experiments it has been found that radioactive elements disintegrate into other more stable elements by emitting radiation, and that the rate at which a radioactive element decays (disintegrates) is proportional to the amount of the radioactive element present at that time. Using these experimental facts, it is shown in calculus that the amount Q of a radioactive element present after time t is given by

$$Q = Q_0 e^{-kt}, \qquad\qquad (6-10)$$

where Q_0 represents the initial amount (the amount at $t = 0$) of the radioactive element present and k is a positive constant of proportionality which depends upon the radioactive element involved in the particular experiment. Equation (6–10) is frequently referred to as the **exponential law of decay.**

EXAMPLE 1

A certain radioactive element X decays according to the exponential law of decay $Q = Q_0 e^{-t/5}$, where Q is the number of grams of X present after t years and Q_0 is the number of grams of X present initially. If there are 100 grams of X present initially, how many grams will be present after 3 years?

Solution   The number of grams Q present after 3 years is given by

$$Q = 100e^{-3/5}.$$

Using logarithms to evaluate Q, we get

$$\begin{aligned}
\log Q &= \log 100 + (-\tfrac{3}{5}) \log e \\
&= \log 100 + (-\tfrac{3}{5}) \log 2.718 \\
&= 2 + (-\tfrac{3}{5})(0.4343) \\
&= 2 - .2606 = 1.7394.
\end{aligned}$$

Hence $Q = 54.88$ grams.   ∎

The time required for half of a given amount of a radioactive element to decay is known as the **half-life** of the element.

EXAMPLE 2

If the half-life of a certain radioactive element Q is 16 days, determine the exponential law of decay that gives the amount of Q present after t days.

Solution We know that the element Q decays according to the exponential law of decay,

$$Q = Q_0 e^{-kt}.$$

In this case, we need to calculate k. Since the half-life of Q is 16 days, we have

$$Q = \tfrac{1}{2} Q_0 \qquad \text{when } t = 16 \text{ days.}$$

Substituting the given data into the exponential law of decay, we get

$$\tfrac{1}{2} Q_0 = Q_0 e^{-k\,(16)}$$
$$\tfrac{1}{2} = e^{-k\,(16)}$$
$$\ln \tfrac{1}{2} = -16k.$$

Hence

$$k = \frac{\ln \tfrac{1}{2}}{-16} = \frac{\ln 1 - \ln 2}{-16} = \frac{0 - .6932}{-16} = .0433.$$

Thus the desired exponential law of decay is $Q = Q_0 e^{-.0433t}$. ∎

In biological experiments it has been found that the rate at which certain populations increase is proportional to the size of the population present at that time. Using this experimental fact, it is shown in calculus that the size N of the population present after time t is given by

$$N = N_0 e^{kt}, \tag{6-11}$$

where N_0 is the initial size (the size at $t = 0$) of the population present and k is a positive constant of proportionality which depends upon the type of population involved. Equation (6-11) is frequently referred to as the **exponential law of growth.**

EXAMPLE 3

In a biology experiment it is found that the number N of bacteria present in a certain culture after t minutes is given by the exponential law of growth, $N = N_0 e^{.02t}$, where N_0 is the initial number of bacteria present in the culture. If 1000 bacteria are present initially, how many will be present after 1 hour?

Solution The number of bacteria present after 1 hour is given by

$$N = 1000 e^{.02\,(60)}.$$

Using logarithms to evaluate N, we get

$$\begin{aligned}
\log N &= \log 1000 + (.02)(60) \log e \\
&= \log 1000 + 1.20 \log 2.718 \\
&= 3 + (1.20)(0.4343) \\
&= 3 + .5212 = 3.5212.
\end{aligned}$$

Therefore, $N = 3321$.   ∎

Suppose that P dollars is invested at an annual interest rate of r (in decimal form). If the interest is compounded m times per year, the amount of dollars A at the end of t years is given by

$$A = P\left(1 + \frac{r}{m}\right)^{mt}. \tag{6-12}$$

EXAMPLE 4

If $\$1000$ is invested at 8 percent interest compounded quarterly for 5 years, determine the total amount of dollars at the end of the 5 years.

Solution   Using Eq. (6–12), the total amount of dollars A at the end of 5 years is

$$\begin{aligned}
A &= (\$1000)\left(1 + \frac{.08}{4}\right)^{4(5)} \\
&= (\$1000)(1.02)^{20}.
\end{aligned}$$

Using logarithms to evaluate A, we get

$$\begin{aligned}
\log A &= \log 1000 + 20 \log 1.02 \\
&= 3 + 20(.0086) \\
&= 3 + .1720 = 3.1720.
\end{aligned}$$

Therefore, $A = \$1486$.   ∎

When P, r, and t are fixed in Eq. (6–12), the total number of dollars A increases as m increases. As an example, let $P = \$1$, $r = 100$ percent, and $t = 1$ year.

$$\text{If } m = 1, \text{ then } A = \$1\left(1 + \frac{1.00}{1}\right)^{1} = \$2.00.$$

$$\text{If } m = 2, \text{ then } A = \$1\left(1 + \frac{1.00}{2}\right)^{2} = \$2.25.$$

$$\text{If } m = 4, \text{ then } A = \$1\left(1 + \frac{1.00}{4}\right)^{4} = \$2.44.$$

$$\text{If } m = 12, \text{ then } A = \$1\left(1 + \frac{1.00}{12}\right)^{12} = \$2.61.$$

Therefore, if $1 is invested for 1 year at 100 percent interest compounded yearly, semiannually, quarterly, or monthly, the total amount of money at the end of 1 year is $2.00, $2.25, $2.44, and $2.61, respectively. Hence it appears desirable to have the interest compounded as often as possible. That is, we would like to have the interest compounded *continuously*. It is shown in calculus that

$$\left(1 + \frac{1}{m}\right)^m$$

become closer and closer to e as m takes on larger and larger integer values. Therefore, if P dollars is invested at an annual interest rate of r (in decimal form) with the interest compounded continuously, the total number of dollars A at the end of t years is given by

$$A = Pe^{rt}. \tag{6-13}$$

EXAMPLE 5

If $1000 is invested at 8 percent interest compounded continuously for 5 years, determine the total amount of dollars at the end of 5 years.

Solution   Using Eq. (6-13), the total number of dollars A at the end of 5 years is

$$A = (\$1000)e^{(.08)5}.$$

Using logarithms to evaluate A, we get

$$\begin{aligned} \log A &= \log 1000 + (.08)(5) \log e \\ &= \log 1000 + (.4) \log 2.718 \\ &= 3 + (.4)(0.4343) \\ &= 3 + 0.1737 = 3.1737. \end{aligned}$$

Therefore, $A = \$1492$. Compare this result with the result of Example 4.

∎

Problems 6.8

In problems 1-6, solve for the variable t.

1. $6 = 3e^{-.01t}$ 2. $3.4 = 1.2e^{-.2t}$ 3. $2 = 5e^{-.25t}$
4. $7 = 3e^{.62t}$ 5. $6 = 7e^{.35t}$ 6. $7.2 = 1.2e^{.72t}$
7. Radium decays according to the exponential law of decay, $Q = Q_0 e^{-.038t}$, where Q is the number of grams of radium present after t years and Q_0 is the number of grams of radium present initially. Calculate the half-life of radium.

8. A certain radioactive element X decays according to the exponential law of decay, $Q = Q_0 e^{-.217t}$, where Q is the number of grams of X present after t hours and Q_0 is the number of grams of X present initially. If there are 150 grams of X present initially, how many grams will be present after 8 hours?

9. If the half-life of a certain radioactive element Q is 20 minutes, determine the exponential law of decay which gives the amount of Q present after t minutes. If 100 grams of Q are present initially, how many grams of Q will remain after 30 minutes?

10. In a certain biology experiment it is found that the number N of bacteria present in a certain culture after t minutes is given by the exponential law of growth, $N = N_0 e^{.08t}$, where N_0 is the initial number of bacteria present in the culture. If 500 bacteria are present initially, how many will be present after 30 minutes?

11. If the number of ants in an ant colony doubles in 10 days, determine the exponential law of growth which gives the number N of ants present after t days.

12. The number of bacteria in a certain culture increases from 1000 to 1400 in 5 minutes. Determine the time required for the initial 1000 bacteria to double.

13. If $500 is invested at 6 percent interest compounded semiannually for 10 years, determine the total number of dollars at the end of 10 years.

14. If $800 is invested at 12 percent interest compounded monthly for 3 years, determine the total amount of dollars present at the end of 3 years.

15. If $2000 is invested at 12 percent interest compounded monthly for 5 years, determine the total amount of dollars at the end of 5 years.

16. If $500 is invested at 6 percent interest compounded continuously for 10 years, determine the total number of dollars at the end of 10 years.

17. If $800 is invested at 12 percent interest compounded continuously for 3 years, determine the total amount of dollars at the end of 3 years.

18. If $2000 is invested at 12 percent interest compounded continuously for 5 years, determine the total amount of dollars at the end of 5 years.

Answers 6.8

1. −69.32	**2.** −5.208	**4.** 1.367	**5.** −.4403
7. 1824 years	**8.** 26.44 grams	**10.** 5511	**11.** $N = N_0 e^{.06932t}$
13. $901.60	**14.** $1139	**16.** $911.20	**17.** $1147

chapter 6 review problems

1. Explain why the given function is (or is not) a one-to-one function.
   (a) $f(x) = \sqrt{x-2}$ (b) $f(x) = 2x - x^2$

2. Determine the inverse of each given one-to-one function f.
   (a) $f(x) = 3 - 7x$ (b) $f(x) = \sqrt{x-5}$

3. Graph $f(x) = 4^x$ and $g(x) = \frac{1}{4}^x$, and indicate what properties of exponential functions are displayed by the graphs of f and g.

4. Graph $f(x) = e^{-x^2}$.
5. Graph $f(x) = \log_3 x$ and $g(x) = \log_{(1/3)} x$, and indicate what properties of logarithmic functions are displayed by the graphs of f and g.
6. Use Eq. (6–6) to evaluate each of the following:
   (a) $\log_4 32$ (b) $\log_{(1/3)} 81$ (c) $2^{1-\log_3 27}$
7. Evaluate each of the following in terms of N:
   (a) $3^{\log_3 N}$ (b) $9^{\log_3 N}$
8. Express $\log(x^2\sqrt{y}/z^3)$ in terms of logarithms of x, y, and z.
9. Express $2 \log x - 3 \log y - \frac{1}{2} \log z + \log \pi$ as a single logarithm.
10. Use Table A and Eq. (6–8) to approximate the following:
    (a) $\log 722$ (b) $\log .0258$ (c) $\log 31.36$
11. Use Table A and Eq. (6–8) to approximate x for each of the following:
    (a) $\log x = 2.8774$ (b) $\log x = .8647 - 3$ (c) $\log x = -1.1713$
12. Use logarithms to calculate $\sqrt{.765/34.5}$ correct to three significant digits.
13. Use Eq. (6–9) to evaluate $\log_{51} 71.7$.
14. If $\log_a x = N$, express the following in terms of N:
    (a) $\log_{(a^4)} x$ (b) $\log_{(2/a)} x$
15. Solve each of the following equations for x:
    (a) $4^{3x} = 8^{3x-1}$ (b) $(4.44)^{x+1} = 55.5$
    (c) $5^{x+1} = 2^{6x-1}$ (d) $\log_2(x^2 + 4x + 11) = 4$
    (e) $\log_3(4x - 1) - \log_3(x - 4) = 2$ (f) $(\log x)^3 = \log x^3$
16. A radioactive element decays from 12 grams to 7 grams in 8 hours. Determine the half-life of the element.   _10.29 hr_
17. If $600 is invested at 8 percent compounded semiannually for 6 years, determine the total number of dollars at the end of 6 years.   _959.80_
18. If $600 is invested at 8 percent compounded continuously for 6 years, determine the total number of dollars at the end of 6 years.   _967.20_

answers

1. (a) is a one-to-one function (b) is not
2. (a) $f^{-1}(x) = \frac{3}{7} - x/7$ (b) $f^{-1}(x) = x + 5, x \geq 0$
4.

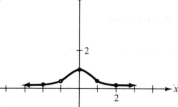

6. (a) $\frac{5}{2}$ (b) -4 (c) $\frac{1}{4}$
7. (a) N (b) N^2
8. $2 \log x + \frac{1}{2} \log y - 3 \log z$
9. $\log(\pi x^2/y^3\sqrt{z})$
10. (a) 2.8585   (b) -1.5884 (c) 1.4963

11. (a) 754   (b) .007323   (c) .0674   **12.** .0254   **13.** 1.09
14. (a) $N/4$ (b) $-N/(1 - \log_a 2)$
15. (a) 1   (b) 1.69   (c) .903   (d) $1, -5$ (e) 7   (f) $1, 10^{\sqrt{3}}, 10^{-\sqrt{3}}$
16. 10.29 hours   **17.** \$959.80   **18.** \$969.20

7

systems of equations
and inequalities

7.1 Systems of Linear Equations in Two Variables

If $P(x, y)$, $Q(x, y)$, $R(x, y)$, and $S(x, y)$ are expressions involving the two variables x and y, then the pair of equations

$$\begin{cases} P(x, y) = Q(x, y) \\ R(x, y) = S(x, y) \end{cases}$$

is called **a system of two equations in the two variables x and y.** An ordered pair (x, y) is said to be a **solution** of such a system of equations provided that the ordered pair is a solution of each of the equations in the system. To *solve* a system of equations means to determine all the solutions of the system. The set consisting of all the solutions of a system is called the **solution set** of the system.

In elementary algebra you learned how to solve systems of the form

$$\begin{cases} a_1x + b_1y = c_1 \\ a_2x + b_2y = c_2, \end{cases} \tag{7-1}$$

where $a_1, a_2, b_1, b_2, c_1, c_2 \in R$ with a_1 or $b_1 \neq 0$ and a_2 or $b_2 \neq 0$. System $(7-1)$ is called a **system of linear equations** in the variables x and y.

Recall from Chapter 4 that the graph of each equation in system $(7-1)$

is a straight line. When we graph these lines on a coordinate plane, the lines must (a) intersect at a unique point, (b) intersect at no point (i.e., be parallel to and distinct from one another), or (c) intersect at an infinite number of points (i.e., be parallel to and coincident with one another). See Figure 7.1. Thus the number of solutions of system (7–1) is (a) one solution, (b) no solution, or (c) an infinite number of solutions.

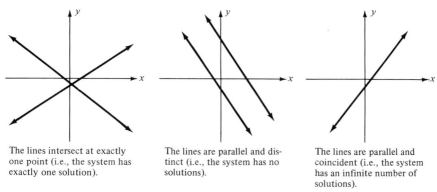

The lines intersect at exactly one point (i.e., the system has exactly one solution).

The lines are parallel and distinct (i.e., the system has no solutions).

The lines are parallel and coincident (i.e., the system has an infinite number of solutions).

Figure 7.1

If the lines in system (7–1) intersect at a unique point, the equations in the system are said to be **independent.** When the lines in system (7–1) are parallel to and distinct from one another, the equations are said to be **inconsistent,** and when the lines are parallel to and coincident with one another, the equations are said to be **dependent.**

In the remainder of this section we shall review how to solve systems of linear equations by the elimination method.

Two systems of equations are called equivalent systems if they have the same solution set. The following theorem is useful in justifying the equivalence of certain systems of equations.

Theorem 7.1   If $k_1, k_2 \in R$ with $k_2 \neq 0$, the system

$$\begin{cases} P(x, y) = Q(x, y) \\ R(x, y) = S(x, y) \end{cases} \tag{7–2}$$

is equivalent to the system

$$\begin{cases} P(x, y) = Q(x, y) \\ k_1 P(x, y) + k_2 R(x, y) = k_1 Q(x, y) + k_2 S(x, y) \end{cases} \tag{7–3}$$

for all values of x and y for which $P(x, y)$, $Q(x, y)$, $R(x, y)$, and $S(x, y)$ have real values.

Proof Suppose that (x_0, y_0) is a solution of system (7–2). Then it is clear that (x_0, y_0) satisfies the first equation of system (7–3). Since

$$P(x_0, y_0) = Q(x_0, y_0) \quad \text{and} \quad R(x_0, y_0) = S(x_0, y_0),$$

it follows by Theorem 1.2 that

$$k_1 P(x_0, y_0) = k_1 Q(x_0, y_0) \quad \text{and} \quad k_2 R(x_0, y_0) = k_2 S(x_0, y_0).$$

Now, using Theorem 1.1 and axiom E4, it follows that

$$k_1 P(x_0, y_0) + k_2 R(x_0, y_0) = k_1 Q(x_0, y_0) + k_2 S(x_0, y_0).$$

Hence (x_0, y_0) also satisfies the second equation of system (7–3). Thus every solution of system (7–2) is also a solution of system (7–3). A similar argument can be used to show that every solution of system (7–3) is also a solution of system (7–2). ∎

By properly choosing the constants k_1 and k_2 in Theorem 7.1, we can eliminate one of the variables in the second equation of system (7–3). We can then solve this equation in one variable for its solution. Finally, we can find the corresponding value of the other variable by using one of the equations in the original system. This procedure is known as the **elimination method** for solving a system of equations.

EXAMPLE 1

Solve the system

$$\begin{cases} x - 3y = -1 \\ 3x + 2y = 8. \end{cases}$$

Solution We begin by eliminating y between the two equations in the given system. Multiplying the first equation by 2 and the second equation by 3 and then adding the corresponding sides of the resulting equations, we get

$$\begin{array}{r} 2x - 6y = -2 \\ 9x + 6y = 24 \\ \hline 11x = 22. \end{array}$$

Solving the last equation for x, we get $x = 2$. Replacing 2 for x in the first equation of the given system, we find that the corresponding value of y is $y = 1$. Hence the solution set is $\{(2, 1)\}$. From a geometrical point of view, the point of intersection (see Figure 7.2) of the lines determined by the given system represents the unique solution of the system. ∎

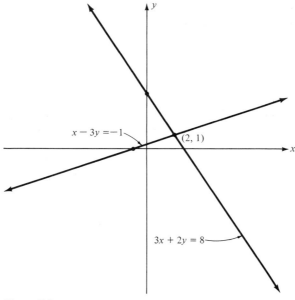

Figure 7.2

EXERCISE 1

Solve the system

$$\begin{cases} x-2y=13 \\ 3x+5y=\ \ 6. \end{cases}$$

Answer $(7,-3)$

When we eliminate one of the variables from the equations in system $(7-1)$, it is possible that the other variable in the system is eliminated at the same time. When this occurs the two equations are either *inconsistent* or *dependent*. That is, the system either has *no solutions* or *an infinite number of solutions*.

EXAMPLE 2

Solve the system

$$\begin{cases} 2x-\ \ y=\ \ 2 \\ 4x-2y=12. \end{cases}$$

Solution We begin by eliminating y. Multiplying the first equation by

−2 and the second equation by 1, and then adding the corresponding sides of the resulting equations, we get

$$-4x+2y=-4$$
$$\underline{4x-2y=12}$$
$$0=8.$$

Since the resulting equation is *never true*, the equations in the original system are inconsistent. That is, the given system has no solutions. This can be seen graphically in Figure 7.3.

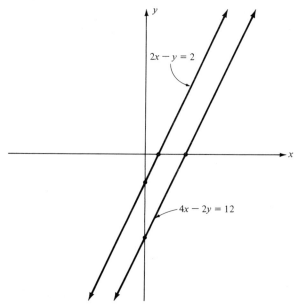

Figure 7.3

EXAMPLE 3

Solve the system

$$\begin{cases} 2x-y=2 \\ 6x-3y=6. \end{cases}$$

Solution   We begin by eliminating y. Multiplying the first equation by −3 and the second equation by 1, and then adding the corresponding sides of the resulting equations, we get

$$-6x+3y=-6$$
$$\underline{6x-3y=6}$$
$$0=0.$$

Since the resulting equation is *always true*, the equations in the given system are dependent. That is, one equation is a constant times the other equation. In this case, the second equation is three times the first equation. Thus their graphs are the same line, and hence any ordered pair that satisfies one of the equations must also satisfy the other equation. Thus the solution set is $\{(x, y)| y = 2x - 2\}$.   ∎

EXERCISE 2

Determine if the given system has exactly one solution, no solutions, or an infinite number of solutions.

(a) $\begin{cases} x - 3y = 3 \\ 3x - 9y = 9 \end{cases}$ (b) $\begin{cases} x - 3y = 3 \\ 2x + y = 1 \end{cases}$ (c) $\begin{cases} x - 3y = 3 \\ 2x - 6y = 3 \end{cases}$

Answer   (a) infinite number   (b) one   (c) none

Problems 7.1

In problems 1 – 15, graph the equations in the given system to determine the number of solutions of the given system. Then use the elimination method to determine the solution set of the given linear system.

1. $\begin{cases} x - 2y = 7 \\ 3x + y = 0 \end{cases}$ 2. $\begin{cases} x + 3y = -4 \\ 2x - y = 6 \end{cases}$ 3. $\begin{cases} x + 4y = 22 \\ 3x - y = 1 \end{cases}$

4. $\begin{cases} 2x - y = 3 \\ 4x - 2y = 5 \end{cases}$ 5. $\begin{cases} 3x + y = 7 \\ 6x + 2y = 2 \end{cases}$ 6. $\begin{cases} 2x - 3y = 1 \\ 4x - 6y = 3 \end{cases}$

7. $\begin{cases} 4x - y = 2 \\ 8x - 2y = 4 \end{cases}$ 8. $\begin{cases} x + y = 3 \\ 3x + 3y = 9 \end{cases}$ 9. $\begin{cases} 2x + 3y = 4 \\ 6x + 9y = 12 \end{cases}$

10. $\begin{cases} 2x - 3y = 5 \\ x - 6y = 1 \end{cases}$ 11. $\begin{cases} 3x - 2y = -9 \\ 2x + 6y = 5 \end{cases}$ 12. $\begin{cases} 3x - 5y = 12 \\ 6x + y = 2 \end{cases}$

13. $\begin{cases} 4x + 3y = 4 \\ 2x - 9y = 9 \end{cases}$ 14. $\begin{cases} 5x - 2y = 4 \\ 5x - 6y = 10 \end{cases}$ 15. $\begin{cases} 2x - 7y = 5 \\ 11x - 3y = 1 \end{cases}$

In problems 16 – 18, use the elimination method to solve the given system.

16. $\begin{cases} \dfrac{2}{x} - \dfrac{3}{y} = 4 \\ \dfrac{1}{x} + \dfrac{1}{y} = 7 \end{cases}$ 17. $\begin{cases} \dfrac{1}{x} - \dfrac{6}{y} = 6 \\ \dfrac{2}{x} + \dfrac{3}{y} = 7 \end{cases}$ 18. $\begin{cases} \dfrac{3}{x} - \dfrac{4}{y} = 17 \\ \dfrac{5}{x} + \dfrac{1}{y} = 13 \end{cases}$

19. Determine a and b so that the graph of $ax + by = 3$ contains the points $(2, 3)$ and $(-1, -6)$.

20. A man is 26 years older than his son. In 12 years he will be twice as old as his son. Determine their present ages.

21. The sum of two integers is 79. If the larger integer is divided by the smaller integer, the quotient is 4 and the remainder is 9. What are the integers?

22. A piggy bank contains $4.55 in nickels and dimes. If the nickels were dimes and the dimes were nickels, the bank would contain $5.05. Determine the number of nickels and the number of dimes in the bank.

23. A total of 68 tickets were sold to a fraternity banquet. If a ticket for a member and his date costs $7.50 and a ticket for a member alone costs $4.50, determine how many members came by themselves if the total income from the ticket sales was $459.

24. The sum of the reciprocals of two numbers is 5. If twice the reciprocal of the larger number is equal to three times the reciprocal of the smaller number, determine the numbers.

25. If Lenis and Matt work together, they can paint a room in 4 hours. If both men work for 2 hours and then Matt leaves, it takes Lenis 3 hours to finish the job alone. Determine how long it takes each man to complete the job alone.

26. The speed of a boat downstream is 2 miles per hour less than 3 times its speed upstream. If the boat travels upstream at the rate of 3 mph, determine its rate in still water and determine the rate of the current.

27. Bill can run 100 yards in the same time that Jim can run 120 yards. If Jim runs 20 yards per minute faster than Bill, determine the rate at which each runs.

28. Complete the proof of Theorem 7.1.

Answers 7.1

1. $\{(1, -3)\}$	**2.** $\{(2, -2)\}$	**4.** $\varnothing$
5. $\varnothing$	**7.** $\{(x, y)\mid y = 4x - 2\}$	**8.** $\{(x, y)\mid y = 3 - x\}$
10. $\{(3, \frac{1}{4})\}$	**11.** $\{(-2, \frac{3}{2})\}$	**13.** $\{(\frac{3}{2}, -\frac{2}{3})\}$
14. $\{(\frac{1}{5}, -\frac{3}{2})\}$	**16.** $\{(\frac{1}{5}, \frac{1}{2})\}$	**17.** $\{(\frac{1}{4}, -3)\}$
19. $a = 3, b = -1$	**20.** 14, 40	**22.** 37 nickels, 27 dimes
23. 17	**25.** Lenis 6 hours, Matt 12 hours	
26. boat 5 mph, current 2 mph		

7.2 Systems Involving Nonlinear Equations

The following theorem is also useful for justifying the equivalence of certain systems of equations.

Theorem 7.2 The system

$$\begin{cases} P(x, y) = Q(x, y) \\ \quad y = F(x) \end{cases}$$

is equivalent to the system

$$\begin{cases} P(x, F(x)) = Q(x, F(x)) \\ \quad y = F(x) \end{cases}$$

for all values of x and y for which $P(x, y)$, $Q(x, y)$, and $F(x)$ have real values.

Proof The proof, which is similar to that of Theorem 7.1, is left as a problem. ∎

Note that Theorem 7.2 states that when one of the equations of a given system has the form $y = F(x)$, then $F(x)$ can be substituted for y in the other equation to obtain an equation in the single variable x. The resulting equation in the variable x can then be solved for x. Finally, the corresponding value (or values) of y can be found by substituting for x in the equation $y = F(x)$. This procedure is known as the **substitution method** for solving a system of equations.

In our first example, we use the substitution method to solve a system of linear equations.

EXAMPLE 1

Solve the system

$$\begin{cases} x - 2y = -9 \\ 3x + y = 1. \end{cases}$$

Solution Solving the second linear equation for y in terms of x, we get

$$y = 1 - 3x. \tag{7-4}$$

Then, substituting $1 - 3x$ for y in the first equation of the given system, we get

$$x - 2(1 - 3x) = -9,$$

which is equivalent to

$$7x = -7.$$

The last equation is satisfied only when $x = -1$. Substituting -1 for x in Eq. (7-4), we find that the corresponding value of y is $y = 4$. Hence the solution set is $\{(-1, 4)\}$.

EXERCISE 1

Solve

$$\begin{cases} x - 3y = 7 \\ 3x + y = 11 \end{cases}$$

by the substitution method.

Answer $(4, -1)$

Next we illustrate the substitution method on a system of equation involving one linear and one nonlinear equation.

EXAMPLE 2

Solve the system

$$\begin{cases} x^2 + y^2 & = 25 \\ 2x - y - 5 = & 0. \end{cases}$$

Solution Solving the linear equation of the given system for y in terms of x, we get

$$y = 2x - 5. \tag{7-5}$$

Then, replacing y with $2x - 5$ in the first equation of the given system, we get

$$x^2 + (2x - 5)^2 = 25$$
$$x^2 + 4x^2 - 20x + 25 = 25$$

and hence

$$5x(x - 4) = 0.$$

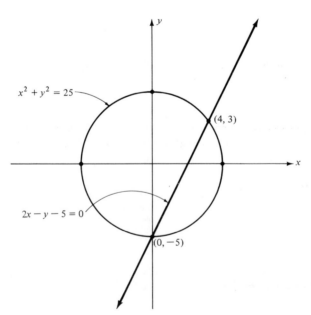

Figure 7.4

The last equation is satisfied when $x = 0$ or $x = 4$. Replacing x with 0 in Eq. $(7-5)$, we find that the corresponding value of y is -5. Replacing x with 4 in Eq. $(7-5)$, we find that $y = 3$. Hence the solution set is $\{(0, -5), (4, 3)\}$. Graphically, the points of the solution set are the points of intersection of the line $2x - y = 5$ and the circle $x^2 + y^2 = 25$ shown in Figure 7.4.   ■

EXERCISE 2

Solve

$$\begin{cases} x^2 - y^2 = 16 \\ 3x + y = 12 \end{cases}$$

by the substitution method.

Answer $(5, -3)$ and $(4, 0)$

Certain systems of nonlinear equations can also be solved by using the substitution method.

EXAMPLE 3

Solve the system

$$\begin{cases} x^2 + y^2 = 16 \\ 4x^2 - y^2 = 4 \end{cases}$$

by the substitution method.

Solution   Solving the first equation for y^2, we get

$$y^2 = 16 - x^2. \tag{7-6}$$

Then, replacing y^2 with $16 - x^2$ in the second equation, we get

$$4x^2 - (16 - x^2) = 4,$$
$$5x^2 = 20,$$

and hence

$$x^2 = 4.$$

The last equation is satisfied when $x = 2$ or when $x = -2$. When $x = 2$ in Eq. $(7-6)$, the corresponding values of y are $\pm\sqrt{12}$. When $x = -2$ in Eq. $(7-6)$, the corresponding values of y are $\pm\sqrt{12}$. Hence the solution set is $\{(2, \sqrt{12}), (2, -\sqrt{12}), (-2, \sqrt{12}), (-2, -\sqrt{12})\}$. Graphically the points of the solution set are the intersection points of the circle $x^2 + y^2 = 16$ and the hyperbola $4x^2 - y^2 = 4$ shown in Figure 7.5.   ■

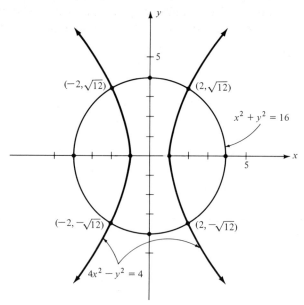

Figure 7.5

Problems 7.2

In problems 1–18, graph the given system to determine the number of solutions of the system. Then use the substitution method to determine the solution set of the given system.

1. $\begin{cases} x - 3y = 10 \\ 5x + y = 34 \end{cases}$

2. $\begin{cases} 3x - 2y = 13 \\ 5x + 3y = 9 \end{cases}$

3. $\begin{cases} 5x - 2y = 3 \\ x + 3y = 2 \end{cases}$

4. $\begin{cases} x^2 + y^2 = 4 \\ x + 2 = 2y \end{cases}$

5. $\begin{cases} x^2 + y^2 = 13 \\ x + y = 1 \end{cases}$

6. $\begin{cases} x^2 + y^2 = 2 \\ y - 2x = 1 \end{cases}$

7. $\begin{cases} 4y - 3x^2 = 0 \\ y = 3x - 3 \end{cases}$

8. $\begin{cases} y = 2x^2 - x - 6 \\ x - 3y = 2 \end{cases}$

9. $\begin{cases} y = x^2 + 4x - 2 \\ x - y + 8 = 0 \end{cases}$

10. $\begin{cases} 4y^2 - 9x^2 = 28 \\ x = 2y - 6 \end{cases}$

11. $\begin{cases} x^2 - 4y^2 = 96 \\ x + 2y + 8 = 0 \end{cases}$

12. $\begin{cases} x^2 - y^2 = 9 \\ 4x + 5y = 0 \end{cases}$

13. $\begin{cases} 4x^2 + 3y^2 = 1 \\ 2x + 3y - 1 = 0 \end{cases}$

14. $\begin{cases} 4x^2 + 9y^2 = 45 \\ 2x - y = 5 \end{cases}$

15. $\begin{cases} 9x^2 + 5y^2 = 81 \\ 3x - 5y + 9 = 0 \end{cases}$

16. $\begin{cases} xy = 6 \\ 3x - 2y = 5 \end{cases}$

17. $\begin{cases} xy = 4 \\ x - 3y = 1 \end{cases}$

18. $\begin{cases} xy = 4 \\ x - 2y + 2 = 0 \end{cases}$

In problems 19–27, graph the given system to determine the number of solutions of the system. Then use the substitution method to determine the solution set of the given system.

19. $\begin{cases} x^2 + y^2 = 7 \\ x^2 - y^2 = 1 \end{cases}$ **20.** $\begin{cases} x^2 + y^2 \quad\;\; = 12 \\ x^2 + y^2 - 6x = 0 \end{cases}$ **21.** $\begin{cases} 4x^2 + y^2 = 25 \\ y^2 - 2x^2 = 1 \end{cases}$

22. $\begin{cases} x^2 + 5y^2 = 36 \\ x^2 + y^2 = 20 \end{cases}$ **23.** $\begin{cases} 9x^2 - 4y^2 = 44 \\ 16x^2 - 9y^2 = 31 \end{cases}$ **24.** $\begin{cases} x^2 - 4y^2 = 4 \\ x^2 + y^2 = 9 \end{cases}$

25. $\begin{cases} x^2 + y^2 - 8x = 0 \\ x^2 - y^2 \quad\;\; = 10 \end{cases}$ **26.** $\begin{cases} x^2 + y^2 = 9 \\ x^2 + 4y^2 = 36 \end{cases}$ **27.** $\begin{cases} x^2 + y^2 \quad\;\; = 4 \\ x^2 + y^2 - 2y = 0 \end{cases}$

28. The sum of two positive numbers is 30. If the square of the larger number is subtracted from twice the square of the smaller number, the difference is 49. Determine the numbers.

29. The sum of the squares of two positive numbers is 74, and the difference of the squares is 24. Determine the numbers.

30. If the sum of two numbers is $\frac{9}{4}$ and their product is $\frac{9}{8}$, determine the numbers.

31. Prove Theorem 7.2.

Answers 7.2

1. $\{(7, -1)\}$ **2.** $\{(3, -2)\}$ **4.** $\{(-2, 0), (\frac{6}{5}, \frac{8}{5})\}$

5. $\{(-2, 3), (3, -2)\}$ **7.** $\{(2, 3)\}$ **8.** $\{(2, 0), (-\frac{4}{3}, -\frac{10}{9})\}$

10. $\{(2, 4), (-\frac{1}{2}, \frac{11}{4})\}$ **11.** $\{(-10, 1)\}$ **13.** $\{(\frac{1}{2}, 0), (-\frac{1}{4}, \frac{1}{2})\}$

14. $\{(\frac{3}{2}, -2), (3, 1)\}$ **16.** $\{(3, 2), (-\frac{4}{3}, -\frac{9}{2})\}$ **17.** $\{(4, 1), (-3, -\frac{4}{3})\}$

19. $\{(2, \sqrt{3}), (2, -\sqrt{3}), (-2, \sqrt{3}), (-2, -\sqrt{3})\}$ **20.** $\{(2, 2\sqrt{2}), (2, -2\sqrt{2})\}$

22. $\{(4, 2), (4. -2), (-4, 2), (-4, -2)\}$ **23.** $\{(4, 5), (4, -5), (-4, 5), (-4, -5)\}$

25. $\{(5, \sqrt{15}), (5, -\sqrt{15})\}$ **26.** $\{(0, 3), (0, -3)\}$

28. 13 and 17   **29.** 5 and 7

7.3 Systems of Inequalities

In Section 4.7, we found that the graph of an inequality in the two variables x and y was frequently a region of a coordinate plane. A similar situation exists for systems of inequalities in the two variables x and y.

EXAMPLE 1

Graph the solution set of

$$\begin{cases} x - y < 2 \\ 2x + y > 2. \end{cases}$$

Solution   The graph of $x - y < 2$ is the region above the line $x - y = 2$ in Figure 7.6. Similarly, the graph of $2x + y > 2$ is the region above the line

$2x + y = 2$ in Figure 7.6. Thus the solution set of the given system consists of those points which are above the line $x - y = 2$ and above the line $2x + y = 2$. That is, the solution set of the given system consists of those points in the shaded region of Figure 7.6. ∎

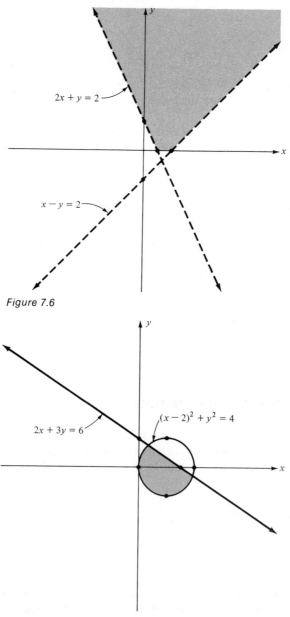

Figure 7.6

Figure 7.7

EXAMPLE 2

Graph the solution set of

$$\begin{cases} (x-2)^2 + y^2 \le 4 \\ 2x + 3y \le 6. \end{cases}$$

Solution See Figure 7.7. The graph of $(x-2)^2 + y^2 \le 4$ is the region inside the circle $(x-2)^2 + y^2 = 4$, and the graph of $2x + 3y \le 6$ is the region below the line $2x + 3y = 6$. Hence the solution set of the given system consists of those points which are inside the circle $(x-2)^2 + y^2 = 4$ and below the line $2x + 3y = 6$. That is, the solution set of the given system consists of those points in the shaded region of Figure 7.7. ∎

Problems 7.3

In problems 1–24, graph the solution set of the given system of inequalities.

1. $\begin{cases} x - 3y > 3 \\ 2x + y < 2 \end{cases}$

2. $\begin{cases} 2x - 3y < 6 \\ x + y < 2 \end{cases}$

3. $\begin{cases} 2x + y > 4 \\ x < y \end{cases}$

4. $\begin{cases} x + 1 \le y \\ 2x + y \le 4 \end{cases}$

5. $\begin{cases} 3x + y \ge -3 \\ 2x + 3 \le y \end{cases}$

6. $\begin{cases} x - y \ge -2 \\ y + 2x \ge 2 \end{cases}$

7. $\begin{cases} y \le x \\ x \le 2 \\ y \le -1 \end{cases}$

8. $\begin{cases} x + y \ge 2 \\ y \le 3 \\ x \ge 1 \end{cases}$

9. $\begin{cases} y \le x + 1 \\ x \le 3 \\ y \ge -1 \end{cases}$

10. $\begin{cases} x - 2y > 4 \\ x + 3y \le 3 \\ x \ge -2 \end{cases}$

11. $\begin{cases} x \ge y \\ x + 2y < 2 \\ y > -2 \end{cases}$

12. $\begin{cases} y < -x \\ y - x \ge 1 \\ x > -3 \end{cases}$

13. $\begin{cases} y > x^2 - 1 \\ 3y - 6 < 2x \end{cases}$

14. $\begin{cases} x \ge y^2 - 2y - 1 \\ 2x + y \ge 2 \end{cases}$

15. $\begin{cases} y \le -x^2 + 2x + 2 \\ 4y + x + 1 \le 0 \end{cases}$

16. $\begin{cases} (x-1)^2 + (y+1)^2 \le 4 \\ 2x - y < 2 \end{cases}$

17. $\begin{cases} 9x^2 + y^2 < 9 \\ x - y + 1 \ge 0 \end{cases}$

18. $\begin{cases} x^2 - 4y^2 \le 4 \\ 2y > x \end{cases}$

19. $\begin{cases} x^2 + y^2 \ge 4 \\ x^2 + (y+2)^2 < 4 \end{cases}$

20. $\begin{cases} y^2 - x^2 \ge 1 \\ x^2 + y^2 \le 9 \end{cases}$

21. $\begin{cases} y > x^2 - 2 \\ y < -x^2 + 1 \end{cases}$

22. $\begin{cases} y < x^2 - 2x - 1 \\ (x-2)^2 + (y+1)^2 \le 4 \end{cases}$

23. $\begin{cases} x^2 - y^2 \le 1 \\ 4y^2 - x^2 \le 4 \end{cases}$

24. $\begin{cases} y \le x - 1 \\ 4 \le x^2 + y^2 \le 9 \end{cases}$

Answers 7.3

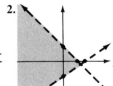

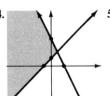

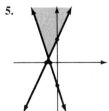

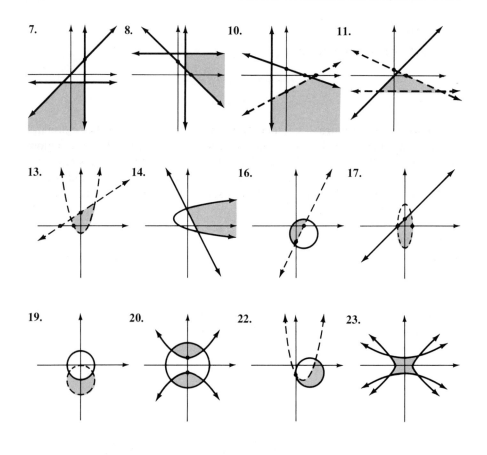

7.4 Introduction to Linear Programming

A region R of a coordinate plane is said to be a **convex region** if and only if, whenever P and Q are any two points of R, the line segment joining P and Q lies entirely in R. For example, the set of points represented by the shaded region in Figure 7.8 is a convex region, whereas the shaded region in Figure 7.9 is not a convex region, since part of the line segment joining P and Q lies outside the region.

The region of a coordinate plane that is the graph of the inequality $ax + by \geq c$ or of the inequality $ax + by \leq c$, where $a,b,c \in R$, is called a **closed half-plane.** For example, the shaded region in Figure 7.10, which represents the graph of $2x + y \geq 2$, is a closed half-plane. Note that any closed half-plane is a convex region.

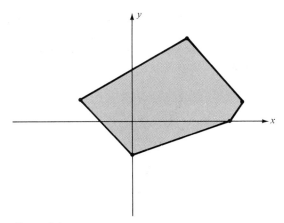

Figure 7.8

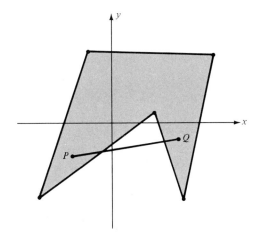

Figure 7.9

Any region of a plane that is the intersection of a finite number of closed half-planes is called a **convex polygonal region.** For example, the shaded region in Figure 7.11 is a convex polygonal region, since this region is the intersection of the two closed half-planes $2x + y \geq 2$ and $y \geq 1$.

If the boundary of a convex polygonal region is a closed polygon, the region is called a **closed convex polygonal region.** For example, the shaded region in Figure 7.8 is a closed convex polygonal region, whereas the region in Figure 7.11 is not a closed convex polygonal region.

In many business and economics situations, we are confronted with the problem of determining the particular point or points of a convex polygonal region R at which the linear expression $ax + by + c$ has its greatest (or its least) value. Such a problem is called a **linear programming problem.** The points of the region R are called the **feasible solutions** of the problem. Those feasible solutions for which $ax + by + c$ has its greatest (or its least) value are called **optimal solutions.**

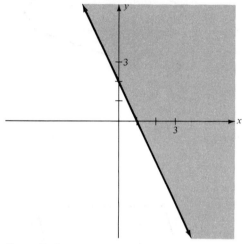

Figure 7.10

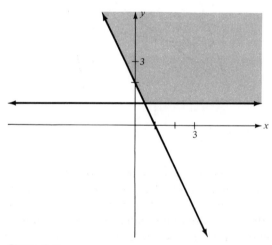

Figure 7.11

Certain linear programming problems can be solved by using the following theorem, whose proof is omitted in this text.

Theorem 7.3 If R is a closed convex polygonal region of a coordinate plane, then the linear expression $ax + by + c$, where a, b, and c are real numbers with $a \neq 0$ or $b \neq 0$, obtains its maximum (or its minimum) value over R at one of the vertices of R. If two adjacent vertices have the same maximum (or minimum) value for $ax + by + c$, then every point on that side of the polygon has the same value for $ax + by + c$.

Note that Theorem 7.3 states that we need only check the vertices of R to determine the maximum (or the minimum) value of $ax + by + c$ over R.

EXAMPLE 1

Determine the maximum value and the minimum value of the linear expression $2x - 3y$ over the closed convex polygonal region R which is the graph of the system

$$\begin{cases} 0 \leq x \\ 0 \leq y \leq 2 \\ x + y \leq 4. \end{cases}$$

Solution   The graph of the given system is shown in Figure 7.12. Observe that the shaded region R in Figure 7.12 is a closed convex polygonal region. Therefore, according to Theorem 7.3, the linear expression $2x - 3y$

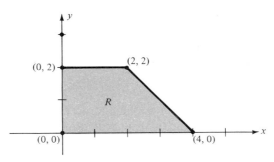

Figure 7.12

obtains its maximum (or its minimum) value over R at one of the vertices $(0, 0)$, $(0, 2)$, $(2, 2)$, and $(4, 0)$. The value of $2x - 3y$ at each of these vertices is shown in the following table:

Vertices	$(0, 0)$	$(0, 2)$	$(2, 2)$	$(4, 0)$
Corresponding Value of $2x - 3y$	0	-6	-2	8

By examining this table, we find that the linear expression $2x - 3y$ has a maximum value of 8 at $(4, 0)$ and a minimum value of -6 at $(0, 2)$. ∎

EXERCISE 1

Determine the maximum value and the minimum value of the linear expression $3x - 5y + 3$ over the closed convex polygonal region R shown below:

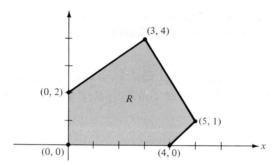

Answer   Maximum value of 15 at $(4, 0)$, minimum value of -8 at $(3, 4)$.

EXAMPLE 2

A farmer plans to plant two crops, A and B, on his 50-acre farm. To receive a government subsidy that he cannot afford to lose, he must plant at least twice as many acres in crop A as he does in crop B. The cost of planting and taking care of crop A is $40 per acre, while the cost of planting and taking care of crop B is $50 per acre. If the expected revenue per acre of crop A is $110 and the expected revenue per acre of crop B is $130, how many of his 50 acres should the farmer plant in each crop to realize the maximum expected profit?

Solution   Let x represent the number of acres planted in crop A and let y represent the number of acres planted in crop B. Since

$$\text{profit} = \text{revenue} - \text{cost},$$

the profit per acre on crop A is $110 − $40 = $70, and the profit per acre on crop B is $130 − $50 = $80. Hence the total profit P in dollars is given by the linear expression

$$P = 70x + 80y.$$

We wish to maximize the profit P subject to the following restrictions:

1. $x \geq 0$ and $y \geq 0$ (the farmer cannot plant a negative number of acres in either crop).
2. $0 \leq x + y \leq 50$ (the number of acres planted in crops A and B cannot exceed 50 acres).

3. $x \geq 2y$ (the farmer must plant at least twice as many acres in crop A as he plants in crop B).

Graphing the inequalities (1), (2), and (3), we see that the graph of the region R in Figure 7.13 determined by these inequalities is a convex polygonal region. Thus according to Theorem 7.3, the linear expression $70x + 80y$,

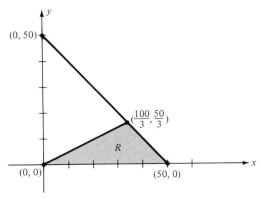

Figure 7.13

which represents the profit, obtains its maximum value at one of the vertices $(0, 0)$, $(50, 0)$, and $(\frac{100}{3}, \frac{50}{3})$. The value of $70x + 80y$ at each of these vertices is shown in the following table:

Vertices	$(0, 0)$	$(50, 0)$	$(100/3, 50/3)$
Corresponding Value of $70x + 80y$	0	3500	$3666 \frac{2}{3}$

Since the expression $70x + 80y$ obtains its maximum value of $3666\frac{2}{3}$ at $(\frac{100}{3}, \frac{50}{3})$, the farmer realizes a maximum profit of \$3666.67 by planting $33\frac{1}{3}$ acres of crop A and $16\frac{2}{3}$ acres of crop B. ∎

Problems 7.4

In problems 1-6, determine if the given region is a convex region. If it is a convex region, determine if it is a convex polygonal region. If it is a convex polygonal region, determine if it is a closed convex polygonal region.

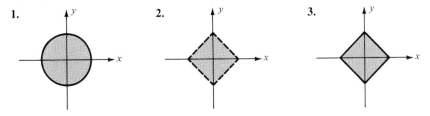

4.
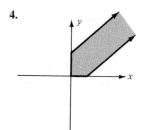

5.
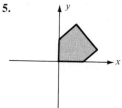

6.
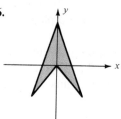

In problems 7–12, determine the maximum (and the minimum) values of the given linear expression over the given shaded region R.

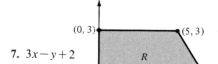

7. $3x - y + 2$

8. $2x + y - 5$

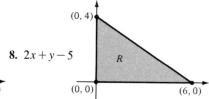

9. $4x - 2y + 2$

10. $5x - 3y - 1$

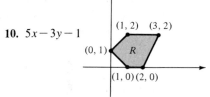

11. $3x - 4y + 1$

12. $2x + y - 6$

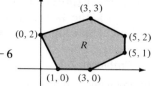

In problems 13–24, determine the maximum (and the minimum) values of the given linear expression over the region R determined by the given system of inequalities.

13. $3x - 4y$; $\quad \begin{cases} x \geq 0 \\ y \geq 0 \\ x + y \leq 1 \end{cases}$

14. $4x - 2y$; $\quad \begin{cases} x \geq 0 \\ y \geq 0 \\ 2x + 3y \leq 6 \end{cases}$

15. $5x - 3y + 1$; $\begin{cases} x \geq 0 \\ y \geq 0 \\ 3x + 4y \leq 12 \end{cases}$

16. $x + y - 3$; $\quad \begin{cases} x \geq 1 \\ y \geq 0 \\ x + 2y \leq 2 \end{cases}$

17. $3x - 5y$; $\begin{cases} x \geq 0 \\ y \geq 1 \\ 3x + 2y \leq 6 \end{cases}$

18. $2x - 5y + 2$; $\begin{cases} x + y \geq 1 \\ 0 \leq x \leq 3 \\ 0 \leq y \leq 2 \end{cases}$

19. $5x - 4y$; $\begin{cases} x \geq 0 \\ y \geq 0 \\ 2x + y \leq 16 \\ x - 2y \leq -2 \end{cases}$

20. $4x - 7y$; $\begin{cases} 2 \leq x \leq 6 \\ y \geq 0 \\ x + 2y \leq 8 \end{cases}$

21. $6x - 4y$; $\begin{cases} 0 \leq x \leq 6 \\ y \geq 1 \\ x - y \geq -3 \\ x + 4y \leq 22 \end{cases}$

22. $3x - 5y$; $\begin{cases} 0 \leq x \\ 0 \leq y \leq 4 \\ 2x + y \leq 10 \\ x + y \leq 6 \end{cases}$

23. $3x - 5y$; $\begin{cases} x \geq 0 \\ y \leq 5 \\ x - y \geq -2 \\ x + 8y \geq 8 \\ 2x + y \leq 16 \end{cases}$

24. $3x - 4y$; $\begin{cases} 0 \leq x \\ 0 \leq y \\ x + y \geq 1 \\ x + 2y \leq 4 \\ x - y \geq -1 \end{cases}$

25. A company manufactures two products, A and B. The company, which has a maximum of 8000 man-hours of labor available per week, has a maximum budget of $10,000 per week for materials. Let x be the number of units of product A produced per week, and let y be the number of units of product B produced per week.

   (a) Write inequalities that indicate the minimum number of units of each product which can be produced per week.

   (b) If the material to produce one unit of product A costs $2 and the material to produce one unit of product B costs $1, write an inequality which indicates that the company has a maximum budget of $10,000 per week for materials.

   (c) If it takes 1 man-hour of labor to produce one unit of A and 2 man-hours of labor to produce one unit of B, write an inequality which indicates that the company has a maximum of 8000 man-hours of labor available per week.

   (d) Graph the inequalities of parts (a) to (c) and determine the vertices of the the graph.

   (e) If the profit on one unit of A is 30 cents and the profit on one unit of B is 50 cents, how many units of each of the products A and B should the company produce per week to realize the maximum profit?

26. A chemical refinery produces two chemicals, A and B. The refinery is capable of producing any number of barrels of chemical A up to 500 barrels per week and any number of barrels of chemical B up to 400 barrels per week. However, the total weekly production of chemicals A and B is limited to 600 barrels because of the limited availability of a certain product that is necessary, in equal amounts, for the production of a barrel of either chemical. The total weekly production of chemicals A and B is also limited because of a maximum budget of $14,000 per week for raw materials.

   (a) Write inequalities indicating the minimum and maximum number of barrels of each chemical that can be produced per week.

(b) If the raw materials to produce one barrel of chemical A cost \$20 and the raw materials to produce one barrel of chemical B cost \$30, write an inequality which indicates that the company has a maximum budget of \$14,000 per week for raw materials.

(c) Write an inequality which indicates that the total weekly production of chemicals A and B is limited to 600 barrels.

(d) Graph the inequalities in parts (a) to (c) and determine the vertices of the graph.

(e) If the profit per barrel of chemical A is \$17 and the profit per barrel of chemical B is \$19, how many barrels of each of the chemicals should the company produce per week to realize the maximum profit?

Answers 7.4

1. convex; not convex polygonal
2. convex; not convex polygonal
4. convex; convex polygonal; not closed
5. convex; convex polygonal; closed
7. max $= 23$, min $= -1$ 8. max $= 7$, min $= -5$
10. max $= 9$, min $= -4$ 11. max $= 4$, min $= -4$
13. max $= 3$, min $= -4$ 14. max $= 12$, min $= -4$
16. max $= -1$, min $= -2$ 17. max $= -1$, min $= -15$
19. max $= 40$, min $= -4$ 20. max $= 24$, min $= -13$
22. max $= 15$, min $= -20$ 23. max $= 24$, min $= -16$
25. (a) $x \geq 0$, $y \geq 0$ (b) $2x + y \leq 10,000$ (c) $x + 2y \leq 8000$
    (d) (0, 0), (0, 4000), (4000, 2000), (5000, 0)
    (e) 4000 units of A, 2000 units of B
26. (a) $0 \leq x \leq 500, 0 \leq y \leq 400$ (b) $20x + 30y \leq 14,000$ (c) $x + y \leq 600$
    (d) (0, 0), (0, 400), (100, 400), (400, 200), (500, 100), (500, 0)
    (e) 400 barrels of chemical A, 200 barrels of chemical B

7.5 Systems of Linear Equations in Three Variables

A statement of the form

$$ax + by + cz = d, \tag{7-7}$$

where $a,b,c,d \in R$ with $a \neq 0$, $b \neq 0$, or $c \neq 0$, is called a **linear equation** in the three variables x, y, and z. If a true statement is obtained when the x, y, and z coordinates of an ordered triple (x, y, z) are substituted for the variables x, y, and z, respectively, in Eq. (7–7), the ordered triple (x, y, z) is said to be a **solution** of the equation.

A system of linear equations in the three variables x, y, and z is a system of the form

$$\begin{cases} a_1x + b_1y + c_1z = d_1 \\ a_2x + b_2y + c_2z = d_2 \\ a_3x + b_3y + c_3z = d_3. \end{cases} \qquad (7\text{-}8)$$

Since Theorem 7.1 can be extended to a system of equations in three variables, system $(7-8)$ can also be solved by the elimination method.

EXAMPLE 1

Solve the system

$$\begin{cases} x - y + 2z = 3 \\ 3x + 4y - 3z = 20 \\ 2x - y - z = 15. \end{cases}$$

Solution We begin by eliminating z between the first and second equations of the given system. Multiplying the first equation by 3 and the second equation by 2, and then adding the corresponding sides of the resulting equations, we get

$$\begin{array}{r} 3x - 3y + 6z = 9 \\ 6x + 8y - 6z = 40 \\ \hline 9x + 5y \phantom{{}- 6z} = 49. \end{array} \qquad (7\text{-}9)$$

Next we eliminate z between the first and third equations of the given system. Multiplying the first equation by 1 and the third equation by 2 and then adding the corresponding sides of the resulting equations, we get

$$\begin{array}{r} x - y + 2z = 3 \\ 4x - 2y - 2z = 30 \\ \hline 5x - 3y \phantom{{}- 2z} = 33. \end{array} \qquad (7\text{-}10)$$

Next we eliminate y between Eqs. $(7-9)$ and $(7-10)$. Multiplying Eq. $(7-9)$ by 3 and Eq. $(7-10)$ by 5, and then adding the corresponding sides of the resulting equation, we get

$$\begin{array}{r} 27x + 15y = 147 \\ 25x - 15y = 165 \\ \hline 52x \phantom{{}- 15y} = 312. \end{array} \qquad (7\text{-}11)$$

Solving Eq. $(7-11)$ for x, we get $x = 6$. Replacing 6 for x in Eq. $(7-10)$, we get $5(6) - 3y = 33$ and hence $y = -1$. Then replacing 6 for x and -1 for y in the first equation of the original system, we get $6 - (-1) + 2z = 3$ and hence $z = -2$. Consequently, the solution is $(6, -1, -2)$. ∎

Problems 7.5

In problems 1–12, use the elimination method to determine the solution of the given linear system.

1. $\begin{cases} x - y + 2z = 5 \\ x + 3y - z = 4 \\ 5x + 2y + z = 12 \end{cases}$

2. $\begin{cases} 3x - y - z = 10 \\ 4x + 3y + z = 2 \\ 2x + 4y - 3z = 9 \end{cases}$

3. $\begin{cases} 2x - 3y + z = 11 \\ 3x + 4y - 2z = 1 \\ 3x - 4y - 3z = 7 \end{cases}$

4. $\begin{cases} 2x - y - 6z = 15 \\ 3x + 2y + 2z = 8 \\ 4x - 3y - 3z = 22 \end{cases}$

5. $\begin{cases} 3x + y - 2z = 9 \\ 4x + 2y + 3z = 5 \\ x - 2y + z = 6 \end{cases}$

6. $\begin{cases} 3x - y - 5z = -2 \\ 2x - 3y + 2z = 14 \\ 5x + 2y + 3z = 12 \end{cases}$

7. $\begin{cases} 2x - 3y + 2z = 3 \\ 3x - z = -11 \\ 2x + 2y + 3z = 13 \end{cases}$

8. $\begin{cases} 3x + 2y - 3z = 10 \\ 2x - y = 7 \\ 3x + y + z = 7 \end{cases}$

9. $\begin{cases} 3x - 5y - 3z = 13 \\ 2x + y = 10 \\ x - 2y + 4z = 30 \end{cases}$

10. $\begin{cases} x - 3y + z = 10 \\ x + 5y - z = -2 \\ x - y + 2z = 10 \end{cases}$

11. $\begin{cases} x - y + z = 1 \\ 2x + y - 2z = 9 \\ 3x - 2y - 3z = 10 \end{cases}$

12. $\begin{cases} x - y - z = 4 \\ 3x + 2y - z = 15 \\ x - 4y + 5z = -5 \end{cases}$

13. Determine a, b, and c so that the graph of $y = ax^2 + bx + c$ contains the points $(1, 1)$, $(2, 3)$, and $(-2, 0)$.

14. Determine D, E, and F so that the graph of $x^2 + y^2 + Dx + Ey + F = 0$ contains the points $(1, 0)$, $(4, -4)$, and $(5, 3)$.

15. The sum of the digits of a three-digit number is 14. The tens digit is two smaller than the units digit. If the order of the digits is reversed, the number is decreased by 99. Determine the numbers.

16. A jar contains \$3.55 in nickels, dimes, and quarters. There are two thirds as many nickels as quarters. If there are 25 coins in all, determine how many coins of each type are in the jar.

17. Mark and Clint can paint a fence together in 2 hours. Mark and Nick can paint the same fence together in $2\frac{2}{3}$ hours, and Clint and Nick can do the job together in 4 hours. Determine how long it would take each of them to paint the fence by himself.

18. A certain swimming pool has two input pipes and one drain pipe. The two input pipes can fill the pool alone in 15 hours and 20 hours, respectively. When the pool is completely full, the drain pipe can empty it in 25 hours. If the pool is empty and both input pipes and the drain pipe are completely open, how long will it take to fill the pool?

19. The length of a certain rectangular box is twice its width. If the volume of the box is 980 cubic inches and the surface area is 616 square inches, determine the dimensions of the box. (*Hint:* Solve by using the substitution method.)

Answers 7.5

1. (1, 2, 3)   **2.** (2, −1, −3)   **4.** (4, −1, −1)   **5.** (3, −2, −1)

7. (−2, 1, 5)   **8.** (3, −1, −1)   **10.** (5, −1, 2)   **11.** (3, 1, −1)

13. $a = \frac{5}{12}$, $b = \frac{3}{4}$, $c = -\frac{1}{6}$ **14.** $D = -9$, $E = 1$, $F = 8$

16. 6 nickels, 10 dimes, 9 quarters

17. Mark 3 hours, Clint 6 hours, Nick 12 hours

19. 14 inches by 7 inches by 10 inches

chapter 7 review problems

1. Determine the solution set of the given linear system.

(a) $\begin{cases} 3x - y = 6 \\ 7x + 2y = 1 \end{cases}$ (b) $\begin{cases} x - 3y = 5 \\ 2x - 6y = 7 \end{cases}$ (c) $\begin{cases} 2x - 3y = 16 \\ 5x + 4y = 17 \end{cases}$

2. Determine the solution set of the given system.

(a) $\begin{cases} y = -x^2 + x + 8 \\ 3x - y + 5 = 0 \end{cases}$ (b) $\begin{cases} xy = 3 \\ x - 2y = 5 \end{cases}$ (c) $\begin{cases} x^2 + 4y^2 = 25 \\ x^2 - y^2 = 5 \end{cases}$

3. Determine the solution set of the given system of inequalities.

(a) $\begin{cases} x \geq 0 \\ x + y \geq 1 \\ x^2 + y^2 \leq 4 \end{cases}$ (b) $\begin{cases} 2y \geq x + 2 \\ y \geq -3x - 3 \\ x \leq 2 \end{cases}$ (c) $\begin{cases} y < x^2 + 2x - 2 \\ 4y^2 - x^2 < 4 \end{cases}$

4. Determine the maximum (and the minimum) values of the linear expression $3x - 4y + 1$ over the given region R.

(a)

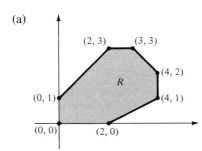

(2, 3)   (3, 3)   (4, 2)   R   (0, 1)   (4, 1)   (0, 0)   (2, 0)

R is defined by   R is defined by

(b) $\begin{cases} x \geq 1 \\ y \geq 0 \\ x + y \leq 3 \\ x + y \geq 2 \end{cases}$ (c) $\begin{cases} 0 \leq y \leq 2 \\ x \geq 1 \\ 3x + 5y \leq 15 \end{cases}$

5. Determine the solution set of the given system.

(a) $\begin{cases} x - 3y - 3z = 0 \\ 3x \quad\quad + z = 11 \\ 2x + y - 2z = 1 \end{cases}$ (b) $\begin{cases} x - 3y + 3z = 12 \\ 3x + 4y - z = 3 \\ 2x + 5y + z = 3 \end{cases}$

6. A total of 6400 tickets were sold to a football game. If an adult's ticket costs $5 and a child's ticket costs $3, determine how many tickets of each kind were sold if the total income from the ticket sales was $28,400.

7. A motorboat can go upstream a certain distance in 5 hours and downstream the same distance in 2 hours. In 7 hours the boat can go upstream 2 miles less than it can go downstream in 3 hours. Determine the speed of the motorboat in still water and determine the rate of the current.

8. The sum of the digits of a three-digit number is 12. The sum of the first and third digits is equal to the second digit. If the second and third digits are interchanged, the new number is 9 less than the original number. Determine the original number.

answers

1. (a) $\{(1, -3)\}$ (b) $\varnothing$ (c) $\{(5, -2)\}$
2. (a) $\{(1, 8), (-3, -4)\}$ (b) $\{(-1, -3), (6, \frac{1}{2})\}$
   (c) $\{(3, 2), (3, -2), (-3, 2), (-3, -2)\}$

3.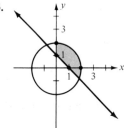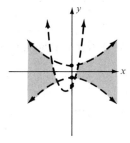

4. (a) max $= 9$, min $= -5$ (b) max $= 10$, min $= -4$ (c) max $= 16$, min $= -4$
5. (a) $\{(3, -1, 2)\}$ (b) $\{(3, -1, 2)\}$
6. 4600 adult's tickets, 1800 children's tickets
7. boat 7 mph, current 3 mph   8. 165

8

matrices and determinants

8.1 Basic Algebraic Properties of Matrices

A **matrix** (plural, **matrices**) is a rectangular array of numbers. The numbers in the array are called the **elements** of the matrix. A matrix is customarily displayed by enclosing the array of numbers inside brackets or parentheses. For example,

$$[-2 \quad 3 \quad 5] \quad \text{and} \quad \begin{pmatrix} -2 & 0 \\ 5 & 7 \end{pmatrix}$$

are matrices. The elements of the first matrix are the numbers -2, 3, and 5.

In a matrix, the horizontal lines of numbers are called **rows,** and the vertical lines of numbers are called **columns.** A matrix that has m rows and n columns is called an **$m \times n$ matrix** (read "m by n" matrix). An $m \times n$ matrix is said to have dimensions $m \times n$. It is important to note that the number of *rows* is given *first* in the previous notation, and the number of *columns* is given *second.* For example,

$$\begin{bmatrix} -1 & 2 & 0 \\ 0 & 5 & 3 \end{bmatrix}, \quad [0 \quad 6], \quad \text{and} \quad \begin{bmatrix} -1 \\ 3 \\ 5 \end{bmatrix}$$

are 2×3, 1×2, and 3×1 matrices, respectively.

Matrices are frequently designated by capital letters. When a matrix is denoted by a capital letter, the elements of the matrix are sometimes denoted by attaching double subscripts to the corresponding lowercase letter, where the first subscript gives the row of the element and the second subscript gives the column of the element. Thus a_{ij} represents the element in the ith row and the $j$ith column of matrix A. For example, in the matrix

$$A = \begin{bmatrix} a_{11} & a_{12} & a_{13} \\ a_{21} & a_{22} & a_{23} \end{bmatrix},$$

a_{12} denotes the element in the first row and the second column of matrix A. We are now ready to begin developing the algebra of matrices.

Definition 8.1   Two matrices, A and B, are said to be **equal,** written $A = B$, if they have the same dimensions and their corresponding elements are equal.

For example,

$$\begin{bmatrix} 2 & 1 \\ 3 & 5 \end{bmatrix} \neq \begin{bmatrix} 2 & 3 \\ 1 & 5 \end{bmatrix},$$

since their corresponding elements are not equal, whereas

$$\begin{bmatrix} 2 & 1 \\ 3 & 5 \end{bmatrix} = \begin{bmatrix} 2 & 1 \\ \sqrt{a} & b \end{bmatrix}$$

provided that $a = 9$ and $b = 5$.

Definition 8.2   The **sum** of two $m \times n$ matrices, A and B, is the $m \times n$ matrix $A + B$ whose elements are the sums of the corresponding elements of A and B.

For example,

$$\begin{bmatrix} 2 & 1 \\ 0 & 5 \end{bmatrix} + \begin{bmatrix} 3 & 1 \\ -1 & 3 \end{bmatrix} = \begin{bmatrix} 2+3 & 1+1 \\ 0+(-1) & 5+3 \end{bmatrix} = \begin{bmatrix} 5 & 2 \\ -1 & 8 \end{bmatrix}.$$

Note that the sum of two matrices is undefined when the matrices have different dimensions.

Definition 8.3   The **negative** of an $m \times n$ matrix A, denoted by $-A$, is the $m \times n$ matrix obtained by replacing each element of A with its negative.

For example,

$$\text{if } A = \begin{bmatrix} 3 & -1 \\ 0 & -6 \end{bmatrix}, \text{ then } -A = \begin{bmatrix} -3 & 1 \\ 0 & 6 \end{bmatrix}.$$

Definition 8.4   The **difference** of two $m \times n$ matrices, A and B, is the $m \times n$ matrix $A - B$ defined by $A - B = A + (-B)$.

For example,

$$\begin{bmatrix} 2 & 1 \\ 0 & 5 \end{bmatrix} - \begin{bmatrix} 3 & 1 \\ -1 & 3 \end{bmatrix} = \begin{bmatrix} 2 & 1 \\ 0 & 5 \end{bmatrix} + \begin{bmatrix} -3 & -1 \\ 1 & -3 \end{bmatrix} = \begin{bmatrix} -1 & 0 \\ 1 & 2 \end{bmatrix}.$$

Definition 8.5 The **product** of a number k times an $m \times n$ matrix A is the $m \times n$ matrix kA obtained by multiplying each element of A by the number k. For example,

$$\text{if } A = \begin{bmatrix} 3 & 0 \\ -2 & 5 \end{bmatrix}, \quad \text{then } 3A = \begin{bmatrix} 3(3) & 3(0) \\ 3(-2) & 3(5) \end{bmatrix} = \begin{bmatrix} 9 & 0 \\ -6 & 15 \end{bmatrix}.$$

Definition 8.6 The **product** of an $m \times n$ matrix A and an $n \times p$ matrix B is the $m \times p$ matrix AB whose element in the ith row and jth column is the sum of the products obtained by multiplying each element of the ith row of A by the corresponding element of the jth column of B.

In subscript notation, if the ith row of A is $a_{i1}a_{i2} \cdots a_{in}$ and the jth column of B is $b_{1j}b_{2j} \cdots b_{nj}$, then the element in the ith row and the jth column of AB is $a_{i1}b_{1j} + a_{i2}b_{2j} + \cdots + a_{in}b_{nj}$. Note that the product AB of the $m \times n$ matrix A and the $n \times p$ matrix B is defined only when the number of columns in A is equal to the number of rows in B. Also note that the product AB will be an $m \times p$ matrix (see Figure 8.1).

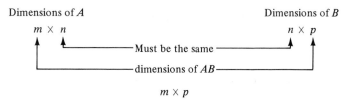

Figure 8.1

EXAMPLE 1

If

$$A = \begin{bmatrix} 1 & 0 \\ 2 & 3 \\ -1 & 2 \end{bmatrix} \quad \text{and} \quad B = \begin{bmatrix} 4 & 5 & 0 \\ 8 & -2 & 1 \end{bmatrix},$$

determine AB and BA.

Solution

$$AB = \begin{bmatrix} 1 & 0 \\ 2 & 3 \\ -1 & 2 \end{bmatrix} \begin{bmatrix} 4 & 5 & 0 \\ 8 & -2 & 1 \end{bmatrix}$$

$$= \begin{bmatrix} (1)(4)+(0)(8) & (1)(5)+(0)(-2) & (1)(0)+(0)(1) \\ (2)(4)+(3)(8) & (2)(5)+(3)(-2) & (2)(0)+(3)(1) \\ (-1)(4)+(2)(8) & (-1)(5)+(2)(-2) & (-1)(0)+(2)(1) \end{bmatrix}$$

$$= \begin{bmatrix} 4 & 5 & 0 \\ 32 & 4 & 3 \\ 12 & -9 & 2 \end{bmatrix}.$$

$$BA = \begin{bmatrix} 4 & 5 & 0 \\ 8 & -2 & 1 \end{bmatrix} \begin{bmatrix} 1 & 0 \\ 2 & 3 \\ -1 & 2 \end{bmatrix}$$

$$= \begin{bmatrix} (4)(1)+(5)(2)+(0)(-1) & (4)(0)+(5)(3)+(0)(2) \\ (8)(1)+(-2)(2)+(1)(-1) & (8)(0)+(-2)(3)+(1)(2) \end{bmatrix}$$

$$= \begin{bmatrix} 14 & 15 \\ 3 & -4 \end{bmatrix}. \qquad ■$$

Note that this example shows that matrix multiplication is not commutative.

EXAMPLE 2

If

$$A = \begin{bmatrix} 1 & 2 & 3 \\ 4 & 5 & 6 \end{bmatrix} \quad \text{and} \quad B = \begin{bmatrix} 1 & 1 & 1 & 0 \\ 0 & 0 & 0 & 1 \end{bmatrix},$$

determine AB.

Solution Since the number of columns in A, namely 3, is not equal to the number of rows in B, namely 2, the product AB is undefined.   ■

Problems 8.1

In problems 1–6, determine the dimensions of the given matrix.

1. $\begin{bmatrix} 2 & -1 \\ 3 & 0 \end{bmatrix}$ 2. $\begin{bmatrix} 3 \\ -2 \end{bmatrix}$ 3. $\begin{bmatrix} 2 & -1 & 2 \\ 5 & 0 & 2 \end{bmatrix}$

4. $[4 \quad 5 \quad 0]$ 5. $\begin{bmatrix} 1 & 2 \\ 0 & 3 \\ 7 & 0 \end{bmatrix}$ 6. $\begin{bmatrix} 1 & 2 & 3 \\ 4 & 5 & 6 \\ 7 & 8 & 9 \end{bmatrix}$

7. Is $[1 \quad 2] = \begin{bmatrix} 1 \\ 2 \end{bmatrix}$? Explain.

8. Under what conditions (if any) is $\begin{bmatrix} x & x+y \\ 3 & 4 \end{bmatrix} = \begin{bmatrix} 3 & 4 \\ 3 & 4 \end{bmatrix}$?

9. Under what conditions (if any) is $\begin{bmatrix} x & x+y \\ 3 & 4 \end{bmatrix} = \begin{bmatrix} 3 & 4 \\ 3 & 5 \end{bmatrix}$?

In problems 10–18, perform the indicated operations.

10. $\begin{bmatrix} 2 \\ 1 \\ 3 \end{bmatrix} + \begin{bmatrix} 5 \\ -1 \\ 3 \end{bmatrix}$

11. $\begin{bmatrix} 2 & 1 & 2 \\ 3 & 5 & -1 \end{bmatrix} + \begin{bmatrix} 6 & 1 & 0 \\ 5 & -3 & 2 \end{bmatrix}$

12. $\begin{bmatrix} 2 & 6 \\ 1 & -3 \end{bmatrix} + \begin{bmatrix} 1 & 5 \\ -1 & 3 \end{bmatrix}$

13. $\begin{bmatrix} -1 & 2 \\ -3 & 4 \\ -5 & 6 \end{bmatrix} - \begin{bmatrix} 5 & 2 \\ 0 & 0 \\ 2 & 5 \end{bmatrix}$

14. $\begin{bmatrix} 2 & -4 & 5 \\ 3 & 0 & 5 \end{bmatrix} - \begin{bmatrix} 0 & 1 & 4 \\ 7 & 4 & 2 \end{bmatrix}$

15. $\begin{bmatrix} 3 \\ 1 \\ 9 \end{bmatrix} - \begin{bmatrix} -2 \\ -2 \\ 5 \end{bmatrix}$

16. $\begin{bmatrix} 1 & 2 & 0 \\ 3 & -1 & 0 \end{bmatrix} + 2\begin{bmatrix} 1 & 5 & 1 \\ -1 & 2 & 0 \end{bmatrix} - 3\begin{bmatrix} 2 & -1 & 1 \\ 1 & -1 & 2 \end{bmatrix}$

17. $[2 \quad 1 \quad 0 \quad 5] - 3[1 \quad 4 \quad 0 \quad -1] + 4[2 \quad 4 \quad 1 \quad -1]$

18. $3\begin{bmatrix} 1 & 2 & 3 \\ 4 & 5 & 6 \\ 7 & 8 & 9 \end{bmatrix} - 2\begin{bmatrix} 1 & 0 & 1 \\ 0 & 1 & 0 \\ 1 & 0 & 1 \end{bmatrix} - \begin{bmatrix} 4 & 5 & 6 \\ 4 & 5 & 6 \\ 4 & 5 & 6 \end{bmatrix}$

In problems 19–30, perform the indicated multiplications when possible.

19. $[2 \quad 2 \quad 5]\begin{bmatrix} 3 \\ -1 \\ 0 \end{bmatrix}$

20. $\begin{bmatrix} 3 \\ -1 \\ 0 \\ 1 \end{bmatrix}[2 \quad -3]$

21. $\begin{bmatrix} -4 & 2 \\ 0 & 6 \end{bmatrix}\begin{bmatrix} -3 & 3 \\ 8 & 7 \end{bmatrix}$

22. $\begin{bmatrix} 1 & 2 \\ 3 & 4 \end{bmatrix}\begin{bmatrix} 1 \\ 2 \\ 1 \end{bmatrix}$

23. $\begin{bmatrix} 1 \\ 2 \end{bmatrix}\begin{bmatrix} 1 & 3 & 1 \\ 0 & 1 & 5 \end{bmatrix}$

24. $\begin{bmatrix} 1 \\ 1 \\ 5 \end{bmatrix}\begin{bmatrix} 1 & 2 \\ 5 & 1 \end{bmatrix}$

25. $\begin{bmatrix} -1 & 0 \\ 3 & -2 \end{bmatrix}\begin{bmatrix} -2 & 1 \\ 1 & 2 \end{bmatrix}$

26. $\begin{bmatrix} 1 & 1 & 5 \\ 4 & -1 & 3 \end{bmatrix}\begin{bmatrix} 2 \\ -1 \\ 3 \end{bmatrix}$

27. $\begin{bmatrix} 0 & 4 \\ 5 & 8 \\ 5 & 8 \end{bmatrix}\begin{bmatrix} 6 & 5 \\ 3 & 4 \end{bmatrix}$

28. $\begin{bmatrix} 1 & 2 & 3 \\ 4 & 0 & -1 \end{bmatrix}\begin{bmatrix} -1 & 0 \\ 1 & 3 \\ 2 & 2 \end{bmatrix}$

29. $\begin{bmatrix} 1 & 0 & 1 \\ 2 & -1 & 2 \\ 1 & 2 & 3 \end{bmatrix}\begin{bmatrix} 0 & 0 & 5 \\ 4 & 3 & -2 \\ 1 & 1 & -1 \end{bmatrix}$

30. $\begin{bmatrix} 3 & 1 & 2 \\ 1 & 0 & 3 \\ 4 & 1 & -1 \end{bmatrix}\begin{bmatrix} 2 & 1 & 0 \\ 1 & -2 & 1 \\ 0 & 1 & 2 \end{bmatrix}$

31. (a) If $A = \begin{bmatrix} 1 & 2 \\ 3 & 2 \end{bmatrix}$ and $B = \begin{bmatrix} 1 & 2 \\ -1 & 3 \end{bmatrix}$, show that $A + B = B + A$.

    (b) Prove that $A + B = B + A$ for all 2×2 matrices A and B.

32. Use the matrices $A = \begin{bmatrix} 1 & 2 \\ 3 & 2 \end{bmatrix}$ and $B = \begin{bmatrix} 1 & 2 \\ -1 & 3 \end{bmatrix}$ to show that $AB = BA$ fails to be true for all 2×2 matrices.

33. (a) If $A = \begin{bmatrix} 1 & 2 \\ 3 & 1 \end{bmatrix}$, $B = \begin{bmatrix} 1 & 2 \\ -1 & 3 \end{bmatrix}$, and $C = \begin{bmatrix} 1 & 3 \\ 3 & 1 \end{bmatrix}$, show that $A + (B + C) = (A + B) + C$.

   (b) Prove that $A + (B + C) = (A + B) + C$ for all 2×2 matrices A, B, and C.

34. (a) If $A = \begin{bmatrix} 1 & 2 \\ 3 & 1 \end{bmatrix}$, $B = \begin{bmatrix} 1 & 2 \\ -1 & 3 \end{bmatrix}$, and $C = \begin{bmatrix} 1 & 3 \\ 3 & 1 \end{bmatrix}$, show that $A(BC) = (AB)C$.

   (b) Prove that $A(BC) = (AB)C$ for all 2×2 matrices A, B, and C.

35. (a) If $A = \begin{bmatrix} 1 & 2 \\ 3 & 1 \end{bmatrix}$, $B = \begin{bmatrix} 1 & 2 \\ -1 & 3 \end{bmatrix}$, and $C = \begin{bmatrix} 1 & 3 \\ 3 & 1 \end{bmatrix}$, show that $A(B + C) = AB + AC$.

   (b) Prove that $A(B + C) = AB + AC$ for all 2×2 matrices A, B, and C.

Answers 8.1

1. 2×2

2. 2×1

4. 1×3

5. 3×2

7. No

8. $x = 3$, $y = 1$

10. $\begin{bmatrix} 7 \\ 0 \\ 6 \end{bmatrix}$

11. $\begin{bmatrix} 8 & 2 & 2 \\ 8 & 2 & 1 \end{bmatrix}$

13. $\begin{bmatrix} -6 & 0 \\ -3 & 4 \\ -7 & 1 \end{bmatrix}$

14. $\begin{bmatrix} 2 & -5 & 1 \\ -4 & -4 & 3 \end{bmatrix}$

16. $\begin{bmatrix} -3 & 15 & -1 \\ -2 & 6 & -6 \end{bmatrix}$

17. $[7 \quad 5 \quad 4 \quad 4]$

19. $[4]$

20. $\begin{bmatrix} 6 & -9 \\ -2 & 3 \\ 0 & 0 \\ 2 & -3 \end{bmatrix}$

22. product undefined

23. product undefined

25. $\begin{bmatrix} 2 & -1 \\ -8 & -1 \end{bmatrix}$

26. $\begin{bmatrix} 16 \\ 18 \end{bmatrix}$

28. $\begin{bmatrix} 7 & 12 \\ -6 & -2 \end{bmatrix}$

29. $\begin{bmatrix} 1 & 1 & 4 \\ -2 & -1 & 10 \\ 11 & 9 & -2 \end{bmatrix}$

8.2 Solving Linear Systems Using Matrices

Matrices can be used as a convenient way of solving systems of linear equations. One way of doing this is to use the concept of row-equivalent matrices.

Definition 8.7 Two matrices, A and B, are said to be **row-equivalent matrices**, written $A \sim B$, if each of the matrices can be obtained from the other matrix by performing a finite number of the following *row operations*:

1. Any two rows of a matrix may be interchanged.
2. Any row of a matrix may be replaced with a nonzero multiple of that row.
3. Any given row of a matrix may be replaced with a new row formed by adding the elements of the given row to k times the elements of any other row.

EXAMPLE 1

$A = \begin{bmatrix} 2 & 1 \\ 3 & 5 \end{bmatrix} \sim \begin{bmatrix} 3 & 5 \\ 2 & 1 \end{bmatrix} = B$, since the first and second rows of matrix A
have been interchanged to give matrix B.

EXAMPLE 2

$A = \begin{bmatrix} 1 & 5 & 6 \\ 3 & 2 & 0 \end{bmatrix} \sim \begin{bmatrix} 1 & 5 & 6 \\ 9 & 6 & 0 \end{bmatrix} = B$, since the second row of matrix A has
been replaced with 3 times that row to give matrix B.

EXAMPLE 3

$A = \begin{bmatrix} -1 & 2 & 0 \\ 1 & 2 & 3 \\ 2 & 3 & 2 \end{bmatrix} \sim \begin{bmatrix} -1 & 2 & 0 \\ 1 & 2 & 3 \\ 0 & 7 & 2 \end{bmatrix} = B$, since the third row of matrix A has
been replaced with a new row formed by adding the given row (the third row
of A) to 2 times the first row of A:

$$
\begin{array}{rrrl}
 & 2 & 3 & 2 \quad \text{(third row of } A) \\
\text{(add)} & -2 & 4 & 0 \quad \text{(2 times the first row of } A) \\
\hline
 & 0 & 7 & 2 \quad \text{(third row of } B) \\
\end{array}
$$

to give matrix B.

Note that the row operations listed in Definition 8.7 correspond to the
following operations, which may be performed on a system of linear equations to obtain an equivalent system:

1. Any two equations of the system may be interchanged.
2. Any equation of a system may be replaced with a nonzero multiple
   of the equation.
3. Any given equation of a system may be replaced with a new equation
   formed by adding the given equation to k times any other equation in
   the system.

In a linear system of the form

$$
\begin{cases} a_1 x + b_1 y = c_1 \\ a_2 x + b_2 y = c_2, \end{cases} \tag{8-1}
$$

the matrices

$$
\begin{bmatrix} a_1 & b_1 \\ a_2 & b_2 \end{bmatrix} \quad \text{and} \quad \begin{bmatrix} a_1 & b_1 & c_1 \\ a_2 & b_2 & c_2 \end{bmatrix}
$$

are called the **coefficient matrix** of the system and the **augmented matrix** of
the system, respectively. A similar definition can be given for a system of n
linear equations containing n variables. Note that the augmented matrix
represents system $(8-1)$.

In light of the comments that follow Example 3, it follows that the steps required to replace system (8-1) with an equivalent system of the form

$$\begin{cases} x & = a \\ & y = b \end{cases} \tag{8-2}$$

are the same as the steps required to replace the augmented matrix of system (8-1) with a row-equivalent matrix of the form

$$\begin{bmatrix} 1 & 0 & a \\ 0 & 1 & b \end{bmatrix}. \tag{8-3}$$

Thus we can solve system (8-1) by first replacing the systems-augmented matrix with a row-equivalent matrix of the form of matrix (8-3). Then, rewriting matrix (8-3) as the linear system (8-2), it is easy to see that (a, b) is the only solution of system (8-2) and hence is the only solution of the equivalent system (8-1). The method just described for solving a system of linear equations is known as the **Gaussian method.**

EXAMPLE 4

Use the Gaussian method to solve

$$\begin{cases} x - 3y = 5 \\ 4x + 5y = 3. \end{cases}$$

Solution To solve the given system, we must first transform the augmented matrix $\begin{bmatrix} 1 & -3 & 5 \\ 4 & 5 & 3 \end{bmatrix}$ into a row-equivalent matrix of the form $\begin{bmatrix} 1 & 0 & a \\ 0 & 1 & b \end{bmatrix}$. This is done in the following sequence of row-equivalent matrices. Each matrix in the sequence is obtained from the preceding matrix by performing the indicated operations on the corresponding rows of the previous matrix.

$$\begin{bmatrix} 1 & -3 & 5 \\ 4 & 5 & 3 \end{bmatrix}$$
$$\sim \begin{bmatrix} 1 & -3 & 5 \\ 0 & 17 & -17 \end{bmatrix} \longleftarrow (\text{row } 2) + (-4)(\text{row } 1)$$
$$\sim \begin{bmatrix} 1 & -3 & 5 \\ 0 & 1 & -1 \end{bmatrix} \longleftarrow (\tfrac{1}{17})(\text{row } 2)$$
$$\sim \begin{bmatrix} 1 & 0 & 2 \\ 0 & 1 & -1 \end{bmatrix} \longleftarrow (\text{row } 1) + (3)(\text{row } 2)$$

Rewriting the last equation as a linear system, we have

$$\begin{cases} x & = 2 \\ & y = -1. \end{cases}$$

Since the last system is equivalent to the given system, it follows that the solution of the given system is $(2, -1)$. ∎

EXAMPLE 5

Use the Gaussian method to solve

$$\begin{cases} x - y + 5z = 11 \\ 2x \quad\quad - z = 7 \\ 3x + y + z = 11. \end{cases}$$

Solution To solve the given system, we must transform the aug-
mented matrix $\begin{bmatrix} 1 & -1 & 5 & 11 \\ 2 & 0 & -1 & 7 \\ 3 & 1 & 1 & 11 \end{bmatrix}$ into a row-equivalent matrix of the form

$\begin{bmatrix} 1 & 0 & 0 & a \\ 0 & 1 & 0 & b \\ 0 & 0 & 1 & c \end{bmatrix}$. This is done in the following sequence of row-equivalent

matrices. Each matrix in the sequence is obtained from the preceding matrix
by performing the indicated operations on the corresponding rows of the
previous matrix.

$$\begin{bmatrix} 1 & -1 & 5 & 11 \\ 2 & 0 & -1 & 7 \\ 3 & 1 & 1 & 11 \end{bmatrix}$$

$$\sim \begin{bmatrix} 1 & -1 & 5 & 11 \\ 0 & 2 & -11 & -15 \\ 0 & 4 & -14 & -22 \end{bmatrix} \begin{matrix} \\ \longleftarrow (\text{row } 2) + (-2)(\text{row } 1) \\ \longleftarrow (\text{row } 3) + (-3)(\text{row } 1) \end{matrix}$$

$$\sim \begin{bmatrix} 1 & -1 & 5 & 11 \\ 0 & 1 & -\frac{11}{2} & -\frac{15}{2} \\ 0 & 4 & -14 & -22 \end{bmatrix} \begin{matrix} \\ \longleftarrow (\tfrac{1}{2})(\text{row } 2) \\ \\ \end{matrix}$$

$$\sim \begin{bmatrix} 1 & 0 & -\frac{1}{2} & \frac{7}{2} \\ 0 & 1 & -\frac{11}{2} & -\frac{15}{2} \\ 0 & 0 & 8 & 8 \end{bmatrix} \begin{matrix} \longleftarrow (\text{row } 1) + (1)(\text{row } 2) \\ \\ \longleftarrow (\text{row } 3) + (-4)(\text{row } 2) \end{matrix}$$

$$\sim \begin{bmatrix} 1 & 0 & -\frac{1}{2} & \frac{7}{2} \\ 0 & 1 & -\frac{11}{2} & -\frac{15}{2} \\ 0 & 0 & 1 & 1 \end{bmatrix} \begin{matrix} \\ \\ \longleftarrow (\tfrac{1}{8})(\text{row } 3) \end{matrix}$$

$$\sim \begin{bmatrix} 1 & 0 & 0 & 4 \\ 0 & 1 & 0 & -2 \\ 0 & 0 & 1 & 1 \end{bmatrix} \begin{matrix} \longleftarrow (\text{row } 1) + (\tfrac{1}{2})(\text{row } 3) \\ \longleftarrow (\text{row } 2) + (\tfrac{11}{2})(\text{row } 3) \\ \\ \end{matrix}$$

Rewriting the last matrix as a linear system, we get

$$\begin{cases} x \quad\quad = 4 \\ \quad y \quad = -2 \\ \quad\quad z = 1. \end{cases}$$

Since the last system is equivalent to the given system, it follows that the
solution of the given system is $(4, -2, 1)$. ∎

Problems 8.2

In problems 1–21, use the Gaussian method to determine the solution set of the given system.

1. $\begin{cases} x-2y= 7 \\ 4x+3y=-5 \end{cases}$

2. $\begin{cases} x-5y= 23 \\ 3x+2y=-16 \end{cases}$

3. $\begin{cases} 3x+5y= 9 \\ x-4y=-14 \end{cases}$

4. $\begin{cases} 2x-5y=-7 \\ 3x+4y= 24 \end{cases}$

5. $\begin{cases} 3x+4y= 6 \\ 5x-2y=-16 \end{cases}$

6. $\begin{cases} 2x+3y= 19 \\ 5x-4y= 13 \end{cases}$

7. $\begin{cases} x- y=-6 \\ 3x+2y= 17 \end{cases}$

8. $\begin{cases} 2x-3y= 3 \\ 5x+ y= 33 \end{cases}$

9. $\begin{cases} x+3y=-4 \\ 4x- y= 23 \end{cases}$

10. $\begin{cases} x+ y- z= 1 \\ 2y-3z=-6 \\ 3x- y+2z= 11 \end{cases}$

11. $\begin{cases} x+3y+ z= 15 \\ 2x-3y =-1 \\ 5y-3z= 9 \end{cases}$

12. $\begin{cases} 2y+ z= 7 \\ x- y-5z=-3 \\ 3x+ y-3z= 15 \end{cases}$

13. $\begin{cases} x- y- z= 6 \\ 3x- y- z= 10 \\ 2x+4y-3z= 9 \end{cases}$

14. $\begin{cases} x+3y-2z= 3 \\ 2x- y-6z= 15 \\ 4x-3y-3z= 22 \end{cases}$

15. $\begin{cases} x+2y- z= 3 \\ 3x+ y+2z= 4 \\ 2x+4y-3z= 4 \end{cases}$

16. $\begin{cases} 3x+ y-2z= 9 \\ 4x+2y+3z= 5 \\ x-2y+ z= 6 \end{cases}$

17. $\begin{cases} 2x-3y+2z= 3 \\ x+5y+ z= 8 \\ 3x - z=-11 \end{cases}$

18. $\begin{cases} 5x+2y+ z= 12 \\ x- y+2z= 2 \\ x+3y- z= 1 \end{cases}$

19. $\begin{cases} x+4y+ z- w=4 \\ x- y+3z-2w=0 \\ 2x -3z+2w=2 \\ 3x+2y - w=2 \end{cases}$

20. $\begin{cases} x+ y+ z+w=1 \\ x- y- z-w=1 \\ 2x-3y-2z-w=1 \\ 4x+ y +w=1 \end{cases}$

21. $\begin{cases} x- y+ z- w= 1 \\ x+ y-2z+3w= 5 \\ 2x - z+5w= 3 \\ 3x+ y -2w= 12 \end{cases}$

Answers 8.2

1. $(1, -3)$	2. $(-2, -5)$	4. $(4, 3)$	5. $(-2, 3)$
7. $(1, 7)$	8. $(6, 3)$	10. $(2, 3, 4)$	11. $(4, 3, 2)$
13. $(2, -1, -3)$	14. $(4, -1, -1)$	16. $(3, -2, -1)$	17. $(-2, 1, 5)$
19. $(1, 1, 2, 3)$	20. $(1, -1, 3 -2)$		

8.3 Determinants

A matrix that has the same number or rows and columns is called a **square matrix.** Associated with each such matrix A is a number that is referred to as the *determinant of A*. This number is denoted by $\delta(A)$ (read "the determinant of A"). We begin by defining the determinant of a 2×2 matrix.

Definition 8.8 The **determinant** of the 2×2 matrix $A = \begin{bmatrix} a_{11} & a_{12} \\ a_{21} & a_{22} \end{bmatrix}$, denoted by $\delta(A)$ or $\begin{vmatrix} a_{11} & a_{12} \\ a_{21} & a_{22} \end{vmatrix}$, is the number $a_{11}a_{22} - a_{12}a_{21}$.

EXAMPLE 1

If $A = \begin{bmatrix} 1 & 2 \\ 3 & 5 \end{bmatrix}$, then $\delta(A) = \begin{vmatrix} 1 & 2 \\ 3 & 5 \end{vmatrix} = (1)(5) - (2)(3) = -1$.

Before we define the determinant of a 3×3 matrix, we must first consider some preliminary concepts.

Definition 8.9 The **minor** of an element a_{ij} of a matrix A, denoted by M_{ij}, is the determinant of the matrix obtained by deleting the row and the column containing a_{ij}.

EXAMPLE 2

The minor M_{23} of the element a_{23} of the matrix

$$A = \begin{bmatrix} a_{11} & a_{12} & a_{13} \\ a_{21} & a_{22} & a_{23} \\ a_{31} & a_{32} & a_{33} \end{bmatrix}$$

is the determinant of the 2×2 matrix $\begin{bmatrix} a_{11} & a_{12} \\ a_{31} & a_{32} \end{bmatrix}$ obtained by striking out the row and column containing a_{23}. Thus

$$M_{23} = \begin{vmatrix} a_{11} & a_{12} \\ a_{31} & a_{32} \end{vmatrix} = a_{11}a_{32} - a_{12}a_{31}.$$

Other minors are as follows:

element a_{ij} of A	minor M_{ij} of the element a_{ij}
a_{21}	$M_{21} = \begin{vmatrix} a_{12} & a_{13} \\ a_{32} & a_{33} \end{vmatrix} = a_{12}a_{33} - a_{13}a_{32}$
a_{33}	$M_{33} = \begin{vmatrix} a_{11} & a_{12} \\ a_{21} & a_{22} \end{vmatrix} = a_{11}a_{22} - a_{12}a_{21}$.

EXERCISE 1

Determine the minor of the element whose value is 7 (and of the element whose value is 5) in the matrix

$$A = \begin{bmatrix} 0 & 7 & 1 \\ -1 & 0 & 3 \\ 5 & 3 & 3 \end{bmatrix}.$$

Answer Minor of $7 = \begin{vmatrix} -1 & 3 \\ 5 & 3 \end{vmatrix} = -18$, minor of $5 = \begin{vmatrix} 7 & 1 \\ 0 & 3 \end{vmatrix} = 21.$

Definition 8.10 The **cofactor** of an element a_{ij} of a matrix A, denoted by A_{ij}, is defined as $A_{ij} = (-1)^{i+j} M_{ij}$, where M_{ij} is the minor of the element a_{ij}.

Note that $A_{ij} = M_{ij}$ when $i + j$ is even, and $A_{ij} = -M_{ij}$ when $i + j$ is odd.

EXAMPLE 3

The cofactors of certain elements of the matrix

$$A = \begin{bmatrix} a_{11} & a_{12} & a_{13} \\ a_{21} & a_{22} & a_{23} \\ a_{31} & a_{32} & a_{33} \end{bmatrix}$$

are as follows:

element a_{ij} of A	cofactor A_{ij} of the element a_{ij}	
a_{21}	$A_{21} = -M_{21} = -\begin{vmatrix} a_{12} & a_{13} \\ a_{32} & a_{33} \end{vmatrix}$	since $2 + 1$ is odd
a_{33}	$A_{33} = M_{33} = \begin{vmatrix} a_{11} & a_{12} \\ a_{21} & a_{22} \end{vmatrix}$	since $3 + 3$ is even.

EXERCISE 2

Determine the cofactor of the element whose value is 7 (and of the element whose value is 5) in the matrix

$$A = \begin{bmatrix} 0 & 7 & 1 \\ -1 & 0 & 3 \\ 5 & 3 & 3 \end{bmatrix}.$$

Answer Cofactor of $7 = -\begin{vmatrix} -1 & 3 \\ 5 & 3 \end{vmatrix} = 18$, cofactor of $5 = +\begin{vmatrix} 7 & 1 \\ 0 & 3 \end{vmatrix} = 21.$

With the previous definition in mind, we are now prepared to define the determinant of a 3×3 matrix.

Definition 8.11 The **determinant** of the 3×3 matrix

$$A = \begin{bmatrix} a_{11} & a_{12} & a_{13} \\ a_{21} & a_{22} & a_{23} \\ a_{31} & a_{32} & a_{33} \end{bmatrix},$$

denoted by $\delta(A)$ or $\begin{vmatrix} a_{11} & a_{12} & a_{13} \\ a_{21} & a_{22} & a_{23} \\ a_{31} & a_{32} & a_{33} \end{vmatrix}$, is the sum of the products obtained by

multiplying each element of a particular row (or column) of the matrix A by its corresponding cofactor.

At first it might appear that Definition 8.11 would yield different values for the determinant of a 3×3 matrix A depending upon the row or column we expand about. Fortunately, however, this is not the case. In problems 1–6 you will be asked to prove this fact by showing that the value of $\delta(A)$ is

$$(a_{11}a_{22}a_{33} + a_{12}a_{23}a_{31} + a_{13}a_{32}a_{21}) - (a_{31}a_{13}a_{22} + a_{32}a_{23}a_{11} + a_{33}a_{21}a_{12})$$

for $A = \begin{bmatrix} a_{11} & a_{12} & a_{13} \\ a_{21} & a_{22} & a_{23} \\ a_{31} & a_{32} & a_{33} \end{bmatrix}$, regardless of the row or column we expand about.

EXAMPLE 4

If

$$A = \begin{bmatrix} 0 & 1 & 5 \\ 2 & -1 & 3 \\ 3 & 2 & 5 \end{bmatrix},$$

determine $\delta(A)$ by using the first column, and then determine $\delta(A)$ by using the second row.

Solution using the first column Expanding about the first column, Definition 8.11 gives

$$\begin{aligned} \delta(A) &= a_{11}A_{11} + a_{21}A_{21} + a_{31}A_{31} \\ &= a_{11}(-1)^{1+1}M_{11} + a_{21}(-1)^{2+1}M_{21} + a_{31}(-1)^{3+1}M_{31} \\ &= (0)(-1)^2 \begin{vmatrix} -1 & 3 \\ 2 & 5 \end{vmatrix} + (2)(-1)^3 \begin{vmatrix} 1 & 5 \\ 2 & 5 \end{vmatrix} + (3)(-1)^4 \begin{vmatrix} 1 & 5 \\ -1 & 3 \end{vmatrix} \\ &= (0)(1)(-11) + (2)(-1)(-5) + (3)(1)(8) = 34. \end{aligned}$$

Solution using the second row Expanding about the second row,

Definition 8.11 gives

$$\begin{aligned}
\delta(A) &= a_{21}A_{21} + a_{22}A_{22} + a_{23}A_{23} \\
&= a_{21}(-1)^{2+1}M_{21} + a_{22}(-1)^{2+2}M_{22} + a_{23}(-1)^{2+3}M_{23} \\
&= (2)(-1)^3 \begin{vmatrix} 1 & 5 \\ 2 & 5 \end{vmatrix} + (-1)(-1)^4 \begin{vmatrix} 0 & 5 \\ 3 & 5 \end{vmatrix} + (3)(-1)^5 \begin{vmatrix} 0 & 1 \\ 3 & 2 \end{vmatrix} \\
&= (2)(-1)(-5) + (-1)(1)(-15) + (3)(-1)(-3) = 34.
\end{aligned}$$
∎

EXERCISE 3

Determine $\delta(A)$ for the matrix A in Example 4 by expanding about the third row.

Answer   Once again the answer is the same as that obtained in Example 4.

The determinant of a 4×4 matrix, and in general an $n \times n$ matrix, is defined in the same manner as the determinant of a 3×3 matrix. In the case of a 4×4 matrix, the minors are the determinants of certain 3×3 matrices which we now know how to calculate.

EXAMPLE 5

If $A = \begin{bmatrix} 0 & 1 & 2 & 5 \\ 2 & -1 & 2 & 3 \\ 3 & 2 & 1 & 5 \\ 1 & 0 & 4 & 0 \end{bmatrix}$, determine $\delta(A)$ by expanding about the most

suitable row or column.

Solution   If we expand about the row or column containing the *most zeros* as elements, we will have to evaluate the determinants of fewer 3×3 matrices. For example, if we expand about row four, it will only be necessary to evaluate the determinants of two 3×3 matrices. The determinants of the other two 3×3 matrices will not matter, since we are multiplying each of them by zero. Therefore, we expand about row four. Doing this we get

$$\begin{aligned}
\delta(A) &= a_{41}A_{41} + a_{42}A_{42} + a_{43}A_{43} + a_{44}A_{44} \\
&= -a_{41}M_{41} + a_{42}M_{42} - a_{43}M_{43} + a_{44}M_{44} \\
&= -(1) \begin{vmatrix} 1 & 2 & 5 \\ -1 & 2 & 3 \\ 2 & 1 & 5 \end{vmatrix} + (0) \begin{vmatrix} 0 & 2 & 5 \\ 2 & 2 & 3 \\ 3 & 1 & 5 \end{vmatrix} - (4) \begin{vmatrix} 0 & 1 & 5 \\ 2 & -1 & 3 \\ 3 & 2 & 5 \end{vmatrix} + (0) \begin{vmatrix} 0 & 1 & 2 \\ 2 & -1 & 2 \\ 3 & 2 & 1 \end{vmatrix}.
\end{aligned}$$

In general, at this point we would have to evaluate the determinants of the four 3×3 matrices indicated above. However, since two of them are multiplied by zero, their is no need to evaluate these determinants. Evaluating the other two determinants using Definition 8.11, we find that

$$\begin{vmatrix} 1 & 2 & 5 \\ -1 & 2 & 3 \\ 2 & 1 & 5 \end{vmatrix} = 4 \quad \text{and} \quad \begin{vmatrix} 0 & 1 & 5 \\ 2 & -1 & 3 \\ 3 & 2 & 5 \end{vmatrix} = 34.$$

Returning to our original problem, it follows that

$$\delta(A) = -(1)(4) + (0)(?) - (4)(34) + (0)(?) = -140. \qquad \blacksquare$$

Problems 8.3

In problems 1–6, calculate the determinant of

$$A = \begin{bmatrix} a_{11} & a_{12} & a_{13} \\ a_{21} & a_{22} & a_{23} \\ a_{31} & a_{32} & a_{33} \end{bmatrix}$$

by expanding about the indicated row or column, and show that the resulting value is

$$(a_{11}a_{22}a_{33} + a_{12}a_{23}a_{31} + a_{13}a_{32}a_{21}) - (a_{31}a_{13}a_{22} + a_{32}a_{23}a_{11} + a_{33}a_{12}a_{21}).$$

1. the first row   **2.** the second row   **3.** the third row
4. the first column   **5.** the second column   **6.** the third column

In problems 7–24, evaluate the determinant of the given matrix.

7. $\begin{bmatrix} 1 & 2 \\ 4 & 2 \end{bmatrix}$ **8.** $\begin{bmatrix} 1 & 3 \\ -2 & 5 \end{bmatrix}$ **9.** $\begin{bmatrix} 3 & -2 \\ 1 & -5 \end{bmatrix}$

10. $\begin{bmatrix} -1 & 4 \\ -3 & 7 \end{bmatrix}$ **11.** $\begin{bmatrix} 5 & -3 \\ -2 & -1 \end{bmatrix}$ **12.** $\begin{bmatrix} 7 & -3 \\ -2 & 1 \end{bmatrix}$

13. $\begin{bmatrix} 2 & 1 & 0 \\ 0 & 1 & 3 \\ -1 & 1 & -2 \end{bmatrix}$ **14.** $\begin{bmatrix} 1 & 2 & 4 \\ 0 & -1 & 1 \\ 3 & 2 & 0 \end{bmatrix}$ **15.** $\begin{bmatrix} 1 & 2 & 3 \\ 0 & 5 & 1 \\ -2 & 0 & 1 \end{bmatrix}$

16. $\begin{bmatrix} 1 & 0 & 2 \\ 0 & 3 & 0 \\ -1 & 1 & 2 \end{bmatrix}$ **17.** $\begin{bmatrix} 0 & 1 & 2 \\ 3 & 0 & 0 \\ -1 & 2 & 1 \end{bmatrix}$ **18.** $\begin{bmatrix} 1 & 2 & 3 \\ -1 & 0 & 1 \\ 0 & 0 & 2 \end{bmatrix}$

19. $\begin{bmatrix} 1 & 2 & 1 \\ 2 & 1 & 2 \\ 1 & 2 & 1 \end{bmatrix}$ **20.** $\begin{bmatrix} 1 & 1 & 3 \\ -1 & 2 & 3 \\ 2 & 1 & -1 \end{bmatrix}$ **21.** $\begin{bmatrix} 1 & 2 & 3 \\ 4 & 5 & 6 \\ 7 & 8 & 9 \end{bmatrix}$

22. $\begin{bmatrix} 1 & 2 & 0 & 1 \\ -1 & 1 & 1 & 1 \\ 0 & 0 & 1 & -2 \\ 1 & 1 & 1 & 0 \end{bmatrix}$ **23.** $\begin{bmatrix} 1 & 2 & 0 & 3 \\ -1 & 1 & 0 & 1 \\ 1 & 0 & 1 & 1 \\ 2 & 1 & 1 & 0 \end{bmatrix}$ **24.** $\begin{bmatrix} 1 & 0 & 1 & 2 \\ 0 & 0 & 1 & -1 \\ 3 & 1 & 0 & 2 \\ 1 & 0 & 1 & 0 \end{bmatrix}$

Answers 8.3

7. −6   **8.** 11   **10.** 5   **11.** −11   **13.** −13   **14.** 16
16. 12   **17.** 9   **19.** 0   **20.** −15   **22.** 7   **23.** −8

8.4 Properties of Determinants

In the previous section, we found that we must evaluate the determinants of four 3×3 matrices in order to evaluate the determinant of a 4×4 matrix. Since we must evaluate the determinants of three 2×2 matrices to evaluate the determinant of each of the four 3×3 matrices, it follows that we must evaluate the determinants of twelve 2×2 matrices to evaluate the determinant of a 4×4 matrix. Using similar reasoning, we find that to evaluate the determinant of a 5×5 matrix, we must eventually evaluate the determinant of sixty 2×2 matrices. Since the required calculations become longer and longer as the dimensions of the matrix increase, it will be beneficial to investigate certain properties of determinants that can be used to shorten the calculations involved in evaluating the determinant of a matrix. We do this in the following three theorems. We prove these theorems for 3×3 matrices. In each case, the proof is similar for $n \times n$ matrices.

Theorem 8.1   If two rows (or columns) of a square matrix A are identical, then $\delta(A) = 0$.

Proof of 3×3 matrices   Without loss of generality, suppose that the first and second columns of A are identical. Hence matrix A has the form

$$A = \begin{bmatrix} a_{11} & a_{11} & a_{13} \\ a_{21} & a_{21} & a_{23} \\ a_{31} & a_{31} & a_{33} \end{bmatrix}.$$

Expanding about the third column using Definition 8.11, we get

$$\delta(A) = a_{13} \begin{vmatrix} a_{21} & a_{21} \\ a_{31} & a_{31} \end{vmatrix} - a_{23} \begin{vmatrix} a_{11} & a_{11} \\ a_{31} & a_{31} \end{vmatrix} + a_{33} \begin{vmatrix} a_{11} & a_{11} \\ a_{21} & a_{21} \end{vmatrix}$$

$$= (a_{13})(0) - (a_{23})(0) + (a_{33})(0) = 0. \qquad \blacksquare$$

EXAMPLE 1

Since the first and third rows are identical,

$$\begin{vmatrix} 1 & 2 & 1 \\ 2 & 1 & 2 \\ 1 & 2 & 1 \end{vmatrix} = 0.$$

Theorem 8.2   If each element of a particular row (or column) of a square matrix A is multiplied by the number k to obtain the matrix B, then $\delta(B) = k \cdot \delta(A)$.

Proof for 3 × 3 matrices   Without loss of generality, suppose that each element of the second column of

$$A = \begin{bmatrix} a_{11} & a_{12} & a_{13} \\ a_{21} & a_{22} & a_{23} \\ a_{31} & a_{32} & a_{33} \end{bmatrix}$$

is multiplied by the number k to obtain

$$B = \begin{bmatrix} a_{11} & k(a_{12}) & a_{13} \\ a_{21} & k(a_{22}) & a_{23} \\ a_{31} & k(a_{32}) & a_{33} \end{bmatrix}.$$

Expanding about the column containing k using Definition 8.11, we get

$$\delta(B) = -(k)(a_{12}) \begin{vmatrix} a_{21} & a_{23} \\ a_{31} & a_{33} \end{vmatrix} + (k)(a_{22}) \begin{vmatrix} a_{11} & a_{13} \\ a_{31} & a_{33} \end{vmatrix} - (k)(a_{32}) \begin{vmatrix} a_{11} & a_{13} \\ a_{21} & a_{23} \end{vmatrix}$$

$$= k \left[-a_{12} \begin{vmatrix} a_{21} & a_{23} \\ a_{31} & a_{33} \end{vmatrix} + a_{22} \begin{vmatrix} a_{11} & a_{13} \\ a_{31} & a_{33} \end{vmatrix} - a_{32} \begin{vmatrix} a_{11} & a_{13} \\ a_{21} & a_{23} \end{vmatrix} \right]$$

$$= k \cdot \delta(A). \qquad ∎$$

EXAMPLE 2

$$\begin{vmatrix} 5 & 5 & 35 \\ 2 & 1 & 7 \\ 0 & 1 & 14 \end{vmatrix} = (5) \begin{vmatrix} 1 & 1 & 7 \\ 2 & 1 & 7 \\ 0 & 1 & 14 \end{vmatrix} = (5)(7) \begin{vmatrix} 1 & 1 & 1 \\ 2 & 1 & 1 \\ 0 & 1 & 2 \end{vmatrix}.$$

Corollary 8.3   If two rows (or columns) of a square matrix A are proportional, then $\delta(A) = 0$.

Proof   The proof, which follows easily from Theorems 8.1 and 8.2, is left as a problem.   ∎

EXAMPLE 3

$$\begin{vmatrix} 2 & -1 & 2 \\ 4 & -2 & 4 \\ 1 & 3 & 1 \end{vmatrix} = (2) \begin{vmatrix} 2 & -1 & 2 \\ 2 & -1 & 2 \\ 1 & 3 & 1 \end{vmatrix} = (2)(0) = 0.$$

Theorem 8.4   If each element of a particular row (or column) of a square matrix A is multiplied by the number k and then each resulting number is added to the corresponding element of another row (or column) to obtain matrix B, then $\delta(A) = \delta(B)$.

Proof for 3 × 3 matrices Without loss of generality, suppose that each element of the third column of

$$A = \begin{bmatrix} a_{11} & a_{12} & a_{13} \\ a_{21} & a_{22} & a_{23} \\ a_{31} & a_{32} & a_{33} \end{bmatrix}$$

is multiplied by the number k and then each resulting number is added to the corresponding element of the second column to obtain

$$B = \begin{bmatrix} a_{11} & a_{12}+(k)a_{13} & a_{13} \\ a_{21} & a_{22}+(k)a_{23} & a_{23} \\ a_{31} & a_{32}+(k)a_{33} & a_{33} \end{bmatrix}.$$

Expanding about the column containing k using Definition 8.11, we get

$$
\begin{aligned}
\delta(B) = & -(a_{12}+ka_{13}) \begin{vmatrix} a_{21} & a_{23} \\ a_{31} & a_{33} \end{vmatrix} + (a_{22}+ka_{23}) \begin{vmatrix} a_{11} & a_{13} \\ a_{31} & a_{33} \end{vmatrix} - (a_{32}+ka_{33}) \begin{vmatrix} a_{11} & a_{13} \\ a_{21} & a_{23} \end{vmatrix} \\
= & \left(-a_{12} \begin{vmatrix} a_{21} & a_{23} \\ a_{31} & a_{33} \end{vmatrix} + a_{22} \begin{vmatrix} a_{11} & a_{13} \\ a_{31} & a_{33} \end{vmatrix} - a_{32} \begin{vmatrix} a_{11} & a_{13} \\ a_{21} & a_{23} \end{vmatrix} \right) \\
& + k\left(-a_{13} \begin{vmatrix} a_{21} & a_{23} \\ a_{31} & a_{33} \end{vmatrix} + a_{23} \begin{vmatrix} a_{11} & a_{13} \\ a_{31} & a_{33} \end{vmatrix} - a_{33} \begin{vmatrix} a_{11} & a_{13} \\ a_{21} & a_{23} \end{vmatrix} \right) \\
= & \ \delta(A) + k[-a_{13}(a_{21}a_{33} - a_{23}a_{31}) + a_{23}(a_{11}a_{33} - a_{13}a_{31}) \\
& \quad - a_{33}(a_{11}a_{23} - a_{13}a_{21})] \\
= & \ \delta(A) + k(0) = \delta(A). \qquad \blacksquare
\end{aligned}
$$

The following example demonstrates why Theorem 8.4 is useful as an aid in evaluating the determinant of a matrix.

EXAMPLE 4

Evaluate the determinant of

$$A = \begin{bmatrix} 1 & 2 & 1 & 1 \\ 2 & -3 & 1 & 0 \\ 1 & 2 & 3 & 1 \\ 1 & 1 & 3 & 5 \end{bmatrix}.$$

Solution Using Theorem 8.4, we will find a sequence of matrices such that each matrix in the sequence has the same determinant as the given matrix, and such that all the elements, except one, of a particular row (or column) are zeros in the final matrix. We can then use this final matrix, which is a matrix whose determinant is easy to calculate, to calculate the determinant of the original matrix. We determine a final matrix having

$$0 \quad 0 \quad 1 \quad 0$$

as its second row as follows. Multiplying the third column of matrix A by -2 and adding the elements to the corresponding elements of the first column of A, we get

$$B = \begin{bmatrix} -1 & 2 & 1 & 1 \\ 0 & -3 & 1 & 0 \\ -5 & 2 & 3 & 1 \\ -5 & 1 & 3 & 5 \end{bmatrix}.$$

Now multiplying the third column of matrix B by 3 and adding the elements to the corresponding elements of the second column of B, we get

$$C = \begin{bmatrix} -1 & 5 & 1 & 1 \\ 0 & 0 & 1 & 0 \\ -5 & 11 & 3 & 1 \\ -5 & 10 & 3 & 5 \end{bmatrix}.$$

Since $\delta(C) = \delta(B) = \delta(A)$ according to Theorem 8.4, we can evaluate $\delta(A)$ by evaluating $\delta(C)$. Since the second row of C contains three zeros, we expand about this row to get

$$\delta(A) = \delta(C) = -(0) \begin{vmatrix} 5 & 1 & 1 \\ 11 & 3 & 1 \\ 10 & 3 & 5 \end{vmatrix} + (0) \begin{vmatrix} -1 & 1 & 1 \\ -5 & 3 & 1 \\ -5 & 3 & 5 \end{vmatrix} - (1) \begin{vmatrix} -1 & 5 & 1 \\ -5 & 11 & 1 \\ -5 & 10 & 5 \end{vmatrix}$$

$$+ (0) \begin{vmatrix} -1 & 5 & 1 \\ -5 & 11 & 3 \\ -5 & 10 & 3 \end{vmatrix}$$

$$= -\begin{vmatrix} -1 & 5 & 1 \\ -5 & 11 & 1 \\ -5 & 10 & 5 \end{vmatrix} = -\left[(-1) \begin{vmatrix} 11 & 1 \\ 10 & 5 \end{vmatrix} - (5) \begin{vmatrix} -5 & 1 \\ -5 & 5 \end{vmatrix} + (1) \begin{vmatrix} -5 & 11 \\ -5 & 10 \end{vmatrix} \right]$$

$$= -[(-1)(45) - (5)(-20) + (1)(5)] = -60. \qquad \blacksquare$$

Problems 8.4

In problems 1 – 18, evaluate the determinant of the given matrix.

1. $\begin{bmatrix} 1 & 3 & 1 \\ 2 & 0 & -1 \\ 3 & 2 & 4 \end{bmatrix}$

2. $\begin{bmatrix} 2 & 5 & 2 \\ 2 & 1 & 2 \\ 3 & 0 & -1 \end{bmatrix}$

3. $\begin{bmatrix} 3 & 1 & 0 \\ -1 & 2 & 2 \\ 5 & 2 & -1 \end{bmatrix}$

4. $\begin{bmatrix} 1 & 2 & 75 \\ -1 & 1 & 69 \\ 2 & 1 & 53 \end{bmatrix}$

5. $\begin{bmatrix} 71 & 91 & 61 \\ 1 & 2 & -1 \\ 3 & 1 & 2 \end{bmatrix}$

6. $\begin{bmatrix} 25 & 1 & 4 \\ 15 & 3 & 1 \\ 13 & -2 & 1 \end{bmatrix}$

7. $\begin{bmatrix} 1 & -1 & 1 & -1 \\ 3 & 0 & 2 & 3 \\ 1 & 2 & 1 & 9 \\ 2 & 1 & 3 & 5 \end{bmatrix}$

8. $\begin{bmatrix} 1 & 1 & 5 & 2 \\ 2 & 2 & 3 & 7 \\ -2 & 1 & 0 & 3 \\ 1 & 1 & 4 & 4 \end{bmatrix}$

9. $\begin{bmatrix} -1 & 1 & 2 & 3 \\ 2 & 1 & 2 & 2 \\ 1 & 1 & 1 & 1 \\ 0 & 3 & 2 & 3 \end{bmatrix}$

10. $\begin{bmatrix} 1 & 3 & 1 & 1 \\ 0 & 2 & 6 & 3 \\ -1 & 4 & 1 & 1 \\ 2 & 1 & 2 & 1 \end{bmatrix}$
11. $\begin{bmatrix} 1 & 2 & -1 & 2 \\ 1 & 0 & -1 & 2 \\ 2 & 4 & -1 & -2 \\ 3 & 2 & 3 & 1 \end{bmatrix}$
12. $\begin{bmatrix} 2 & 1 & 1 & 2 \\ 4 & 3 & 0 & 2 \\ 1 & 2 & 3 & 1 \\ 1 & 5 & -1 & -1 \end{bmatrix}$

13. $\begin{bmatrix} 1 & 1 & 1 & 2 \\ 1 & 1 & 2 & 1 \\ 1 & 2 & 1 & 1 \\ 2 & 1 & 1 & 1 \end{bmatrix}$
14. $\begin{bmatrix} 1 & 1 & 2 & 2 \\ 1 & 2 & 2 & 1 \\ 2 & 2 & 1 & 1 \\ 2 & 1 & 1 & 2 \end{bmatrix}$
15. $\begin{bmatrix} 2 & 1 & 1 & 1 \\ 1 & 3 & 1 & 1 \\ 1 & 1 & 3 & 1 \\ 1 & 1 & 1 & 2 \end{bmatrix}$

16. $\begin{bmatrix} 1 & 2 & 1 & 3 & 0 \\ 2 & 4 & 0 & 4 & 3 \\ 1 & 0 & 2 & 1 & 1 \\ 0 & 3 & -1 & 1 & 2 \\ 1 & 1 & 0 & 2 & 1 \end{bmatrix}$
17. $\begin{bmatrix} 1 & 0 & 2 & -1 & 1 \\ 1 & -1 & 1 & 0 & 2 \\ 0 & 1 & 0 & -5 & 0 \\ 1 & 3 & 0 & 2 & 1 \\ -1 & 3 & 2 & 2 & 0 \end{bmatrix}$
18. $\begin{bmatrix} 2 & 0 & 1 & 3 & 1 \\ -1 & 0 & 1 & 4 & 1 \\ -1 & 2 & 0 & -1 & 2 \\ 1 & 3 & 2 & 1 & 0 \\ 2 & 0 & 1 & 2 & -1 \end{bmatrix}$

19. Prove Corollary 8.3.

Answers 8.4

1. -27	2. 32	4. 141	5. -405	7. -21	8. 33
10. 8	11. -62	13. 3	14. 0	16. 8	17. 130

8.5 Solving Linear Systems Using Determinants

It is possible to use determinants in solving a system of n linear equations involving n variables. This is done by using the following theorem, which is known as *Cramer's rule*.

Theorem 8.5 (Cramer's Rule) Suppose that D is the determinant of the coefficient matrix A of the linear system

$$\begin{cases} a_{11}x_1 + a_{12}x_2 + \cdots + a_{1n}x_n = c_1 \\ a_{21}x_1 + a_{22}x_2 + \cdots + a_{2n}x_n = c_2 \\ \vdots \\ a_{n1}x_1 + a_{n2}x_2 + \cdots + a_{nn}x_n = c_n \end{cases} \qquad (8-4)$$

and that D_{x_i} is the determinant of the matrix obtained from A by replacing the column of A containing the coefficients of x_i with the column of constants. If $D \neq 0$, then system $(8-4)$ has a unique solution, namely $(x_1, x_2, \cdots, x_n)$, where

$$x_i = \frac{D_{x_i}}{D} \qquad \text{for } i = 1, 2, \cdots, n.$$

Proof when n = 2   In this case, the linear system to be solved is

$$\begin{cases} a_1 x + b_1 y = c_1 \\ a_2 x + b_2 y = c_2. \end{cases}$$

The determinant of the coefficient matrix is

$$D = \begin{vmatrix} a_1 & b_1 \\ a_2 & b_2 \end{vmatrix}.$$

Replacing the coefficients of x in D with their corresponding constants, we find that

$$D_x = \begin{vmatrix} c_1 & b_1 \\ c_2 & b_2 \end{vmatrix}.$$

Using Theorem 8.2, it follows that

$$xD = x \begin{vmatrix} a_1 & b_1 \\ a_2 & b_2 \end{vmatrix} = \begin{vmatrix} a_1 x & b_1 \\ a_2 x & b_2 \end{vmatrix}.$$

Multiplying the elements of the second column by y and adding to the corresponding elements of the first column, according to Theorem 8.4 it follows that

$$\begin{vmatrix} a_1 x & b_1 \\ a_2 x & b_2 \end{vmatrix} = \begin{vmatrix} a_1 x + b_1 y & b_1 \\ a_2 x + b_2 y & b_2 \end{vmatrix}.$$

Since $a_1 x + b_1 y = c_1$ and $a_2 x + b_2 y = c_2$, we can combine the two equations above to get

$$xD = \begin{vmatrix} a_1 x & b_1 \\ a_2 x & b_2 \end{vmatrix} = \begin{vmatrix} a_1 x + b_1 y & b_1 \\ a_2 x + b_2 y & b_2 \end{vmatrix} = \begin{vmatrix} c_1 & b_1 \\ c_2 & b_2 \end{vmatrix} = D_x,$$

from which it follows that $x = D_x/D$. Similarly, we can show that $y = D_y/D$. ∎

EXAMPLE 1

Use Cramer's rule to solve

$$\begin{cases} 5x - 7y = 43 \\ 4x + 5y = -8. \end{cases}$$

Solution The determinant of the coefficient matrix is

$$D=\begin{vmatrix} 5 & -7 \\ 4 & 5 \end{vmatrix}=53.$$

If we replace the coefficients of x in D with their corresponding constants, we find that

$$D_x=\begin{vmatrix} 43 & -7 \\ -8 & 5 \end{vmatrix}=159.$$

If we replace the coefficients of y in D with their corresponding constants, we find that

$$D_y=\begin{vmatrix} 5 & 43 \\ 4 & -8 \end{vmatrix}=-212.$$

Then according to Cramer's rule, we have

$$x=\frac{D_x}{D}=\frac{159}{53}=3 \quad \text{and} \quad y=\frac{D_y}{D}=\frac{-212}{53}=-4.$$

Thus the solution is $(3, -4)$. ∎

EXAMPLE 2

Use Cramer's rule to solve

$$\begin{cases} x-\ y+\ z=6 \\ 2x+\ y+3z=7 \\ x-2y-\ z=6. \end{cases}$$

Solution The determinant of the coefficient matrix is

$$D=\begin{vmatrix} 1 & -1 & 1 \\ 2 & 1 & 3 \\ 1 & -2 & -1 \end{vmatrix}=(1)\begin{vmatrix} 1 & 3 \\ -2 & -1 \end{vmatrix}-(-1)\begin{vmatrix} 2 & 3 \\ 1 & -1 \end{vmatrix}+(1)\begin{vmatrix} 2 & 1 \\ 1 & -2 \end{vmatrix}$$
$$=(1)(5)-(-1)(-5)+(1)(-5)=-5.$$

If we replace the coefficients of x in D with their corresponding constants, we find that

$$D_x=\begin{vmatrix} 6 & -1 & 1 \\ 7 & 1 & 3 \\ 6 & -2 & -1 \end{vmatrix}=(6)\begin{vmatrix} 1 & 3 \\ -2 & -1 \end{vmatrix}-(-1)\begin{vmatrix} 7 & 3 \\ 6 & -1 \end{vmatrix}+(1)\begin{vmatrix} 7 & 1 \\ 6 & -2 \end{vmatrix}$$
$$=(6)(5)-(-1)(-25)+(1)(-20)=-15.$$

If we replace the coefficients of y in D with their corresponding constants, we find that

$$D_y = \begin{vmatrix} 1 & 6 & 1 \\ 2 & 7 & 3 \\ 1 & 6 & -1 \end{vmatrix} = (1) \begin{vmatrix} 7 & 3 \\ 6 & -1 \end{vmatrix} - (6) \begin{vmatrix} 2 & 3 \\ 1 & -1 \end{vmatrix} + (1) \begin{vmatrix} 2 & 7 \\ 1 & 6 \end{vmatrix}$$
$$= (1)(-25) - (6)(-5) + (1)(5) = 10.$$

If we replace the coefficients of z in D with their corresponding constants, we find that

$$D_z = \begin{vmatrix} 1 & -1 & 6 \\ 2 & 1 & 7 \\ 1 & -2 & 6 \end{vmatrix} = (1) \begin{vmatrix} 1 & 7 \\ -2 & 6 \end{vmatrix} - (-1) \begin{vmatrix} 2 & 7 \\ 1 & 6 \end{vmatrix} + (6) \begin{vmatrix} 2 & 1 \\ 1 & -2 \end{vmatrix}$$
$$= (1)(20) - (-1)(5) + (6)(-5) = -5.$$

According to Cramer's rule, we have

$$x = \frac{D_x}{D} = \frac{-15}{-5} = 3, \quad y = \frac{D_y}{D} = \frac{10}{-5} = -2, \quad \text{and} \quad z = \frac{D_z}{D} = \frac{-5}{-5} = 1.$$

Thus the solution is $(3, -2, 1)$. ∎

Problems 8.5

In problems 1–15, use Cramer's rule to determine the solution of the given system.

1. $\begin{cases} x - y = 7 \\ 3x + 4y = 7 \end{cases}$

2. $\begin{cases} 2x - y = -8 \\ 3x + 5y = 1 \end{cases}$

3. $\begin{cases} 2x - 3y = 19 \\ 5x + 4y = 13 \end{cases}$

4. $\begin{cases} x - 2y = 1 \\ 5x - 3y = 3 \end{cases}$

5. $\begin{cases} 3x + y = 1 \\ 5x + 3y = 4 \end{cases}$

6. $\begin{cases} 2x - 3y = 5 \\ x + 5y = 7 \end{cases}$

7. $\begin{cases} x - y + z = 3 \\ 2x + y - z = -9 \\ 3x + 2y + z = 8 \end{cases}$

8. $\begin{cases} 2x + 3y + z = 5 \\ x - y - z = 0 \\ 3x - y + 4z = 31 \end{cases}$

9. $\begin{cases} 2x - y + 3z = 12 \\ 3x + y - 2z = 3 \\ 4x + 2y + z = 27 \end{cases}$

10. $\begin{cases} x - y - z = 0 \\ 2x + 2y + z = 5 \\ 5x + 2y - z = 5 \end{cases}$

11. $\begin{cases} x - 2y - 4z = 7 \\ x + y - 2z = 11 \\ 3x + y + z = 22 \end{cases}$

12. $\begin{cases} x + 2y + 3z = 1 \\ 3x - y - z = 2 \\ 4x + 3y - z = 15 \end{cases}$

13. $\begin{cases} 2x + y + z = 3 \\ x - y + w = 7 \\ 2x + 3y + w = 2 \\ 3x - 2z + w = 13 \end{cases}$

14. $\begin{cases} 3x + y + 2z - w = 14 \\ x + 2y - w = 3 \\ 2x + z = 8 \\ y - z + w = -5 \end{cases}$

15. $\begin{cases} x+y \quad +w= 8 \\ 2x \quad + z-w= 3 \\ x+y-2z+w=28 \\ x-y \quad +w= 4 \end{cases}$

16. Use Cramer's rule to solve for z only: $\begin{cases} x-y+ z+ w= 2 \\ 2x+y-2z+ w= 13 \\ x-y+3z- w=-6 \\ 3x-y- z-5w= 0. \end{cases}$

17. Use Cramer's rule to solve for w only: $\begin{cases} x+2y+ z+w \quad = 10 \\ y- z+w+2t= 14 \\ x \quad +2z \quad - t=-3 \\ 3y \quad +w+ t= 13 \\ x+ y+2z+w+ t= 10. \end{cases}$

Answers 8.5

1. $(5, -2)$ 2. $(-3, 2)$ 4. $(\frac{3}{7}, -\frac{2}{7})$ 5. $(-\frac{1}{4}, \frac{7}{4})$ 7. $(-2, 3, 8)$
8. $(3, -2, 5)$ 10. $(2, -1, 3)$ 11. $(7, 2, -1)$ 13. $(3, -2, -1, 2)$
14. $(3, -1, 2, -2)$ 16. -2 17. 8

8.6 Inverse of a Square Matrix

In this section, we continue our discussion of the algebra of matrices which we started in Section 8.1.

The **principal diagonal** of a square matrix A is the ordered set of numbers, $a_{11}, a_{22}, \ldots, a_{nn}$, extending from the upper left-hand corner to the lower right-hand corner of A. For example, the principal diagonal of

$$\begin{bmatrix} 3 & -1 & 3 \\ 1 & 2 & 7 \\ 5 & 5 & 4 \end{bmatrix}$$

consists of the ordered set of numbers 3, 2, and 4.

A **diagonal matrix** is a square matrix in which all the elements off the principal diagonal are zeros. For example, each of the matrices

$$\begin{bmatrix} 1 & 0 \\ 0 & 5 \end{bmatrix} \quad \text{and} \quad \begin{bmatrix} 1 & 0 & 0 \\ 0 & 3 & 0 \\ 0 & 0 & -1 \end{bmatrix}$$

is a diagonal matrix.

It is now possible to prove that there exists a unique diagonal matrix I having only 1's on its principal diagonal such that $IA = AI = A$ for every $n \times n$ matrix A. The matrix I is called the $n \times n$ **identity matrix.** For example,

$$\begin{bmatrix} 1 & 0 \\ 0 & 1 \end{bmatrix} \quad \text{and} \quad \begin{bmatrix} 1 & 0 & 0 \\ 0 & 1 & 0 \\ 0 & 0 & 1 \end{bmatrix}$$

are the 2×2 and 3×3 identity matrices, respectively.

Theorem 8.6   There exists a unique $n \times n$ matrix I, namely the $n \times n$ identity matrix, such that $AI = IA = A$ for every $n \times n$ matrix A.

Proof for 2×2 matrices   Given that $A = \begin{bmatrix} a_{11} & a_{12} \\ a_{21} & a_{22} \end{bmatrix}$, we wish to determine a matrix $I = \begin{bmatrix} x & y \\ z & w \end{bmatrix}$ such that $AI = A$. Using Definitions 8.1 and 8.6, it follows that

$$AI = \begin{bmatrix} a_{11} & a_{12} \\ a_{21} & a_{22} \end{bmatrix} \begin{bmatrix} x & y \\ z & w \end{bmatrix} = \begin{bmatrix} a_{11}x + a_{12}z & a_{11}y + a_{12}w \\ a_{21}x + a_{22}z & a_{21}y + a_{22}w \end{bmatrix} = \begin{bmatrix} a_{11} & a_{12} \\ a_{21} & a_{22} \end{bmatrix} = A$$

if and only if

$$a_{11}x + a_{12}z = a_{11} \qquad\qquad a_{21}x + a_{22}z = a_{21} \qquad (8-5)$$
$$\text{and}$$
$$a_{11}y + a_{12}w = a_{12} \qquad\qquad a_{21}y + a_{22}w = a_{22}. \qquad (8-6)$$

Solving system (8–5), we get $x = 1$ and $z = 0$. Similarly, solving system (8–6), we get $y = 0$ and $w = 1$. Therefore,

$$I = \begin{bmatrix} x & y \\ z & w \end{bmatrix} = \begin{bmatrix} 1 & 0 \\ 0 & 1 \end{bmatrix}.$$

It can be shown by direct matrix multiplication that not only does $AI = A$ but that $IA = A$ also.   ∎

If A is an $n \times n$ square matrix, we define the **inverse** of the matrix A as the $n \times n$ square matrix A^{-1} satisfying $AA^{-1} = A^{-1}A = I$ when such a matrix exists. The following theorem shows that the inverse of a matrix A exists only when $\delta(A) \neq 0$.

Theorem 8.7 For each $n \times n$ matrix A with $\delta(A) \neq 0$, there exists a unique $n \times n$ matrix A^{-1} such that $AA^{-1} = A^{-1}A = I$.

Proof for 2 × 2 matrices Given that $A = \begin{bmatrix} a_{11} & a_{12} \\ a_{21} & a_{22} \end{bmatrix}$, we wish to determine a matrix $A^{-1} = \begin{bmatrix} x & y \\ z & w \end{bmatrix}$ such that $AA^{-1} = I$. Using Definitions 8.1 and 8.6, it follows that

$$AA^{-1} = \begin{bmatrix} a_{11} & a_{12} \\ a_{21} & a_{22} \end{bmatrix}\begin{bmatrix} x & y \\ z & w \end{bmatrix} = \begin{bmatrix} a_{11}x + a_{12}z & a_{11}y + a_{12}w \\ a_{21}x + a_{22}z & a_{21}y + a_{22}w \end{bmatrix} = \begin{bmatrix} 1 & 0 \\ 0 & 1 \end{bmatrix} = I$$

if and only if

$$a_{11}x + a_{12}z = 1 \qquad a_{21}x + a_{22}z = 0 \tag{8-7}$$
$$\text{and}$$
$$a_{11}y + a_{12}w = 0 \qquad a_{21}y + a_{22}w = 1. \tag{8-8}$$

Solving system (8–7), we get

$$x = \frac{a_{22}}{a_{11}a_{22} - a_{12}a_{21}} \qquad \text{and} \qquad z = \frac{-a_{21}}{a_{11}a_{22} - a_{12}a_{21}}.$$

Similarly solving system (8–8), we get

$$y = \frac{-a_{12}}{a_{11}a_{22} - a_{12}a_{21}} \qquad \text{and} \qquad w = \frac{a_{11}}{a_{11}a_{22} - a_{12}a_{21}}.$$

Since $\delta(A) = a_{11}a_{22} - a_{12}a_{21}$, it follows that

$$x = \frac{a_{22}}{\delta(A)}, \quad y = \frac{-a_{12}}{\delta(A)}, \quad z = \frac{-a_{21}}{\delta(A)}, \quad \text{and} \quad w = \frac{a_{11}}{\delta(A)}.$$

Therefore,

$$A^{-1} = \frac{1}{\delta(A)}\begin{bmatrix} a_{22} & -a_{12} \\ -a_{21} & a_{11} \end{bmatrix} \tag{8-9}$$

provided that $\delta(A) \neq 0$. It can be shown by direct matrix multiplication that not only does $AA^{-1} = I$ but that $A^{-1}A = I$ also. Hence, when $\delta(A) \neq 0$, there exists a unique matrix A^{-1} given by Eq. (8–9) which is the inverse of matrix A. ∎

EXAMPLE 1

If $A = \begin{bmatrix} 4 & 3 \\ 6 & 5 \end{bmatrix}$, determine A^{-1}.

Solution   Since $\delta(A) = (4)(5) - (3)(6) = 2$, A^{-1} exists. Thus it follows by Eq. (8–9) that

$$A^{-1} = \frac{1}{\delta(A)} \begin{bmatrix} a_{22} & -a_{12} \\ -a_{21} & a_{11} \end{bmatrix} = \frac{1}{2} \begin{bmatrix} 5 & -3 \\ -6 & 4 \end{bmatrix} = \begin{bmatrix} \frac{5}{2} & -\frac{3}{2} \\ -3 & 2 \end{bmatrix}.$$

Checking the answer by direct matrix multiplication, we find that

$$AA^{-1} = \begin{bmatrix} 4 & 3 \\ 6 & 5 \end{bmatrix} \begin{bmatrix} \frac{5}{2} & -\frac{3}{2} \\ -3 & 2 \end{bmatrix} = \begin{bmatrix} 1 & 0 \\ 0 & 1 \end{bmatrix} = I. \qquad \blacksquare$$

The following theorem, which we state without proof, gives a formula for calculating the inverse of an $n \times n$ matrix, if such an inverse exists, when $n = 3, 4, 5, \ldots$.

Theorem 8.8   If A_{ij} is the cofactor of the element a_{ij} of the $n \times n$ matrix

$$A = \begin{bmatrix} a_{11} a_{12} \cdots a_{1n} \\ a_{21} a_{22} \cdots a_{2n} \\ \vdots \quad \vdots \quad \quad \vdots \\ a_{n1} a_{n2} \cdots a_{nn} \end{bmatrix},$$

then the multiplicative inverse A^{-1} of A is

$$A^{-1} = \frac{1}{\delta(A)} \begin{bmatrix} A_{11} A_{21} \cdots A_{n1} \\ A_{12} A_{22} \cdots A_{n2} \\ \vdots \quad \vdots \quad \quad \vdots \\ A_{1n} A_{2n} \cdots A_{nn} \end{bmatrix} \qquad (8-10)$$

when $\delta(A) \neq 0$.

EXAMPLE 2

If $A = \begin{bmatrix} 3 & 2 & 1 \\ 2 & 2 & 1 \\ 0 & 0 & 1 \end{bmatrix}$, determine A^{-1}.

Solution Note that A^{-1} exists since $\delta(A) = 2$. Calculating some of the cofactors of the elements of A (you should calculate the others for yourself), we get

$$A_{11} = (-1)^{1+1}\begin{vmatrix} 2 & 1 \\ 0 & 1 \end{vmatrix} = 2, \qquad A_{13} = (-1)^{1+3}\begin{vmatrix} 2 & 2 \\ 0 & 0 \end{vmatrix} = 0,$$

$$A_{21} = (-1)^{2+1}\begin{vmatrix} 2 & 1 \\ 0 & 1 \end{vmatrix} = -2, \qquad A_{32} = (-1)^{3+2}\begin{vmatrix} 3 & 1 \\ 2 & 1 \end{vmatrix} = -1.$$

After calculating the other cofactors, it follows by Eq. (8–10) that

$$A^{-1} = \frac{1}{\delta(A)}\begin{bmatrix} A_{11} & A_{21} & A_{31} \\ A_{12} & A_{22} & A_{32} \\ A_{13} & A_{23} & A_{33} \end{bmatrix} = \frac{1}{2}\begin{bmatrix} 2 & -2 & 0 \\ -2 & 3 & -1 \\ 0 & 0 & 2 \end{bmatrix} = \begin{bmatrix} 1 & -1 & 0 \\ -1 & \frac{3}{2} & -\frac{1}{2} \\ 0 & 0 & 1 \end{bmatrix}.$$

Checking the result by direct matrix multiplication, we find that

$$AA^{-1} = \begin{bmatrix} 3 & 2 & 1 \\ 2 & 2 & 1 \\ 0 & 0 & 1 \end{bmatrix}\begin{bmatrix} 1 & -1 & 0 \\ -1 & \frac{3}{2} & -\frac{1}{2} \\ 0 & 0 & 1 \end{bmatrix} = \begin{bmatrix} 1 & 0 & 0 \\ 0 & 1 & 0 \\ 0 & 0 & 1 \end{bmatrix} = I. \qquad \blacksquare$$

Problems 8.6

In problems 1–18, determine A^{-1}, if it exists, for the given matrix A.

1. $\begin{bmatrix} 1 & 2 \\ 3 & 7 \end{bmatrix}$ 2. $\begin{bmatrix} -2 & 3 \\ -3 & 5 \end{bmatrix}$ 3. $\begin{bmatrix} 3 & 7 \\ 2 & 5 \end{bmatrix}$

4. $\begin{bmatrix} 4 & 6 \\ 6 & 9 \end{bmatrix}$ 5. $\begin{bmatrix} 3 & 2 \\ -1 & 3 \end{bmatrix}$ 6. $\begin{bmatrix} 2 & 3 \\ -1 & 4 \end{bmatrix}$

7. $\begin{bmatrix} 1 & -2 \\ 1 & 1 \end{bmatrix}$ 8. $\begin{bmatrix} 9 & 6 \\ 3 & 2 \end{bmatrix}$ 9. $\begin{bmatrix} -1 & -7 \\ 2 & 14 \end{bmatrix}$

10. $\begin{bmatrix} 1 & 2 & 0 \\ 0 & 1 & 1 \\ 1 & 1 & 0 \end{bmatrix}$ 11. $\begin{bmatrix} 1 & 2 & 3 \\ 1 & 1 & 1 \\ 1 & 1 & 2 \end{bmatrix}$ 12. $\begin{bmatrix} -1 & 0 & 1 \\ 2 & 0 & -3 \\ 3 & -1 & 1 \end{bmatrix}$

13. $\begin{bmatrix} 1 & 2 & 5 \\ -1 & 2 & 3 \\ 2 & 1 & 5 \end{bmatrix}$ 14. $\begin{bmatrix} 1 & 1 & 2 \\ 0 & 2 & 2 \\ 1 & 0 & 2 \end{bmatrix}$ 15. $\begin{bmatrix} 3 & 1 & -1 \\ 2 & 0 & 1 \\ -1 & -1 & 3 \end{bmatrix}$

16. $\begin{bmatrix} 2 & 2 & 3 \\ 1 & 0 & 1 \\ -1 & 1 & 0 \end{bmatrix}$ 17. $\begin{bmatrix} 1 & 0 & 1 \\ -1 & -1 & 0 \\ 2 & 2 & -1 \end{bmatrix}$ 18. $\begin{bmatrix} 1 & 2 & 3 \\ -3 & 0 & -1 \\ 2 & -1 & 1 \end{bmatrix}$

19. Prove that the sum of the products obtained by multiplying each element of a particular row (or column) of an $n \times n$ matrix A by the corresponding cofactor of another row (or column) is zero. (*Hint:* You will need to use Corollary 8.3.)

20. Prove Theorem 8.8. (*Hint:* Show that $AA^{-1} = A^{-1}A = I$ by using Definition 8.11 and problem 19.)

Answers 8.6

1. $\begin{bmatrix} 7 & -2 \\ -3 & 1 \end{bmatrix}$ 2. $\begin{bmatrix} -5 & 3 \\ -3 & 2 \end{bmatrix}$ 4. none

5. $\begin{bmatrix} \frac{3}{11} & -\frac{2}{11} \\ \frac{1}{11} & \frac{3}{11} \end{bmatrix}$ 7. $\begin{bmatrix} \frac{1}{3} & \frac{2}{3} \\ -\frac{1}{3} & \frac{1}{3} \end{bmatrix}$ 8. none

10. $\begin{bmatrix} -1 & 0 & 2 \\ 1 & 0 & -1 \\ -1 & 1 & 1 \end{bmatrix}$ 11. $\begin{bmatrix} -1 & 1 & 1 \\ 1 & 1 & -2 \\ 0 & -1 & 1 \end{bmatrix}$ 13. $\begin{bmatrix} \frac{7}{4} & -\frac{5}{4} & -1 \\ \frac{11}{4} & -\frac{5}{4} & -2 \\ -\frac{5}{4} & \frac{3}{4} & 1 \end{bmatrix}$

14. $\begin{bmatrix} 2 & -1 & -1 \\ 1 & 0 & -1 \\ -1 & \frac{1}{2} & 1 \end{bmatrix}$ 16. $\begin{bmatrix} 1 & -3 & -2 \\ 1 & -3 & -1 \\ -1 & 4 & 2 \end{bmatrix}$ 17. $\begin{bmatrix} 1 & 2 & 1 \\ -1 & -3 & -1 \\ 0 & -2 & -1 \end{bmatrix}$

chapter 8 review problems

1. Perform the indicated operations when possible.

(a) $\begin{bmatrix} 1 & 2 \\ -1 & 3 \end{bmatrix} + 2 \begin{bmatrix} -1 & 1 \\ 0 & 2 \end{bmatrix}$ (b) $\begin{bmatrix} 1 & 2 \\ 3 & 3 \\ 2 & 1 \end{bmatrix} - 3 \begin{bmatrix} 1 & 0 \\ 0 & 2 \\ 3 & 0 \end{bmatrix}$

(c) $\begin{bmatrix} 1 & 2 & -1 \\ 0 & 5 & 4 \end{bmatrix} \begin{bmatrix} 2 & 1 \\ 1 & 2 \end{bmatrix}$ (d) $\begin{bmatrix} 1 & 2 \\ 1 & 4 \\ 4 & -1 \\ 3 & 0 \end{bmatrix} \begin{bmatrix} 1 & 2 & 5 \\ 3 & 1 & 4 \end{bmatrix}$

2. Use the Gaussian method to determine the solution of the given system.

(a) $\begin{cases} 2x - y = 8 \\ 4x + 5y = 2 \end{cases}$ (b) $\begin{cases} 4x + y - 4z = 22 \\ 2x - y + 3z = -1 \\ 3x + 2y - 2z = 11 \end{cases}$

3. Evaluate the determinant of the given matrix.

(a) $\begin{bmatrix} 2 & 1 \\ -3 & 1 \end{bmatrix}$ (b) $\begin{bmatrix} 1 & 2 & 1 \\ 3 & 5 & 5 \\ 7 & 1 & 3 \end{bmatrix}$

(c) $\begin{bmatrix} 1 & 0 & -1 & 2 \\ 3 & 4 & 2 & 1 \\ 1 & 3 & 1 & 1 \\ 1 & 2 & 1 & 1 \end{bmatrix}$ (d) $\begin{bmatrix} 2 & -1 & 0 & 3 & 7 \\ 49 & 59 & 5 & 69 & 49 \\ 3 & 1 & 0 & 5 & 8 \\ 6 & -2 & 0 & -2 & -4 \\ 8 & -4 & 0 & -3 & 3 \end{bmatrix}$

4. Use Cramer's rule to determine the solution of each system in problem 2.
5. Determine the multiplicative inverse, if it exists, of the given matrix.

(a) $\begin{bmatrix} 1 & 3 \\ 2 & 4 \end{bmatrix}$ (b) $\begin{bmatrix} 1 & 2 & 1 \\ -1 & 0 & 0 \\ 1 & 2 & 2 \end{bmatrix}$

answers

1. (a) $\begin{bmatrix} -1 & 4 \\ -1 & 7 \end{bmatrix}$ **(b)** $\begin{bmatrix} -2 & 2 \\ 3 & -3 \\ -7 & 1 \end{bmatrix}$ **(c)** impossible   **(d)** $\begin{bmatrix} 7 & 4 & 13 \\ 13 & 6 & 21 \\ 1 & 7 & 16 \\ 3 & 6 & 15 \end{bmatrix}$

2. (a) $(3, -2)$ **(b)** $(3, -2, -3)$

3. (a) 5   **(b)** 30   **(c)** -5 **(d)** 2000

5. (a) $\begin{bmatrix} -2 & \frac{3}{2} \\ 1 & -\frac{1}{2} \end{bmatrix}$ **(b)** $\begin{bmatrix} 0 & -1 & 0 \\ 1 & \frac{1}{2} & -\frac{1}{2} \\ -1 & 0 & 1 \end{bmatrix}$

9

theory of equations

9.1 Synthetic Division

In this chapter, we shall frequently find it necessary to divide a polynomial $F(x)$ by the binomial $x - k$, where k is a constant. Therefore, it will be useful to develop a shortcut, called *synthetic division*, for doing this. We illustrate synthetic division by an example.

EXAMPLE 1

Divide $F(x) = 2x^3 - 3x^2 - 4x + 5$ by $x - 2$.

Solution   Dividing first by long division, we get

$$
\begin{array}{r}
2x^2 + x - 2 \quad \text{(quotient)} \\
x - 2 \enclose{longdiv}{2x^3 - 3x^2 - 4x + 5} \quad \text{(dividend)} \\
\end{array}
$$

(divisor) $x - 2$ | $2x^3 - 3x^2 - 4x + 5$ (dividend)
$\boldsymbol{2x^3 - 4x^2}$

Subtracting the two polynomials above the line, we get

$x^2 - 4x + 5$
$\boldsymbol{x^2 - 2x}$
$-2x + 5$
$\boldsymbol{-2x + 4}$
1 (remainder)

We can abbreviate our work by omitting the boldface terms, since they are going to cancel anyway. We can shorten our work further by omitting the variable x throughout the division process. Thus we get

$$
\begin{array}{r|l}
 & \underline{2+1-2} \\
-2 & 2-3-4+5 \\
 & \underline{-4} \\
 & 1-4+5 \quad \text{subtracting} \\
 & \underline{-2} \\
 & -2+5 \quad \text{subtracting} \\
 & \underline{+4} \\
 & 1 \qquad \text{subtracting}
\end{array}
$$

We could obtain the same result by replacing the divisor -2 with 2 and adding in each step instead of subtracting. We do this because mistakes are made less often in addition than in subtraction. Thus we have

$$
\begin{array}{r|l}
 & \underline{\mathbf{2+1-2}} \\
2 & 2-3-4+5 \\
 & \underline{4} \\
 & \mathbf{1}-4+5 \quad \text{adding} \\
 & \underline{2} \\
 & -\mathbf{2}+5 \quad \text{adding} \\
 & \underline{-4} \\
 & 1 \qquad \text{adding}
\end{array}
$$

Deleting the boldface numbers, which are repetitious, we can abbreviate the previous division in three lines as follows:

$$
\begin{array}{r|rrrr}
 & \multicolumn{4}{c}{\overbrace{\quad}^{\text{(dividend coefficients)}}} \\
2 & 2 & -3 & -4 & +5 \\
 & & 4 & +2 & -4 \quad \text{adding} \\
\hline
 & 2 & +1 & -2 & +1
\end{array}
$$

(quotient   (remainder)
coefficients)

Thus we have obtained a quotient of $2x^2 + x - 2$ and a remainder of 1. ∎

Steps in Synthetic Division Process

Mechanically, the numbers in the previous abbreviated synthetic division process are obtained as follows:

1. On the top line, write the value of k in the box and arrange the coefficients of the dividend in order of descending powers of x, supplying zero as the coefficient of each missing power of x.
2. Bring down the coefficient of the largest power of x to the bottom line, multiply it by k, place this product beneath the coefficient of the second-largest power of x on the middle line, and add the two numbers in the second column to obtain the second number in the third row.
3. Multiply the second number in the third row by k, place this product beneath the coefficient of the third-largest power of x on the middle line, and add the two numbers in the third column to obtain the third number in the third row.
4. Continue the procedure in step 3 until there is a number added to the last number in the top row. The last number in the third row is the constant remainder R, and the other numbers, reading from left to right, are the coefficients of the quotient in order of descending powers of x.

EXAMPLE 2

Use synthetic division to obtain the quotient $Q(x)$ and the constant remainder R obtained when $x^3 - 2x^2 + x + 40$ is divided by $x + 3$.

Solution In this case, $x - k = x + 3$ and hence $k = -3$. Using the steps described above, we get

$$
\begin{array}{r|rrrr}
& \multicolumn{4}{c}{\text{(dividend coefficients)}} \\
\hline
-3 & 1 & -2 & 1 & 40 \\
& & -3 & 15 & -48 \\
\hline
& 1 & -5 & 16 & -8 \\
\end{array}
$$

(quotient   (remainder)
coefficients)

Therefore, the quotient $Q(x)$ is $x^2 - 5x + 16$ and the constant remainder R is -8.   ∎

EXAMPLE 3

If $F(x) = x^4 - x^2$ and $x - k = x - 2$, use synthetic division to write $F(x)/(x - k)$ in the form $Q(x) + [R/(x - k)]$.

Solution Supplying 0 as the coefficient of each missing power of x, we see that $F(x) = x^4 - x^2 = x^4 + 0x^3 - x^2 + 0x + 0$. Thus

$$
\begin{array}{c}
\quad\quad\quad \text{[coefficients of the} \\
\quad\quad\quad \text{dividend } F(x)] \\
\underline{2\,\rfloor}\quad
\begin{array}{ccccc}
1 & 0 & -1 & 0 & 0 \\
  & 2 & 4 & 6 & 12 \\
\hline
1 & 2 & 3 & 6 & 12
\end{array} \\
\text{[coefficients of the}\quad\quad\text{(remainder)} \\
\text{quotient } Q(x)]
\end{array}
$$

Therefore, the quotient $Q(x)$ is $x^3 + 2x^2 + 3x + 6$ and the remainder R is 12. Consequently,

$$
\frac{x^4 - x^2}{x - 2} = (x^3 + 2x^2 + 3x + 6) + \frac{12}{x - 2} \quad\quad \text{when } x \neq 2. \quad\quad \blacksquare
$$

Multiplying both sides of the final equation in Example 3 by $x - 2$, we get

$$
x^4 - x^2 = (x - 2)(x^3 + 2x^2 + 3x + 6) + 12.
$$

This equation suggests the following theorem, which we state without proof, concerning the division of a polynomial $F(x)$ by a binomial $x - k$.

Theorem 9.1 If $F(x)$ is a polynomial and k is a constant, there exists a unique polynomial $Q(x)$ and a constant R such that the degree of $Q(x)$ is one less than the degree of $F(x)$ and

$$
F(x) = (x - k)\,Q(x) + R, \quad\quad\quad\quad\quad (9-1)
$$

where $Q(x)$ is the quotient and R is the constant remainder obtained in the division of $F(x)$ by $x - k$.

Problems 9.1

In problems 1–6, use synthetic division to determine the constant remainder, which is obtained when the first polynomial is divided by the second polynomial.

1. $x^3 - 2x^2 + 3x - 4$, $x - 2$
2. $x^3 + x^2 - 2x + 5$, $x - 1$
3. $2x^3 - 3x^2 + 5x - 5$, $x - 3$
4. $2x^4 - 3x^3 + x + 3$, $x + 1$
5. $x^4 + 3x^3 + 5x - 1$, $x + 4$
6. $x^4 + 5x^3 - x^2 + 2$, $x + 2$

In problems 7–18, use synthetic division to determine the quotient $Q(x)$ and the constant remainder R obtained when the polynomial $F(x)$ is divided by the binomial $x - k$.

7. $x^4 - 2x^3 + x + 7$, $x - 1$
8. $2x^4 - 8x^3 + x^2 - 12$, $x - 4$
9. $3x^4 - 7x^3 + 11x - 15$, $x + 3$
10. $x^5 - 4x^3 - x + 2$, $x + 2$
11. $x^5 + 2x^4 - x - 5$, $x + 2$
12. $x^5 - x + 10$, $x - 4$
13. $3x^4 + x^2 + 1$, $x - 2$
14. $x^4 - x$, $x - 3$
15. $x^4 + x^3 - 1$, $x + 4$
16. $2x^3 - 100x^2 + 12x^4 - 1$, $x + 3$
17. $3x^2 - 7x + x^4 - 2$, $x + 2$
18. $7 + 3x^4 - x$, $x - 1$

In problems 19–24, use synthetic division to write the expression $F(x)/(x - k)$ in the form $Q(x) + [R/(x - k)]$.

19. $\dfrac{x^3 - 2x + 7}{x + 1}$
20. $\dfrac{x^3 + 7x^2 - 5}{x - 2}$
21. $\dfrac{x^3 - 7x^2 + x + 2}{x - 3}$

22. $\dfrac{x^4 - 2x^3 + 7}{x - 4}$
23. $\dfrac{x^4 + 3x - 9}{x + 2}$
24. $\dfrac{x^4 - x^3 + x - 1}{x + 3}$

Answers 9.1

1. 2   2. 5   4. 7   5. 43
7. $Q(x) = x^3 - x^2 - x$, $R = 7$
8. $Q(x) = 2x^3 + x + 4$, $R = 4$
10. $Q(x) = x^4 - 2x^3 - 1$, $R = 4$
11. $Q(x) = x^4 - 1$, $R = -3$
13. $Q(x) = 3x^3 + 6x^2 + 13x + 26$, $R = 53$
14. $Q(x) = x^3 + 3x^2 + 9x + 26$, $R = 78$
16. $Q(x) = 12x^3 - 34x^2 + 2x - 6$, $R = 17$
17. $Q(x) = x^3 - 2x^2 + 7x - 21$, $R = 40$
19. $x^2 - x - 1 + [8/(x + 1)]$
20. $x^2 + 9x + 18 + [31/(x - 2)]$
22. $x^3 + 2x^2 + 8x + 32 + [135/(x - 4)]$
23. $x^3 - 2x^2 + 4x - 5 + [1/(x + 2)]$

9.2 Remainder and Factor Theorems

In this section we consider several theorems that are useful in factoring polynomials.

Theorem 9.2 (The Remainder Theorem)   If a polynomial $F(x)$ is divided by $x - a$ until a constant remainder R is obtained, then $R = F(a)$.

Proof If $Q(x)$ represents the quotient and R represents the constant remainder obtained when $F(x)$ is divided by $x - a$, then

$$F(x) = (x-a)\,Q(x) + R$$

according to Theorem 7.1. Since the previous equation holds for all values of x, it must be true when $x = a$. Therefore,

$$F(a) = (a-a)\,Q(a) + R = 0 + R,$$

and hence $R = F(a)$. ∎

EXAMPLE 1

Determine the remainder that is obtained when $2x^4 - x^3 - 3x + 4$ is divided by $x + 2$.

Solution According to the remainder theorem, when $F(x) = 2x^4 - x^3 - 3x + 4$ is divided by $x - a = x - (-2)$, the remainder is

$$R = F(-2) = 2(-2)^4 - (-2)^3 - 3(-2) + 4 = 32 + 8 + 6 + 4 = 50.$$ ∎

EXAMPLE 2

Verify the answer in Example 1 by using synthetic division.

Solution Using synthetic division, we get

$$
\begin{array}{r|rrrrr}
-2 & 2 & -1 & 0 & -3 & 4 \\
   &   & -4 & 10 & -20 & 46 \\
\hline
   & 2 & -5 & 10 & -23 & 50 \\
\end{array}
$$

remainder ∎

EXERCISE 1

Use (a) the remainder theorem and (b) synthetic division to determine the remainder obtained when $x^5 - x^3 + 3x - 1$ is divided by $x - 2$.

Answer (a) 29   (b) 29

The remainder theorem can be used to prove the following important theorem.

Theorem 9.3 (The Factor Theorem) If $F(x)$ is a polynomial, then $F(a) = 0$ if and only if $x - a$ is a factor of $F(x)$.

Proof

Proof of: if $F(x)$ is a polynomial such that $F(a)=0$, then $x-a$ is a factor of $F(x)$ Suppose that $F(a) = 0$. Using the remainder theorem, it follows that 0 is the constant remainder obtained when $F(x)$ is divided by $x - a$. Hence

$$F(x)=(x-a)\,Q(x)+0=(x-a)\,Q(x).$$

Thus $x - a$ is a factor of $F(x)$.

Proof of: if $x-a$ is a factor of the polynomial $F(x)$, then $F(a)=0$ Suppose that $x - a$ is a factor of the polynomial $F(x)$. Hence

$$F(x)=(x-a)\,Q(x).$$

Replacing x with a in the previous equation, we get

$$F(a)=(a-a)\,Q(a)=0. \qquad\blacksquare$$

EXAMPLE 3

Show that $x + 2$ is (or is not) a factor of $F(x) = x^4 + 3x^3 - 2x + 4$.

Solution   Since $F(-2) = (-2)^4 + 3(-2)^3 - 2(-2) + 4 = 0$, it follows by the factor theorem that $x - (-2) = x + 2$ is a factor of $F(x) = x^4 + 3x^3 - 2x + 4$. $\qquad\blacksquare$

If F is a polynomial function of degree n, then $F(x)=0$ is called a **polynomial equation** of degree n. If F is a polynomial function of degree n such that $F(a)=0$, then a is a solution (root) of the polynomial equation $F(x)=0$, and vice versa. Hence the factor theorem can be restated as follows.

Theorem 9.4 (The Factor Theorem)   If $F(x)$ is a polynomial, then a is a solution of the equation $F(x) = 0$ if and only if $x - a$ is a factor of $F(x)$.

EXAMPLE 4

Determine the polynomial equation whose roots are $3, -1$, and -2.

Solution   According to the factor theorem, $3, -1$, and -2 are the roots of the polynomial equation $F(x)=0$ if and only if $x-3$, $x+1$, and $x+2$ are the factors of $F(x)$. Therefore,

$$F(x)=(x-3)(x+1)(x+2)=0$$

and hence $x^3 - 7x - 6 = 0$ is the desired polynomial equation. $\qquad\blacksquare$

EXERCISE 2

Determine the polynomial equation whose roots are -3, 5, and 2.

Answer $x^3 - 4x^2 - 11x + 30 = 0$

EXAMPLE 5

Determine the roots of the equation $(x - 2)(x^2 - 2x - 1) = 0$.

Solution   Since $x - 2$ is a factor of $(x - 2)(x^2 - 2x - 1)$, the factor theorem states that 2 is a root of the given equation. The other roots of the given equation are the roots of the quadratic equation $x^2 - 2x - 1 = 0$. Using the quadratic formula to solve $x^2 - 2x - 1 = 0$ for x, we get

$$x = \frac{-(-2) \pm \sqrt{(-2)^2 - 4(1)(-1)}}{2(1)} = \frac{2 \pm \sqrt{8}}{2} = 1 \pm \sqrt{2}.$$

Thus the roots of the given equation are 2, $1 + \sqrt{2}$, and $1 - \sqrt{2}$.   ∎

Problems 9.2

In problems 1–6, use the remainder theorem to determine the constant remainder that is obtained when the first polynomial is divided by the second polynomial. Check your answer by using synthetic division.

1. $3x^3 - 2x + 7$, $x - 2$ **2.** $5x^4 - 2x^2 + 3x - 1$, $x + 1$
3. $x^3 - x^2 + 5x - 7$, $x + 2$ **4.** $x^2 - x^4 + x - 2$, $x + 3$
5. $x^3 - 2x + x^4 + 3$, $x - 3$ **6.** $x - x^3 + 4x^4 - x^2$, $x - 1$

In problems 7–12, use the factor theorem to show that the first polynomial is (or is not) a factor of the second polynomial.

7. $x - 4$, $x^3 - 2x^2 + 3x - 44$ **8.** $x + 3$, $3x^3 + 8x^2 + 3x + 18$
9. $x - 3$, $x^3 - 3x^2 + 6x - 7$ **10.** $x + 1$, $x^4 - 2x^2 + x + 1$
11. $x - 2$, $x^4 - 4x^3 + 3x^2 + 10$ **12.** $x + 1$, $2x^4 + x^3 - 10x - 11$

In problems 13–18, use the factor theorem to determine a polynomial equation of lowest degree that has the given roots.

13. $7, 2, -1$ **14.** $3, -3, 5, -5$ **15.** $a, b, 2$
16. $3, -2, \sqrt{2}, -\sqrt{2}$ **17.** $2, 2 \pm \sqrt{3}$ **18.** $3, -1, 3 \pm \sqrt{2}$

In problems 19–24, determine the roots of the given equation.

19. $(x + 4)(x - 1)(2x - 1) = 0$ **20.** $(x + 4)(x^2 + x - 6) = 0$
21. $(x + 3)(x^2 - 8) = 0$ **22.** $(x^2 - 2x)(x^2 + 2x + 5) = 0$
23. $(x^2 + 3x - 4)(x^2 - 6x + 10) = 0$ **24.** $(x^3 - 4x)(x^2 - 4x + 13) = 0$
25. Determine the value of k so that $x^3 - kx^2 + 1$ is divisible by $x - 1$.

26. Determine the value of k so that the remainder is 5 when $x^2 + x - 1$ is divided by $x - k$.
27. Determine the value of k so that $x - 3$ is a factor of $x^3 + 3x^2 + kx - 7$.
28. Given that 1 is a root of the equation $2x^3 - 11x^2 + 4x + 5 = 0$, determine the other roots.
29. Given that 2 is a root of the equation $4x^3 - 4x^2 - 11x + 6 = 0$, determine the other roots.
30. Given that -2 is a root of the equation $2x^4 - x^3 - 13x^2 - 6x = 0$, determine the other roots.

Answers 9.2

1. 27	**2.** -1	**4.** -77	**5.** 105
7. is	**8.** is	**10.** is not	**11.** is not
13. $x^3 - 8x^2 + 5x + 14 = 0$		**14.** $x^4 - 34x^2 + 225 = 0$	
16. $x^4 - x^3 - 8x^2 + 2x + 12 = 0$		**17.** $x^3 - 6x^2 + 9x - 2 = 0$	
19. $-4, 1, \frac{1}{2}$	**20.** $-4, 2, -3$	**22.** $0, 2, -1 \pm 2i$	**23.** $-4, 1, 3 \pm i$
25. 2	**26.** $2, -3$	**28.** $5, -\frac{1}{2}$	**29.** $\frac{1}{2}, -\frac{3}{2}$

9.3 Theorems About the Roots of Polynomial Equations

In this section, we shall consider several theorems that are of theoretical importance in solving polynomial equations. These theorems will not tell us how to solve a polynomial equation, but they will give us some information about the roots of such an equation. We begin with a theorem whose proof is beyond the scope of this book.

Theorem 9.5 (The Fundamental Theorem of Algebra) If $F(x)$ is a polynomial of degree n where $n \in N$, then the equation $F(x) = 0$ has at least one (real or imaginary) root.

In Chapter 3 we found that each linear equation (a polynomial equation of degree *one*) has exactly *one* solution. In the same chapter we showed that each quadratic equation (a polynomial equation of degree *two*) has precisely *two* solutions. In general, it can be shown that a polynomial equation of degree n has exactly n solutions.

Theorem 9.6 (The Number-of-Roots Theorem) If $F(x)$ is a polynomial of degree n where $n \in N$, then the equation $F(x) = 0$ has exactly n roots.

Proof The equation $F(x) = 0$ has at least one root, call it r_1, according to the fundamental theorem of algebra. Thus it follows by the factor theorem that $x - r_1$ is a factor of $F(x)$. Hence

$$F(x) = (x - r_1) \cdot P_1(x),$$

where $P_1(x)$ is a polynomial of degree $n - 1$. If the polynomial $P_1(x)$ is not a constant, then the equation $P_1(x) = 0$ has at least one root, say r_2, according to the fundamental theorem of algebra. Thus $x - r_2$ is a factor of $P_1(x)$ and hence $P_1(x) = (x - r_2) \cdot P_2(x)$, where $P_2(x)$ is a polynomial of degree $n - 2$. Therefore,

$$F(x) = (x - r_1)(x - r_2) \cdot P_2(x).$$

Repeating this process n times, we get

$$F(x) = (x - r_1)(x - r_2) \cdots (x - r_n) \cdot P_n(x),$$

where $P_n(x)$ is a polynomial of degree $n - n = 0$. Since $P_n(x)$ is a polynomial of degree zero, $P_n(x)$ is a constant, say a. Thus the equation $F(x) = 0$ has exactly n roots. ∎

It is important to note that the number-of-roots theorem does *not* state that the roots of the equation $F(x) = 0$ are all real. For example, the two roots of the quadratic equation $x^2 + 2x + 2 = 0$ are $-1 \pm i$. It is also important to note that the number-of-roots theorem does *not* state that the roots of the equation $F(x) = 0$ are all distinct. For example, the quadratic equation $x^2 - 2x + 1 = 0$ has two roots, namely 1 and 1, which are not distinct.

When r appears twice as a root of an equation, we say that r is a *double root* of the equation. When r appears three times as a root of an equation, we say that r is a *triple root*. In general, when r appears k times as a root of an equation, we say that r is a *root of multiplicity k*.

EXAMPLE 1

(a) In the equation $x^2 - 2x + 1 = (x - 1)(x - 1) = 0$, 1 is a double root.
(b) In the equation $(x - 2)^4(x + 3)^3 = 0$, 2 is a root of multiplicity 4 and -3 is a triple root, or a root of multiplicity 3.

Recalling the quadratic formula, we note that when a quadratic equation with real coefficients has $a + bi$ as a root, it also has $a - bi$ as a root. That is, imaginary roots of a quadratic equation with real coefficients occur in pairs. This result is generalized in the following theorem, which states that when a polynomial equation has real coefficients, the imaginary roots of the equation occur in pairs.

Theorem 9.7   If the imaginary number $a + bi$ is a root of the equation $F(x) = 0$, where $F(x)$ is a polynomial with real coefficients, then the conjugate imaginary number $a - bi$ is also a root of the polynomial equation $F(x) = 0$.

Proof   Since $a + bi$ is a root of $F(x) = 0$, it follows from the factor theorem that $[x - (a + bi)]$ is a factor of $F(x)$. According to the factor theorem, we can show that $a - bi$ is also a root of $F(x) = 0$ by showing that $[x - (a - bi)]$ is also a factor of $F(x)$. We can do this by showing that

$$P(x) = x^2 - 2ax + a^2 + b^2 = [x - (a + bi)][x - (a - bi)]$$

is a factor of $F(x)$. Dividing $F(x)$ by $P(x)$, we obtain a quotient $Q(x)$ and a remainder $R(x)$ of degree less than or equal to one. If we write $R(x) = cx + d$, we have

$$F(x) = Q(x) \cdot P(x) + (cx + d) \qquad (9-2)$$

according to Eq. (2-1). Since $a + bi$ is a root of $F(x) = 0$, we know that $F(a + bi) = 0$. Therefore, substituting $a + bi$ for x in Eq. (9-2) gives

$$F(a + bi) = Q(a + bi) \cdot P(a + bi) + c(a + bi) + d = 0,$$

which in turn gives

$$Q(a + bi) \cdot 0 + c(a + bi) + d = 0,$$
$$c(a + bi) + d = 0,$$

and

$$(ca + d) + cbi = 0,$$

since $a + bi$ is a root of $P(x)$. Using Definition 3.2 it then follows that

$$ca + d = 0 \qquad \text{and} \qquad cb = 0.$$

Since $cb = 0$ and $b \neq 0$ (because $a + bi$ is an imaginary number), it follows that $c = 0$. This in turn means that $d = 0$, since $ca + d = (0)a + d = 0$. Thus $R(x) = cx + d = 0x + 0 = 0$. Hence Eq. (9-2) becomes

$$F(x) = Q(x) \cdot P(x) + 0 = Q(x) \cdot [x - (a + bi)][x - (a - bi)].$$

Thus $[x - (a - bi)]$ is a factor of $F(x)$, and hence $a - bi$ is a root of $F(x) = 0$. ∎

Note that Theorem 9.7 applies only to polynomials *with real coefficients.* For example, the polynomial $2x + i = 0$ has only one solution, namely $x = -i/2$.

EXAMPLE 2

Determine the polynomial equation of lowest degree with real coefficients which has 3 and $-3 - 2i$ as roots.

Solution   Using Theorem 9.7, it follows that $-3 + 2i$ must also be a root of the desired equation. Hence the desired polynomial equation $F(x) = 0$ has the roots 3, $-3 - 2i$, and $-3 + 2i$. Using the factor theorem, it follows that $x - 3$, $x - (-3 - 2i)$, and $x - (-3 + 2i)$ are the factors of $F(x)$. Therefore,

$$F(x) = [x - 3][x - (-3 - 2i)][x - (-3 + 2i)] = 0,$$

and hence

$$x^3 + 3x^2 - 5x - 39 = 0$$

is the desired polynomial equation.   ■

Problems 9.3

1. How many roots does $x^{17} - 17x^3 + 1 = 0$ have?
2. How many roots does $x^{80} + 10x + 7 = 0$ have?
3. How many roots does $x^{55} + 55x^{59} - x + 2 = 0$ have?

In problems 4–9, if the given number is a root of a polynomial equation $F(x) = 0$ with real coefficients, give another number that must also be a root of $F(x) = 0$.

4. $2 - 3i$ 5. $1 + i$ 6. $-3i$
7. $-5i$ 8. $7 - 2i$ 9. $1 + 6i$

In problems 10–18, determine a polynomial equation of lowest degree with real coefficients that has the given roots.

10. $5, 2 + i$ 11. $-2, 5, 2 - i$ 12. $1, 0, 3 - i$
13. $-1, -i, 1 + i$ 14. $0, 2i, 1 - 2i$ 15. $1, -3i, 2 - i$
16. 1 as a double root, $-i$ 17. 2 as a triple root, $1 - i$
18. 0 as a root of multiplicity 4, $1 - i$
19. Use synthetic division to show that -2 is a double root of $x^4 + x^2 + 36x + 52 = 0$. Then find the remaining roots of the given equation.
20. Use synthetic division to show that 1 is a triple root of $x^5 + x^4 - 4x^3 - 4x^2 + 11x - 5 = 0$. Then find the remaining roots of the given equation.
21. Use synthetic division to show that -1 is a triple root of $x^5 + 5x^4 + 11x^3 + 13x^2 + 8x + 2 = 0$. Then find the remaining roots of the given equation.

22. Given that i is a root of the equation $x^4 - 2x^3 - 3x^2 - 2x - 4 = 0$, determine the other roots of the given equation.

23. Given that $2 + i$ is a root of the equation $x^4 - 2x^3 + 7x^2 - 30x + 50 = 0$, determine the other roots of the given equation.

24. Given that $1 - 2i$ is a root of the equation $x^4 - 2x^3 - 2x^2 + 14x - 35 = 0$, determine the other roots of the given equation.

25. If $a + bi$ is a root of the polynomial equation $F(x) = 0$ *with complex coefficients,* give an example which shows that $a - bi$ is *not necessarily* a root of $F(x) = 0$.

26. Prove that a polynomial equation of degree 3 with real coefficients has either three real roots, or one real root and two imaginary roots. (*Hint:* Use Theorems 9.6 and 9.7.)

27. Prove that a polynomial equation of degree four with real coefficients has either four real roots, two real roots and two imaginary roots, or four imaginary roots.

Answers 9.3

1. 17   **2.** 80   **4.** $2 + 3i$

5. $1 - i$ **7.** $5i$ **8.** $7 + 2i$

10. $x^3 - 9x^2 + 25x - 25 = 0$ **11.** $x^4 - 7x^3 + 7x^2 + 25x - 50 = 0$

13. $x^5 - x^4 + x^3 + x^2 + 2 = 0$ **14.** $x^5 - 2x^4 + 9x^3 - 8x^2 + 20x = 0$

16. $x^4 - 2x^3 + 2x^2 - 2x + 1 = 0$ **17.** $x^5 - 8x^4 + 26x^3 - 44x^2 + 40x - 16 = 0$

19. $2 \pm 3i$ **20.** $-2 \pm i$

22. $-i,\ 1 + \sqrt{5},\ 1 - \sqrt{5}$ **23.** $2 - i,\ -1 + 3i,\ -1 - 3i$

9.4 Real Roots of Polynomial Equations

In this section, we shall consider two theorems that can be used to determine certain information concerning the real roots of a polynomial equation. We begin with a theorem, which we will not prove, which yields information concerning the number of positive roots and the number of negative roots of a polynomial equation.

Theorem 9.8 (Descartes' Rule of Signs) Let $F(x) = a_0 x^n + a_1 x^{n-1} + \cdots + a_n$ be a polynomial with real coefficients.

   (a) If k is the number of variations in sign that occur in the coefficients of $F(x)$, then the number of *positive* roots of the equation $F(x) = 0$ is either k or is less than k by an even positive integer.

   (b) If k is the number of variations in sign that occur in the coefficients of $F(-x)$, then the number of *negative* roots of the equation $F(x) = 0$ is either k or is less than k by an even positive integer.

If $F(x) = a_0 x^n + a_1 x^{n-1} + \cdots + a_n$ is a polynomial with real coefficients, a **variation in sign** occurs when two consecutive coefficients of $F(x)$ differ in sign. As an example, the polynomial

$$x^4 - 2x^2 - x + 5$$

has two variations in sign.

EXAMPLE 1

What can be learned about the number of positive roots and the number of negative roots of $2x^4 - 3x^3 - 4x^2 + 1 = 0$ without solving it?

Solution Since the polynomial

$$F(x) = 2x^4 - 3x^3 - 4x^2 + 1$$

has two variations in sign, it follows by Theorem 9.8(a) that the given equation has either two positive roots or no positive roots. Since the polynomial

$$F(-x) = 2(-x)^4 - 3(-x)^3 - 4(-x)^2 + 1$$
$$= 2x^4 + 3x^3 - 4x^2 + 1$$

has two variations in sign, it follows by Theorem 9.8(b) that the given equation has either two negative roots or no negative roots. ∎

EXAMPLE 2

Investigate the equation $x^4 + 2x^3 + x^2 - 2x - 2 = 0$ to see what can be learned about its roots.

Solution Using Theorem 9.6, it follows that the given equation has exactly four roots. Since

$$F(x) = x^4 + 2x^3 + x^2 - 2x - 2 = 0$$

has one variation in sign, it follows by Theorem 9.8(a) that exactly one of these four roots is positive. Since

$$F(-x) = (-x)^4 + 2(-x)^3 + (-x)^2 - 2(-x) - 2$$
$$= x^4 - 2x^3 + x^2 + 2x - 2$$

has three variations in sign, it follows by Theorem 9.8(b) that the given equation has either three negative roots or one negative root. In conclusion, since there are four roots in all, there is either one positive, one negative, and two imaginary roots, or there is one positive and three negative roots. ∎

EXERCISE 1

Investigate the equation $x^5 + x^3 + x - 1 = 0$ to see what can be learned about its roots.

Answer   One positive root and four imaginary roots.

The next theorem can be used to isolate the real roots of a polynomial equation with real coefficients between a fixed positive number and a fixed negative number.

Theorem 9.9   Let $F(x) = a_0 x^n + a_1 x^{n-1} + \cdots + a_n$, where $a_0 > 0$, be a polynomial with real coefficients.
  (a) If there are no negative numbers in the third row of the synthetic division of $F(x)$ by $x - a$, where $a > 0$, then a is an upper bound for the real roots of $F(x) = 0$.
  (b) If the numbers in the third row alternate in sign in the synthetic division of $F(x)$ by $x - a$, where $a < 0$, then a is a lower bound for the real roots of $F(x) = 0$.

Proof of (a)   If $Q(x)$ represents the quotient and R represents the constant remainder obtained when $F(x)$ is divided by $x - a$, then

$$F(x) = (x - a) \cdot Q(x) + R.$$

Recall that the coefficient of the quotient $Q(x)$ and the constant remainder R are the numbers of the third row in the synthetic division of $F(x)$ by $x - a$. Since there are no negative numbers in the third row of the synthetic division of $F(x)$ by $x - a$, it follows that none of the coefficients of $Q(x)$ are negative and that R is zero or positive. Thus the polynomial

$$(x - a) \cdot Q(x) + R$$

is positive for all real numbers $x > a$. That is, $F(x) > 0$ for $x > a$. Hence $F(x) = 0$ has no roots larger than a. Therefore, a is an upper bound for the real roots of $F(x) = 0$.   ∎
  The proof of (b) is left as a problem.

EXAMPLE 3

Determine the smallest positive integer that is an upper bound for the real roots of $4x^3 - x^2 - 13x + 7 = 0$.

Solution We begin by testing the number 1 to see if it is an upper bound for the real roots of the given equation.

$$
\begin{array}{r|rrrr}
1 & 4 & -1 & -13 & 7 \\
  &   & 4 & 3   & -10 \\
\hline
  & 4 & 3 & -10 & -3
\end{array}
$$

Since there are negative numbers in the third row, we next test the number 2 to see if it is an upper bound for the roots.

$$
\begin{array}{r|rrrr}
2 & 4 & -1 & -13 & 7 \\
  &   & 8 & 14 & 2 \\
\hline
  & 4 & 7 & 1   & 9
\end{array}
$$

Thus 2 is an upper bound for the real roots of the given equation, since there are no negative numbers in the third row. ∎

EXAMPLE 4

Determine the largest negative integer that is a lower bound for the real roots of $2x^3 + 5x^2 + 6x + 2 = 0$.

Solution We begin by testing the number -1 to see if it is a lower bound for the real roots of the given equation.

$$
\begin{array}{r|rrrr}
-1 & 2 & 5 & 6 & 2 \\
   &   & -2 & -3 & -3 \\
\hline
   & 2 & 3 & 3 & -1
\end{array}
$$

Since the numbers in the third row do not alternate in sign, we next test the number -2 to see if it is a lower bound for the real roots. After doing this, we find that the number -2 also fails the test. Thus we test the number -3 next.

$$
\begin{array}{r|rrrr}
-3 & 2 & 5 & 6 & 2 \\
   &   & -6 & 3 & -27 \\
\hline
   & 2 & -1 & 9 & -25
\end{array}
$$

Thus -3 is a lower bound for the real roots of the given equation since the numbers in the third row are alternately positive and negative. ∎

EXERCISE 2

Determine the smallest positive integer M that is an upper bound (and the largest negative integer m that is a lower bound) for the real roots of $2x^3 - x^2 - 2x - 9 = 0$.

Answer $M = 3$, $m = -1$

Problems 9.4

In problems 1–9, determine what can be learned about the number of positive roots
and the number of negative roots of the given equation.

1. $x^3 - 2x^2 + 1 = 0$ 2. $x^3 + 3x - 4 = 0$ 3. $x^3 - 3x + 7 = 0$
4. $x^4 + x^3 - 2 = 0$ 5. $x^4 + x^3 + 3 = 0$ 6. $x^4 - x^3 - 7 = 0$
7. $x^4 - x^3 + x^2 - x + 1 = 0$ 8. $x^4 - x^2 - 5x + 3 = 0$ 9. $x^5 - x^3 - 5x^2 + 1 = 0$

In problems 10–15, investigate the given equation to see what can be learned about
its roots.

10. $x^3 - 2x^2 - 2x + 1 = 0$ 11. $x^3 - 3x^2 + 3x - 5 = 0$ 12. $x^3 + 5x^2 - 2x - 3 = 0$
13. $x^4 - 2x^2 + 3x - 2 = 0$ 14. $x^4 + 3x^3 - x - 7 = 0$ 15. $x^4 + x^3 - 3x + 5 = 0$

In problems 16–21, determine the smallest positive integer that is an upper bound
for the real roots of the given equation.

16. $2x^3 - x^2 - 7x + 6 = 0$ 17. $3x^3 - 2x^2 - 7x - 50 = 0$
18. $2x^3 - 11x^2 + 19x + 2 = 0$ 19. $x^4 - 3x^3 - 3x^2 - 17 = 0$
20. $2x^4 - 5x^3 - 12x + 2 = 0$ 21. $3x^4 - 7x^3 - 7x^2 - 7x - 7 = 0$

In problems 22–27, determine the largest negative integer that is a lower bound for
the real roots of the given equation.

22. $3x^3 + 5x^2 - 10x + 21 = 0$ 23. $2x^3 - 7x^2 - 32x + 110 = 0$
24. $3x^3 + 11x^2 - 6x - 8 = 0$ 25. $2x^4 + 8x^2 + 2x - 9 = 0$
26. $2x^4 + 5x^3 - x + 1 = 0$ 27. $3x^4 - 5x^3 - 15x^2 - 40 = 0$
28. Let $F(x) = x^{80} + 4x - 8$.
   (a) How many roots does $F(x) = 0$ have?
   (b) How many positive roots does $F(x) = 0$ have?
   (c) How many negative roots does $F(x) = 0$ have?
   (d) What is the smallest positive integer that is an upper bound for the real roots
       of $F(x) = 0$?
   (e) What is the largest negative integer that is a lower bound for the real roots
       of $F(x) = 0$?
29. If $F(x) = x^{55} - 2x^2 + 2$, answer the questions in problem 28.
30. If $F(x) = x^{69} - 3x^{68} + 2x + 1$, answer the questions in problem 28.
31. Prove Theorem 9.9(b).

Answers 9.4

1. 2 or 0 positive roots; 1 negative root
2. 1 positive root; 0 negative roots
4. 1 positive root; 1 negative root
5. 0 positive roots; 2 or 0 negative roots
7. 4, 2, or 0 positive roots; 0 negative roots
8. 2 or 0 positive roots; 2 or 0 negative roots
10. 2 positive and 1 negative roots; or 1 negative and 2 imaginary roots
11. 3 positive roots; or 1 positive and 2 imaginary roots

13. 3 positive and 1 negative roots; or 1 positive, 1 negative, and 2 imaginary roots
14. 1 positive, 1 negative, and 2 imaginary roots; or 1 positive and 3 negative roots
16. 3   **17.** 4   **19.** 5   **20.** 4   **22.** −4   **23.** −4   **25.** −2   **26.** −3
28. (a) 80   (b) 1   (c) 1   (d) 2   (e) −2
29. (a) 55   (b) 2 or 0   (c) 1   (d) 2   (e) −1

9.5 Rational Roots of Polynomial Equations with Integers As Coefficients

Using the number-of-roots theorem, we can determine the number of roots of the polynomial equation $F(x)=0$, but this theorem does not indicate how to determine the roots. The following theorem can be used to determine each of the *rational roots* of a polynomial equation $F(x)=0$ when the coefficients of $F(x)$ are integers.

Theorem 9.10 (The Rational-Roots Theorem)   Let $F(x)=a_0x^n+a_1x^{n-1}+\cdots a_n$, where $a_0 \neq 0$, be a polynomial with integer coefficients. If p/q is a rational root (in lowest terms) of $F(x)=0$, then p is an integral factor of a_n and q is an integral factor of a_0.

Proof   Since p/q is a root of the equation $F(x)=0$, it follows that

$$a_0\left(\frac{p}{q}\right)^n + a_1\left(\frac{p}{q}\right)^{n-1} + \cdots + a_{n-1}\left(\frac{p}{q}\right) + a_n = 0.$$

Multiplying both sides of the previous equation by q^n and simplifying, we get

$$a_0p^n + a_1p^{n-1}q + \cdots + a_{n-1}pq^{n-1} + a_nq^n = 0,$$

and hence

$$p(a_0p^{n-1} + a_1p^{n-2}q + \cdots + a_{n-1}q^{n-1}) = -a_nq^n.$$

Since the integer p is a factor of the left side of the last equation, p is also a factor of $-a_nq^n$. Since p/q is in lowest terms, p is neither a factor of q nor of q^n. Thus p must be a factor of a_n. To complete the proof, a similar argument can be given to show that q is a factor of a_0.   ∎

EXAMPLE 1

Determine the possible rational roots of $2x^3 - 9x^2 + 7x + 6 = 0$.

Solution If p/q is a rational root of the given equation, then p must be an integral factor of 6 and q must be an integral factor of 2 according to the rational-roots theorem. Hence the possible choices for p are $\pm 1, \pm 2, \pm 3$, and ± 6, and the possible choices for q are ± 1 and ± 2. Consequently, the possible rational roots are $\pm \frac{1}{1}, \pm \frac{2}{1}, \pm \frac{3}{1}, \pm \frac{6}{1}, \pm \frac{1}{2}, \pm \frac{2}{2}, \pm \frac{3}{2}$, and $\pm \frac{6}{2}$. If we eliminate repetitions, we have $-6, -3, -2, -\frac{3}{2}, -1, -\frac{1}{2}, \frac{1}{2}, 1, \frac{3}{2}, 2, 3$, and 6 as the possible rational roots of the given equation. ∎

EXERCISE 1

Determine the possible rational roots of $3x^3 + 5x^2 + 4x - 2 = 0$.

Answer $2, 1, \frac{2}{3}, \frac{1}{3}, -2, -1, -\frac{2}{3}, -\frac{1}{3}$

EXAMPLE 2

Determine the roots of $2x^3 - 9x^2 + 7x + 6 = 0$.

Solution In the previous example, we determined the possible rational roots of the given equation. Thus we need only check these possible rational roots by using synthetic division to see which of them, if any, are roots of the given equation. Testing the possible rational root 1 by synthetic division, we have

$$
\begin{array}{r|rrrr}
1 & 2 & -9 & 7 & 6 \\
  &   & 2 & -7 & 0 \\
\hline
  & 2 & -7 & 0 & 6 \\
\end{array}
$$

Since the remainder is not zero, 1 is not a root. Testing the possible rational root 2 by synthetic division, we have

$$
\begin{array}{r|rrrr}
2 & 2 & -9 & 7 & 6 \\
  &   & 4 & -10 & -6 \\
\hline
  & 2 & -5 & -3 & 0 \\
\end{array}
$$

Since the remainder is zero, 2 is a root. Since $2x^3 - 9x^2 + 7x + 6 = (x - 2)(2x^2 - 5x - 3)$, the other roots of the given equation are the roots of the equation $2x^2 - 5x - 3 = (2x + 1)(x - 3) = 0$. Thus the roots of the original equation are 3, 2, and $-\frac{1}{2}$. ∎

EXAMPLE 3

Determine the roots of $2x^4 + x^3 - 11x^2 - 24x - 18 = 0$.

Solution According to the number-of-roots theorem, the given equation has four roots. The possible rational roots are ± 1, ± 2, ± 3, ± 6, ± 9, ± 18, $\pm\frac{1}{2}$, $\pm\frac{3}{2}$, and $\pm\frac{9}{2}$. Testing the possible rational root 3, we find that 3 is a root, since

$$
\begin{array}{r|rrrrr}
3 & 2 & 1 & -11 & -24 & -18 \\
  &   & 6 & 21 & 30 & 18 \\
\hline
  & 2 & 7 & 10 & 6   & 0
\end{array}
$$

Thus the given equation can be rewritten as

$$(x-3)(2x^3 + 7x^2 + 10x + 6) = 0.$$

Therefore, the remaining roots of the original equation are roots of the equation $2x^3 + 7x^2 + 10x + 6 = 0$. The possible rational roots of the last equation are ± 1, ± 2, ± 3, ± 6, $\pm\frac{1}{2}$, and $\pm\frac{3}{2}$. Testing the possible rational root $-\frac{3}{2}$, we find that $-\frac{3}{2}$ is a root, since

$$
\begin{array}{r|rrrr}
-\frac{3}{2} & 2 & 7 & 10 & 6 \\
             &   & -3 & -6 & -6 \\
\hline
             & 2 & 4 & 4 & 0
\end{array}
$$

Hence the original equation can now be rewritten as

$$(x-3)(x+\tfrac{3}{2})(2x^2 + 4x + 4) = 0,$$

and hence as

$$(x-3)(2x+3)(x^2 + 2x + 2) = 0.$$

The remaining two roots of the original equation are roots of the quadratic equation $x^2 + 2x + 2 = 0$. Using the quadratic formula to obtain the roots of this equation, we have

$$x = \frac{-(2) \pm \sqrt{(2)^2 - 4(1)(2)}}{2(1)} = \frac{-2 \pm \sqrt{-4}}{2} = -1 \pm i.$$

Hence the roots of the original equation are 3, $-\frac{3}{2}$, $-1 + i$, and $-1 - i$. ∎

EXERCISE 2

Determine the roots of $3x^3 + 5x^2 + 4x - 2 = 0$.

Answer $\frac{1}{3}, -1 + i, -1 - i$

Certain inequalities of the form $F(x) > 0$, $F(x) \geq 0$, $F(x) < 0$, or $F(x) \leq 0$, where $F(x)$ is a polynomial with integral coefficients, can be solved by the rational-roots theorem.

EXAMPLE 4

Determine the solution set of $2x^3 - 9x^2 + 7x + 6 > 0$.

Solution In Example 2, we showed that the roots of the corresponding equation $2x^3 - 9x^2 + 7x + 6 = 0$ are $3, 2$, and $-\frac{1}{2}$. Hence the given inequality can be rewritten as

$$(2x + 1)(x - 2)(x - 3) > 0.$$

Above the coordinate line of Figure 9.1, we have indicated where each of the factors $x - 3$, $x - 2$, and $2x + 1$ is positive and where each is negative. Below the same coordinate line, we have indicated where $(2x + 1)(x - 2)(x - 3)$ is positive and where it is negative. Thus the solution set of the given inequality is $\{x \mid -\frac{1}{2} < x < 2 \text{ or } x > 3\}$. ∎

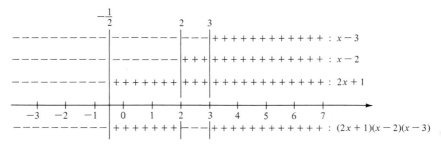

Figure 9.1

Problems 9.5

In problems 1–6, determine the possible rational roots of the given equation.

1. $2x^3 - 3x + 5 = 0$
2. $3x^7 + 5x^3 - 4 = 0$
3. $4x^6 - 2x^5 + x - 3 = 0$
4. $6x^5 + 5x^3 + 2x^2 - 4 = 0$
5. $10x^7 + 2x^6 - x - 9 = 0$
6. $6x^6 - x^5 - 3x^4 + 9 = 0$

In problems 7–15, determine the rational roots of the given equation.

7. $2x^3 + x^2 - 13x + 6 = 0$ **8.** $2x^3 + x^2 - 4x - 3 = 0$

9. $3x^3 - 13x^2 + 16x - 4 = 0$ **10.** $x^3 + 2x^2 - 4x + 1 = 0$

11. $2x^3 - 11x^2 + 16x - 3 = 0$ **12.** $2x^3 + 11x^2 + 12x - 4 = 0$

13. $x^4 - 3x^3 + 4x^2 - 3x + 3 = 0$ **14.** $x^4 - x^3 + 4x^2 + 3x + 5 = 0$

15. $x^4 + 5x^3 + 2x^2 + 15x - 3 = 0$

In problems 16–24, determine all roots of the given equation.

16. $x^3 - 4x^2 - 2x + 12 = 0$ **17.** $2x^3 - 6x^2 + x - 3 = 0$ **18.** $x^3 - 2x - 4 = 0$

19. $2x^4 - x^3 - 5x^2 + 2x + 2 = 0$ **20.** $3x^4 - 11x^3 + 14x^2 - 6x - 4 = 0$

21. $5x^4 - 26x^3 + 35x^2 - 16x + 2 = 0$ **22.** $x^4 - 5x^3 + 7x^2 - 5x + 6 = 0$

23. $x^4 + 2x^3 - 6x^2 - 6x + 9 = 0$ **24.** $2x^4 - 5x^3 + 10x^2 - 20x + 8 = 0$

25. Determine the possible rational roots of $2x^{10} - 3x^7 + x^4 + 3x = 0$.

26. Determine the possible rational roots of $x^5 - \frac{3}{2}x^2 + x - \frac{1}{3} = 0$.

27. Prove that every polynomial equation with rational coefficients can be rewritten as an equivalent polynomial equation with integral coefficients.

In problems 28–36, determine the solution set of the given inequality.

28. $x^3 - 4x^2 + x + 6 \geq 0$ **29.** $x^3 - 2x^2 - 13x - 10 > 0$ **30.** $x^3 + 6x^2 + 11x + 6 \geq 0$

31. $2x^3 + 5x^2 - 11x + 4 < 0$ **32.** $2x^3 + 3x^2 - 11x - 6 \leq 0$

33. $2x^3 - 3x^2 - 23x + 12 \leq 0$ **34.** $2x^4 - 3x^3 - 4x^2 + 3x + 2 > 0$

35. $4x^4 - 8x^3 - x^2 + 8x - 3 < 0$ **36.** $3x^4 - 7x^3 - x^2 + 7x - 2 < 0$

Answers 9.5

1. $\pm 1, \pm 5, \pm \frac{1}{2}, \pm \frac{5}{2}$ **2.** $\pm 1, \pm 2, \pm 4, \pm \frac{1}{3}, \pm \frac{2}{3}, \pm \frac{4}{3}$

4. $\pm 1, \pm 2, \pm 4, \pm \frac{1}{2}, \pm \frac{1}{3}, \pm \frac{2}{3}, \pm \frac{4}{3}, \pm \frac{1}{6}$

5. $\pm 1, \pm 3, \pm 9, \pm \frac{1}{2}, \pm \frac{3}{2}, \pm \frac{9}{2}, \pm \frac{1}{5}, \pm \frac{3}{5}, \pm \frac{9}{5}, \pm \frac{1}{10}, \pm \frac{3}{10}, \pm \frac{9}{10}$

7. $2, -3, \frac{1}{2}$ **8.** $-1, -1, \frac{3}{2}$ **10.** 1

11. 3 **13.** none   **14.** none

16. $2, 1 \pm \sqrt{7}$ **17.** $3, \pm i\sqrt{2}/2$ **19.** $1, -\frac{1}{2}, \pm \sqrt{2}$

20. $2, -\frac{1}{3}, 1 \pm i$ **22.** $2, 3, \pm i$ **23.** $1, -3, \pm \sqrt{3}$

25. $0, \pm 1, \pm 3, \pm \frac{1}{2}, \pm \frac{3}{2}$ **26.** $\pm 1, \pm 2, \pm \frac{1}{2}, \pm \frac{1}{3}, \pm \frac{2}{3}, \pm \frac{1}{6}$

28. 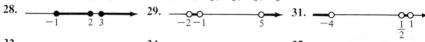   **29.**   **31.**

32. 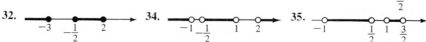   **34.**   **35.**

9.6 Irrational Roots of Polynomial Equations with Real Coefficients

In this section, we shall consider a method for approximating the irrational roots of a polynomial equation with real coefficients. Before doing this, however, we shall consider a theorem, which we shall not prove, which can be used to locate each irrational root of a polynomial equation between two consecutive integers.

Theorem 9.11 (The Location-of-Roots Theorem)   Let $x_1, x_2 \in R$ with $x_1 < x_2$. If $F(x_1)$ and $F(x_2)$ have opposite signs, then the polynomial equation $F(x) = 0$ has at least one real root between x_1 and x_2.

EXAMPLE 1

Locate each real root of $x^3 - 3x^2 - 9x + 6 = 0$ between two consecutive integers.

Solution   We begin by setting up a table of corresponding values of x and $f(x)$ for the function $f(x) = x^3 - 3x^2 - 9x + 6$:

x	-3	-2	-1	0	1	2	3	4	5
$f(x)$	-21	4	11	6	-5	-16	-21	-14	11

Since $f(-3)$ and $f(-2)$ have opposite signs, there exists a real root between -3 and -2. Similarly, there exists a real root between 0 and 1, since $f(0)$ and $f(1)$ have opposite signs. There also exists a third real root between 4 and 5, since $f(4)$ and $f(5)$ have opposite signs. According to Theorem 9.6, we have now isolated each of the three roots of the given equation between pairs of consecutive integers.

Once we have located a real root of a polynomial equation $F(x) = 0$ between two consecutive integers, there are several numerical methods that can be used to determine a decimal approximation of the root to any desired degree of accuracy. One such method, called the **method of successive approximations,** will now be described. To be precise, suppose that we have determined that there is exactly one real root of the polynomial equation $F(x) = 0$ between the consecutive integers 1 and 2. Using synthetic division to calculate $F(1)$, $F(1.1)$, $F(1.2)$, . . ., $F(1.9)$, and $F(2)$, this root can then be located between a consecutive pair of the numbers 1, 1.1, 1.2, . . ., 1.9, and 2, since exactly one pair of consecutive functional values will have opposite signs. To be precise, suppose that the root is between 1.7 and 1.8.

Applying the above process to the numbers 1.7, 1.71, 1.72, . . ., 1.79, and 1.8, the root can then be isolated between a consecutive pair of these numbers. By repeating this process a sufficient number of times, we can obtain a decimal approximation of the root correct to any desired number of decimal places.

Since the calculations involved in the method of successive approximations are long and tedious, it is desirable to find a way to shorten our work. This can be done by using linear interpolation. That is, we assume that a line segment can be used as a good approximation for the graph of a polynomial function F on sufficiently small intervals. In other words, we assume that if x_1 is sufficiently close to x_2, then the graph of the polynomial function F between $(x_1, F(x_1))$ and $(x_2, F(x_2))$ is very close to the line segment connecting these points. If $F(x_1)$ and $F(x_2)$ have opposite signs, we can then use the point where the line segment between $(x_1, F(x_1))$ and $(x_2, F(x_2))$ crosses the x-axis as a rough approximation of the point where the graph of f crosses the x-axis.

Again suppose that we have determined that exactly one real root of the polynomial equation $F(x) = 0$ lies between the consecutive integers 1 and 2. By using the line segment joining the points $(1, F(1))$ and $(2, F(2))$ as an approximation for the graph of F between these points (see Figure 9.2), we find that 1.7 can be used as a rough approximation for the root of $F(x) = 0$ between 1 and 2. ∎

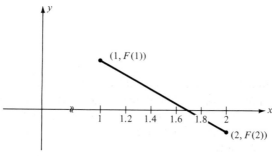

Figure 9.2

EXAMPLE 2

Determine the smallest positive root of $x^3 - 4x + 1 = 0$ correct to two decimal places.

Solution We begin by setting up a table of corresponding values of x and $f(x)$ for the function $f(x) = x^3 - 4x + 1$:

x	-3	-2	-1	0	1	2	3
$f(x)$	-14	1	3	1	-2	1	16

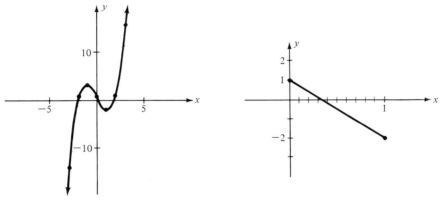

Figure 9.3   Figure 9.4

After graphing f (see Figure 9.3), we see that the smallest positive root of $f(x) = 0$ is between 0 and 1. If we assume that the graph of f between $(0,1)$ and $(1, -2)$ is very close to the straight line connecting these points (see Figure 9.4), we find that the desired root is close to .3. Thus we calculate the following table of values:

x	0.2	0.3	0.4
$f(x)$	+.228	−.173	−.536

Hence the root is between .2 and .3. If we assume that the graph of f between $(.2, .228)$ and $(.3, -.173)$ is very close to the straight line connecting these points (see Figure 9.5), we find that the desired root is close to .26. Thus we calculate the following table of values:

x	0.25	0.26	0.27
$f(x)$	+.016	−.022	−.060

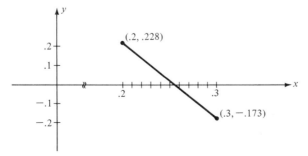

Figure 9.5

Since $f(.25) = +.016$ and $f(.26) = -.022$, it seems reasonable to conclude that the smallest positive root correct to two decimal places is .25. However, to be sure that .25 is the correct two-decimal approximation of the root, we should calculate the root to three decimal places and then round off. ∎

◆ **Problems 9.6**

In problems 1–12, use the location-of-roots theorem to locate each real root of the given equation between consecutive integers.

1. $x^2 - 2x - 2 = 0$ 2. $x^2 + 4x - 1 = 0$ 3. $4x^2 - 4x - 7 = 0$
4. $x^3 - 3x^2 + 1 = 0$ 5. $2x^3 - 5x + 2 = 0$ 6. $x^3 - 7x + 3 = 0$
7. $3x^3 - 11x^2 - x + 1 = 0$ 8. $4x^3 + 27x^2 + 42x + 18 = 0$
9. $8x^3 - 12x^2 - 16x + 10 = 0$ 10. $4x^4 - 24x^3 - 15x^2 + 42x + 14 = 0$
11. $x^4 - 4x^3 - 2x^2 + 12x - 2 = 0$ 12. $3x^4 - 8x^3 - 30x^2 + 72x + 15 = 0$

In problems 13–21, determine the indicated real root of the given polynomial equation correct to one decimal place.

13. $x^3 - 3x^2 - 2 = 0$, the positive root
14. $x^3 - 7x + 3 = 0$, the largest positive root
15. $x^3 - x^2 + 2 = 0$, the negative root
16. $x^3 + 2x^2 - 5x + 1 = 0$, the largest positive root
17. $x^3 + 2x^2 - 5x + 1 = 0$, the negative root
18. $x^3 + 2x^2 - 5x + 1 = 0$, the smallest positive root
19. $x^4 - 3x^3 + x - 1 = 0$, the root between 2 and 3
20. $x^4 - 2x^2 + 2x - 5 = 0$, the root between 1 and 2
21. $x^4 - 4x^3 + 7 = 0$, the root between 3 and 4
22. Determine the largest positive root of $x^3 - 3x^2 + 1 = 0$ correct to two decimal places.
23. Determine the smallest positive root of $x^3 - 6x + 2 = 0$ correct to two decimal places.
24. Determine the largest negative root of $x^3 + x^2 - 20x - 5 = 0$ correct to two decimal places.
25. Determine a decimal approximation of $\sqrt[3]{12}$ correct to two decimal places. (*Hint:* Consider the equation $x^3 - 12 = 0$.)
26. Determine a decimal approximation of $\sqrt[3]{21}$ correct to two decimal places.
27. Determine a decimal approximation of $\sqrt{17}$ correct to two decimal places.

Answers 9.6

1. -1 and 0, 2 and 3   2. -5 and -4, 0 and 1
4. -1 and 0, 0 and 1, 2 and 3   5. -2 and -1, 0 and 1, 1 and 2
7. -1 and 0, 0 and 1, 3 and 4   8. -5 and -4, -2 and -1, -1 and 0
10. -2 and -1, -1 and 0, 1 and 2, 6 and 7
11. -2 and -1, 0 and 1, 1 and 2, 3 and 4
13. 3.2   14. 2.4   16. 1.3   17. -3.5 19. 2.9
20. 1.6   22. 2.88   23. 0.34   25. 2.29   26. 2.14

chapter 9 review problems

1. Use synthetic division to determine the quotient $Q(x)$ and the remainder R obtained when $x^4 - 2x^3 + 3x - 7$ is divided by $x - 3$.
2. Determine the constant remainder R that is obtained when $3x^4 - x + 1$ is divided by $x + 2$ by using (a) synthetic division and (b) the remainder theorem.
3. Determine the polynomial equation of lowest degree with real coefficients that have the given roots.
   (a) $2, 3, -1$ (b) $1, 2, 1 - i$
4. Use synthetic division to show that 2 is a double root of $x^4 + x^2 - 36x + 52 = 0$. Then find the remaining roots of the given equation.
5. Given that $-1 + i$ is a root of $x^4 + 2x^3 - 3x^2 - 10x - 10 = 0$, determine the other roots.
6. Determine the number of positive roots of the equation $x^5 + x^2 + x - 1 = 0$.
7. Determine the number of negative roots of the equation $x^5 + x^2 + x - 1 = 0$.
8. Determine the smallest positive integer that is an upper bound for the real roots of $x^3 + 2x^2 - 5x + 1 = 0$.
9. Determine the largest negative integer that is a lower bound for the real roots of $x^3 + 2x^2 - 5x + 1 = 0$.
10. Determine the rational roots of $2x^3 - x^2 - 7x + 6 = 0$.
11. Determine all the roots of $x^3 + 2x^2 + 2x + 1 = 0$.
12. Determine the largest positive root of $2x^3 - x^2 - 10x - 1 = 0$ correct to two decimal places.
13. Suppose that $f(x) = x^{28} + 2x + 1$.
    (a) How many roots does $f(x) = 0$ have?
    (b) How many positive roots does $f(x) = 0$ have?
    (c) How many negative roots does $f(x) = 0$ have?
    (d) What is the smallest positive integer that is an upper bound for the real roots of $f(x) = 0$?
    (e) What is the largest negative integer that is a lower bound for the real roots of $f(x) = 0$?

answers

1. $Q(x) = x^3 + x^2 + 3x + 12$, $R = 29$
2. 51
3. (a) $x^3 - 4x^2 + x + 6 = 0$ (b) $x^4 - 5x^3 + 10x^2 - 10x + 4 = 0$
4. $-2 + 3i, -2 - 3i$ 5. $-1 - i, \pm\sqrt{5}$
6. 1   7. 2 or 0
8. 2   9. -3
10. $1, -2, \frac{3}{2}$ 11. $-1, (-1 \pm \sqrt{3}i)/2$
12. 2.54   13. (a) 28   (b) 0   (c) 2 or 0   (d) 1   (e) -2

10

sequences; mathematical
induction; the binomial
theorem

10.1 Sequences and Series

We begin by defining a special kind of important function that is called a sequence.

Definition 10.1 An **infinite sequence** is a function whose domain is the set N of natural numbers. A **finite sequence** is a function whose domain is $\{1, 2, 3, \ldots, n\}$, where n is a fixed natural number. Infinite sequences and finite sequences are collectively known as **sequences.**

For example, the function a defined by

$$a(n) = 2n - 1, \quad \text{where } n \in N,$$

is a sequence (in this case, an infinite sequence), since its domain is defined as the set N of natural numbers. This sequence can be represented in order-pair notation as

$$a = \{(1, 1), (2, 3), (3, 5), (4, 7), \ldots, (n, 2n-1), \ldots\}.$$

Since it is understood that the domain of an infinite sequence is the set N of natural numbers, it is traditional to represent such a sequence by indicating only its range elements. Thus the sequence described above is denoted by

$$1, 3, 5, 7, \ldots, 2n-1, \ldots,$$

since

$$a(1) = 1$$
$$a(2) = 3$$
$$a(3) = 5$$
$$\vdots$$

and in general
$$a(n) = 2n - 1.$$

When we represent a sequence by listing the elements of the range of the sequence in the order

$$a(1), a(2), a(3), \ldots, a(n), \ldots, \qquad (10-1)$$

the number $a(1)$ is called the *first term* of the sequence, $a(2)$ is the *second term*, and so forth. The number $a(n)$ is called the *n*th *term* of the sequence.

It is traditional to represent the terms of a sequence by using subscript notation rather than functional notation. Thus we write a_1 instead of $a(1)$, a_2 instead of $a(2)$, and so on. Using this symbolism, sequence $(10-1)$ is denoted as

$$a_1, a_2, a_3, \ldots, a_n, \ldots.$$

A finite sequence with n terms is denoted by

$$a_1, a_2, a_3, \ldots, a_n.$$

EXAMPLE 1
Determine the first four terms of the sequence whose *n*th term is $a_n = n^2$.

Solution

$$a(1) = a_1 = 1^2 = 1, \qquad a(2) = a_2 = 2^2 = 4,$$
$$a(3) = a_3 = 3^2 = 9, \qquad a(4) = a_4 = 4^2 = 16.$$

The given sequence can be represented as

$$1, 4, 9, 16 \ldots, n^2, \ldots. \qquad\blacksquare$$

There are two common ways of describing the terms of a sequence. One is to give a formula that describes the nth term. We saw an example of this method in Example 1. The other way of describing a sequence is to give the first term of the sequence and to give a formula that defines a *recurrence relationship* between each term of the sequence and its preceding term.

EXAMPLE 2

Determine the first four terms of the sequence defined by $a_1 = 5$ and $a_{n+1} = a_n - 3$ for $n \in N$.

Solution   We are given that

$$a_1 = 5.$$

Since $a_{n+1} = a_n - 3$ for $n \in N$, we have

$$a_2 = a_1 - 3 = 5 - 3 = 2,$$
$$a_3 = a_2 - 3 = 2 - 3 = -1,$$
$$a_4 = a_3 - 3 = -1 - 3 = -4.$$ ∎

Given the first few terms in a sequence, it is often possible to determine a formula that defines the nth term of the sequence. For example,

$$2, 4, 6, 8, \ldots \qquad \text{is defined by} \quad a_n = 2n,$$
$$1, \tfrac{1}{2}, \tfrac{1}{3}, \tfrac{1}{4}, \ldots \qquad \text{is defined by} \quad a_n = \frac{1}{n},$$

and $1, -4, 9, -16, \ldots$ is defined by $a_n = (-1)^{n+1} n^2.$

It is important to note that the formula which we determine is not necessarily unique. For example,

$$1, 2, 3, \ldots \qquad \text{is defined by} \quad a_n = n.$$

However,

$$1, 2, 3, \ldots \qquad \text{is also defined by} \quad a_n = (n-2)^3 + 2.$$

Associated with each sequence is a *series*.

Definition 10.2   A **series** is the indicated sum of the terms in a sequence. The series associated with a finite sequence is called a **finite series**. The series associated with an infinite sequence is called an **infinite series**.

For example, associated with the infinite sequence 3, 7, 11, 15, . . ., $4n - 1, \ldots$ is the infinite series $3 + 7 + 11 + 15 + \cdots + (4n - 1) + \cdots$. As other examples,

$$1, 4, 9, 16, 25 \quad \text{is associated with} \quad 1 + 4 + 9 + 16 + 25,$$

$$1, \frac{1}{2}, \frac{1}{3}, \ldots, \frac{1}{n} \quad \text{is associated with} \quad 1 + \frac{1}{2} + \frac{1}{3} + \cdots + \frac{1}{n}.$$

Series are often represented in compact form, called **sigma notation**, by using the Greek letter Σ (sigma) as a means of indicating the summation involved. Thus the finite series

$$a_1 + a_2 + a_3 + \cdots + a_n$$

is abbreviated as

$$\sum_{k=1}^{n} a_k,$$

where the terms of the series are obtained from the sigma notation by successively replacing k with integers, starting with 1 (the first value of k) and ending with n (the last value of k). An infinite series

$$a_1 + a_2 + a_3 + \cdots + a_n + \cdots$$

is abbreviated as

$$\sum_{k=1}^{\infty} a_k.$$

For example,

$$\sum_{k=1}^{4} k \qquad \text{represents the series} \quad 1 + 2 + 3 + 4,$$

$$\sum_{k=1}^{n} k^2 \qquad \text{represents the series} \quad 1 + 4 + 9 + \cdots + n^2,$$

and

$$\sum_{k=1}^{\infty} (2k - 1) \quad \text{represents the series} \quad 1 + 3 + 5 + \cdots + (2n - 1) + \cdots.$$

Problems 10.1

In problems 1 – 12, write the first four terms of the sequence determined by the given conditions.

1. $a_n = 3n - 2$ 2. $a_n = n + 3$ 3. $a_n = 2n - 5$
4. $a_n = 3n$ 5. $a_n = (-1)^n n^2$ 6. $a_n = n^n$
7. $a_1 = 3, a_{n+1} = a_n - 2$ 8. $a_1 = 1, a_{n+1} = a_n + 2n + 1$
9. $a_1 = 2, a_{n+1} = a_n + 3n - 1$ 10. $a_1 = -5, a_{n+1} = a_n + n^2$
11. $a_1 = 1, a_{n+1} = 2a_n + 1$ 12. $a_1 = 4, a_{n+1} = 1/a^n$

In problems 13 – 18, determine a formula for the nth term of a sequence beginning with the given terms.

13. 3, 6, 9, 12, . . .   14. 3, 9, 15, 21, . . .
15. 2, 4, 8, 16, . . .   16. 2, 5, 10, 17, 26, . . .
17. 1, 3, 9, 27, . . .   18. $\frac{1}{2}, \frac{2}{3}, \frac{3}{4}, \frac{4}{5}, \ldots$

In problems 19 – 24, express the given series in sigma notation.

19. $2 + 5 + 8 + 11 + 14$ 20. $2 + 4 + 8 + 16 + 32$
21. $\frac{1}{3} + \frac{1}{4} + \frac{1}{5} + \frac{1}{6}$ 22. $1 + 8 + 27 + \cdots + n^3$
23. $\frac{3}{2} + \frac{4}{3} + \frac{5}{4} + \frac{6}{5} + \cdots$ 24. $\frac{1}{2} + \frac{1}{4} + \frac{1}{6} + \frac{1}{8} + \cdots$

In problems 25 – 30, write the given series in expanded form without sigma notation.

25. $\displaystyle\sum_{k=1}^{3} (5k - 3)$ 26. $\displaystyle\sum_{k=1}^{4} (-1)^k (k + 1)^2$ 27. $\displaystyle\sum_{k=1}^{5} k(k + 1)$

28. $\displaystyle\sum_{k=1}^{\infty} (-1)^{k+1} x^{k-1}$ 29. $\displaystyle\sum_{k=1}^{n} \frac{1}{k(k + 1)}$ 30. $\displaystyle\sum_{k=1}^{n} \frac{k}{k^2 + 1}$

Answers 10.1

1. 1, 4, 7, 10   2. 4, 5, 6, 7   4. 3, 6, 9, 12
5. $-1, 4, -9, 16$ 7. 3, 1, $-1, -3$ 8. 1, 4, 9, 16
10. $-5, -4, 0, 9$ 11. 1, 3, 7, 15   13. $a_n = 3n$
14. $a_n = 6n - 3$ 16. $a_n = n^2 + 1$ 17. $a_n = 3^{n-1}$

19. $\displaystyle\sum_{k=1}^{5} (3K - 1)$ 20. $\displaystyle\sum_{k=1}^{5} 2^k$ 22. $\displaystyle\sum_{k=1}^{n} k^3$

23. $\displaystyle\sum_{k=1}^{\infty} \left(\frac{k + 2}{k + 1}\right)$ 25. $2 + 7 + 12$ 26. $-4 + 9 - 16 + 25$

28. $1 - x + x^2 - x^3 + \cdots + (-1)^{n+1} x^{n-1} + \cdots$
29. $\frac{1}{2} + \frac{1}{6} + \frac{1}{12} + \frac{1}{20} + \cdots + 1/n(n + 1)$

10.2 Arithmetic Sequences and Series

In this section, we are concerned with a particular kind of sequence (called an *arithmetic progression*) and the series associated with such a sequence.

Definition 10.3   An **arithmetic sequence,** or **arithmetic progression,** is a sequence in which each term after the first is obtained by adding a constant, called the **common difference,** to the preceding term.
   For example, the sequence

$$3, 8, 13, 18, \ldots$$

is an arithmetic progression with $a_1 = 3$ and a common difference of 5. As another example, the sequence

$$5, 2, -1, -4, \ldots$$

is an arithmetic progression with $a_1 = 5$ and a common difference of -3.
   If a_1 is the first term of an arithmetic progression that has a common difference of d, then the arithmetic progression is

$$a_1, a_1 + d, a_1 + 2d, \ldots, a_1 + (n-1)d, \ldots.$$

Note that a formula for the nth term a_n of an arithmetic progression is

$$a_n = a_1 + (n-1)d. \tag{10-2}$$

EXAMPLE 1
Find the 17th term of the arithmetic progression $-1, 3, \ldots$.

Solution   In this case, $a_1 = -1$ and $d = 4$. Using Eq. (10–2), it follows that

$$a_{17} = (-1) + (16)(4) = 63. \qquad \blacksquare$$

EXAMPLE 2
If the 6th term of an arithmetic progression is 2 and the 16th term is -18, find the 1st term.

Solution   Using Eq. (10–2), we know that $a_6 = a_1 + (5)d$. Hence

$$2 = a_1 + 5d.$$

Similarly, we find that $a_{16} = -18 = a_1 + 15d$. Solving the last two equations as a system, we find that $a_1 = 12$. ∎

It is often useful to be able to find the sum S_n of the first n terms of an arithmetic progression (i.e., to find the sum of the first n terms of the series associated with the arithmetic progression). We can obtain a formula for the sum $S_n = \sum_{k=1}^{n} a_k$ as follows. Writing the expression for the sum both forward and backward, we get

$$S_n = [a_1] + [a_1 + d] + \cdots + [a_1 + (n-2)d] + [a_1 + (n-1)d]$$

and

$$S_n = [a_1 + (n-1)d] + [a_1 + (n-2)d] + \cdots + [a_1 + d] + [a_1].$$

Adding the corresponding terms of these equations, we obtain

$$2S_n = [2a_1 + (n-1)d] + [2a_1 + (n-1)d] + \cdots + [2a_1 + (n-1)d].$$

Since there are n of the terms $[2a_1 + (n-1)d]$ on the right side of the last equation, we get

$$2S_n = n[2a_1 + (n-1)d].$$

Thus

$$S_n = \frac{n}{2}[2a_1 + (n-1)d]. \tag{10-3}$$

Combining Eqs. (10-2) and (10-3), we obtain another formula, namely

$$S_n = \frac{n}{2}[a_1 + a_n], \tag{10-4}$$

which can be used to calculate the sum S_n.

EXAMPLE 3

Find the sum of the first 30 terms of the arithmetic progression -3, $2, \ldots ..$

Solution In this case, $a_1 = -3$ and $d = 5$. Using Eq. (10-3), we find that

$$S_{30} = \frac{30}{2}[2(-3) + (29)5] = 2085.$$ ∎

EXAMPLE 4

The sum of the first 13 terms of an arithmetic progression is -65. If the 13th term is 7, find the 1st term and the common difference.

Solution In this case, $a_{13} = 7$ and $S_{13} = -65$. Using Eq. $(10-4)$, we have

$$-65 = \frac{13}{2}[a_1 + 7].$$

Solving for a_1, we get $a_1 = -17$. Now using Eq. $(10-2)$, we get

$$7 = (-17) + (13-1)d. \qquad \blacksquare$$

Solving for d, we get $d = 2$.

Problems 10.2

In problems 1–6, determine if the given sequence is an arithmetic progression. If it is, give the common difference.

1. $5, -1, -7, \ldots$ 2. $7, 5, 6, 4, \ldots$ 3. $2, 4, 8, \ldots$
4. $\frac{1}{2}, \frac{5}{6}, \frac{7}{6}, \ldots$ 5. $3, 3+\pi, 3+2\pi, \ldots$ 6. $7.5, 7.1, 6.7, \ldots$

In problems 7–12, determine the next two terms of the given arithmetic progression, and then find a_n and S_n for the given value of n.

7. $1, 4, \ldots; n = 12$ 8. $-\frac{1}{2}, 2, \ldots; n = 10$ 9. $42, 30, \ldots; n = 8$
10. $7, 2, \ldots; n = 15$ 11. $1, -1, \ldots; n = 11$ 12. $-10, -\frac{10}{3}, \ldots; n = 6$

In problems 13–18, three of the five quantities a_1, d, n, a_n, and S_n are given for an arithmetic progression. Determine the missing quantities.

13. $a_1 = 7$, $a_n = -20$, $S_n = -65$ 14. $a_1 = -3$, $n = 8$, $S_n = 18$
15. $n = 12$, $a_n = -31$, $S_n = -108$ 16. $d = 3$, $n = 13$, $S_n = 286$
17. $a_1 = -5$, $d = 3$, $S_n = 85$ 18. $d = 2$, $a_n = 11$, $S_n = 35$
19. The terms that lie between two given terms of an arithmetic progression are called the **arithmetic means** between these two numbers. If only one term lies between two given terms of an arithmetic progression, the term is called the **arithmetic mean** of the other two.
    (a) Insert three arithmetic means between -3 and 15.
    (b) Determine the arithmetic mean of a and b.
20. Insert five arithmetic means between 3 and -21.
21. Determine x so that $x, 5, 1-4x, \ldots$ is an arithmetic progression.
22. Find the sum of the numbers between 50 and 200 that are exactly divisible by 9.
23. Find the sum of the numbers between 200 and 500 that are exactly divisible by 7.
24. If the 16th term of an arithmetic progression is 46 and the 25th term is 19, determine the 1st term.

25. If the 3rd term of an arithmetic progression is 5 and the 7th term is 29, determine the 10th term.

26. Find the sum of the first eight terms of an arithmetic progression in which the 5th term is 2 and the 9th term is 5.

27. Determine the sum of the first n positive odd integers.

28. Find the 1st term and the 6th term in an arithmetic progression whose 3rd term is a and whose 4th term is b.

29. If a clock strikes the number of hours on the hour, how many times will it strike each week?

30. Each row in a theatre contains two more seats than the row in front of it. If the theatre has 27 rows with 16 seats in the 1st row, how many seats are in the theatre?

In problems 31–36, use Eq. (10–4) to determine the following sums.

31. $\displaystyle\sum_{k=1}^{10}(2k-1)$ **32.** $\displaystyle\sum_{k=1}^{10}(3k-5)$ **33.** $\displaystyle\sum_{k=1}^{10}(7-5k)$

34. $\displaystyle\sum_{k=1}^{12}(3k+7)$ **35.** $\displaystyle\sum_{k=1}^{8}(13-2k)$ **36.** $\displaystyle\sum_{k=1}^{15}(4k+1)$

Answers 10.2

1. is, $d=-6$
2. is not
4. is, $d=\frac{1}{3}$
5. is, $d=\pi$
7. 7,10; 34; 210
8. $\frac{9}{2}$, 7; 22; 107.5
10. $-3, -8; -63; -420$
11. $-3, -5; -19; -99$
13. $d=-3$, $n=10$
14. $d=\frac{3}{2}$, $a_n=\frac{15}{2}$
16. $a_1=4$, $a_n=40$
17. $n=10$, $a_n=22$
19. (a) $\frac{3}{2}$, 6, $\frac{21}{2}$ (b) $(a+b)/2$
20. $-1, -5, -9, -13, -17$
22. 2142
23. 15, 246
25. 47
26. 13
28. $3a-2b, 3b-2a$
29. 1092
31. 100 32. 115 34. 318 35. 32

10.3 Geometric Sequences and Series

In this section, we consider another special kind of sequence and series.

Definition 10.4 A **geometric sequence**, or **geometric progression**, is a sequence in which each term after the first is obtained by multiplying the preceding term by a constant, called the **common ratio**.

For example, the sequence

$$2, 4, 8, 16, \ldots$$

is a geometric progression with $a_1=2$ and a common ratio of.2. As another example, the sequence

$$27, -9, 3, -1, \ldots$$

is a geometric sequence with $a_1 = 27$ and a common ratio of $-\frac{1}{3}$.

If a_1 is the first term of a geometric progression that has a common ratio of r, then the geometric progression is

$$a_1, ra_1, r^2a_1, \ldots, r^{n-1}a_1, \ldots .$$

Note that a formula for the nth term a_n of a geometric progression is

$$a_n = r^{n-1}a_1. \tag{10-5}$$

EXAMPLE 1

Find the 7th term of the geometric progression $27, -9, \ldots$.

Solution In this case, $a_1 = 27$ and $r = -\frac{1}{3}$. Using Eq. $(10-5)$, it follows that

$$a_7 = (27)(-\tfrac{1}{3})^6 = \tfrac{1}{27}. \qquad\blacksquare$$

To obtain a formula for the sum S_n of the first n terms of a geometric progression, we proceed as follows. Writing the expression for the sum and multiplying it by r, we get

$$S_n = a_1 + ra_1 + r^2a_1 + \cdots + r^{n-1}a_1$$

and

$$rS_n = ra_1 + r^2a_1 + \cdots + r^{n-1}a_1 + r^na_1.$$

Subtracting the terms of the second equation from the corresponding terms of the first equation, we get

$$S_n - rS_n = a_1 - r^na_1$$

and

$$S_n(1 - r) = a_1(1 - r^n).$$

Thus

$$S_n = \frac{a_1(1 - r^n)}{1 - r} \qquad (r \ne 1). \tag{10-6}$$

Combining Eqs. (10–5) and (10–6), we obtain another formula, namely

$$S_n = \frac{a_1 - ra_n}{1-r} \qquad (r \neq 1), \qquad\qquad (10-7)$$

which can be used to calculate the sum S_n.

EXAMPLE 2

Find the sum of the first 10 terms of the geometric progression 32, $-16, \ldots \ldots$

Solution In this case, $a_1 = 32$ and $r = -\frac{1}{2}$. Using Eq. (10–6), we find that

$$S_{10} = \frac{32[1 - (-\frac{1}{2})^{10}]}{1 - (-\frac{1}{2})} = \frac{341}{16}. \qquad\qquad ▮$$

Problems 10.3

In problems 1–6, determine if the given sequence is a geometric progression. If it is, give the common ratio.

1. $25, -5, 1, \ldots$ 2. $64, 32, 16, 8, \ldots$ 3. $5, 10, 50, \ldots$
4. $2, 8, 24, \ldots$ 5. $3, -\frac{1}{3}, \frac{1}{27}, \ldots$ 6. $2, -.2, .02, \ldots$

In problems 7–12, determine the next two terms of the given geometric progression, and then find a_n and S_n for the given value of n.

7. $3, 6, \ldots; n = 8$ 8. $2, -8, \ldots; n = 5$ 9. $27, -9, \ldots; n = 5$
10. $5, -15, \ldots; n = 6$ 11. $\frac{1}{9}, \frac{1}{3}, \ldots; n = 7$ 12. $\frac{1}{8}, \frac{1}{4}, \ldots; n = 9$

In problems 13–18, three of the five quantities a_1, r, n, a_n, and S_n are given for a geometric progression. Determine the missing quantities.

13. $a_1 = 1, r = 3, S_n = 1093$ 14. $a_1 = 224, a_n = 14, S_n = 154$
15. $a_1 = \frac{1}{2}, n = 7, a_n = 32$ 16. $r = -3, n = 6, a_n = -1701$
17. $a_1 = 5, r = 2, a_n = 320$ 18. $r = -2, a_n = 192, S_n = 129$
19. The terms that lie between the given terms of a geometric progression are called the **geometric means** between these two terms. If only one term lies between two given terms, the term is called the **geometric mean** of the other two.
    (a) Insert four geometric means between 160 and -5.
    (b) Determine the geometric mean of 27 and $\frac{4}{3}$.
20. Insert two geometric means between a and b.
21. Determine x so that $3x - 3, 5x - 4, 7x - 2, \ldots$ is a geometric sequence.
22. Determine x so that $1 - 3x, x + 1, x - 5, \ldots$ is a geometric progression.
23. Find the first two terms of a geometric progression whose 3rd term is 3 and whose 8th term is -96.
24. Find the 5th term of a geometric progression whose 2nd term is 27 and whose 6th term is $\frac{1}{3}$.

25. Find the sum of the first six terms of a geometric progression in which the 3rd term is 2 and the 6th term is -16.
26. Determine the sum of the first n terms of the geometric progression $1, 2, 4, \ldots$.
27. Given that $a, b \neq 0$, find the 1st and 5th terms of a geometric sequence whose 2nd term is a and whose 3rd term is b.
28. If there are no duplicates, how many direct-lineage ancestors do you have in the seven generations that immediately precede you?
29. A man agrees to work for $1 the first day provided that his employer agrees to double his daily wages each day for as long as he works. If the man works every day for 2 weeks and then quits, how much money does he receive for his work?
30. A handball falls from a height of 16 feet. If after each fall it rebounds three fourths of the distance it has fallen, how far has the ball traveled when it strikes the ground the fifth time?

In problems $31-36$, use Eq. $(10-7)$ to determine the following sums.

31. $\sum\limits_{k=1}^{6} (\tfrac{1}{2})^k$ $\qquad$ **32.** $\sum\limits_{k=1}^{6} 3^k$ $\qquad$ **33.** $\sum\limits_{k=1}^{6} (\tfrac{1}{3})^k$

34. $\sum\limits_{k=1}^{8} (-2)^k$ $\qquad$ **35.** $\sum\limits_{k=1}^{10} (-1)^k$ $\qquad$ **36.** $\sum\limits_{k=1}^{12} 2^k$

Answers 10.3

1. is, $r=-\tfrac{1}{5}$
2. is, $r=\tfrac{1}{2}$
4. is not
5. is, $r=-\tfrac{1}{4}$
7. $12, 24; 384; 765$
8. $32, -128; 512; 410$
10. $45, -135; -1215; -910$
11. $1, 3; 81; \frac{1093}{9}$
13. $n=7, a_n=729$
14. $r=-\tfrac{1}{2}, n=5$
16. $a_1=7, S_n=-1274$
17. $n=7, S_n=635$
19. (a) $-80, 40, -20, 10$ $\qquad$ (b) $\tfrac{2}{9}$ or $-\tfrac{2}{9}$
20. $\sqrt[3]{a^2 b}, \sqrt[3]{ab^2}$
22. 3 or $\tfrac{1}{2}$
23. $\tfrac{3}{4}, -\tfrac{3}{2}$
25. $-\tfrac{21}{2}$
26. $2^n - 1$
28. 254
29. $16,383$
31. $\tfrac{63}{64}$ $\qquad$ 32. 1092 $\qquad$ 34. 170 $\qquad$ 35. 0

10.4 Mathematical Induction

In this section, we consider another kind of deductive reasoning (see Section 1.3) which is used frequently in mathematical proofs. It is known as **mathematical induction**, and it is based upon the following axiom.

The Axiom of Mathematical Induction If the statement involving the natural number n is

1. True for $n = 1$, and
2. True for $n = k + 1$ when it is true for $n = k$,

then the statement is true for all $n \in N$.

The principle involved in the previous axiom can be compared to climbing an infinitely tall ladder, where the bottom rung corresponds to $n = 1$, the next rung to $n = 2$, and so on. If we can show that

1. We can climb onto the first rung, and
2. We can climb from any rung to the next higher rung,

then it follows that we can reach *all* rungs of the ladder.

Using the axiom of mathematical induction, we can prove various kinds of mathematical statements. In each such proof, we must do two things:

1. We must *verify* that the statement is true for $n = 1$, and
2. We must *prove* that if the statement is true for $n = k$, then it is also true for $n = k + 1$.

Note that parts 1 and 2 are both necessary in a proof by mathematical induction. You can establish this fact for yourself by working problems 1 and 2.

EXAMPLE 1

Prove that $n^3 + 2n$ is divisible by 3 for all $n \in N$.

Proof

Part (a): we must verify the statement for $n = 1$ Although unnecessary, we shall also verify the statement for $n = 2$ and $n = 3$.

When $n = 1$, $1^3 + 2(1) = 3$, which is divisible by 3.
When $n = 2$, $2^3 + 2(2) = 12$, which is divisible by 3.
When $n = 3$, $3^3 + 2(3) = 33$, which is divisible by 3.

Hence the statement is true when n has the values 1, 2, or 3.

Part (b): we must prove that if the statement is true when $n = k$, then it is also true when $n = k + 1$ That is, given that $k^3 + 2k$ is divisible by 3, we must show that $(k + 1)^3 + 2(k + 1)$ is also divisible by 3. Note that

$$(k + 1)^3 + 2(k + 1) = k^3 + 3k^2 + 3k + 1 + 2k + 2$$
$$= (k^3 + 2k) + 3(k^2 + k + 1).$$

Since each term of the last expression is divisible by 3, it follows that $(k + 1)^3 + 2(k + 1)$ is divisible by 3.

Conclusion. In part (a), we have shown that the statement is true for $n = 1$. In part (b), we have shown that the statement is true for $n = k + 1$ when it is true for $n = k$. Hence we conclude, by the axiom of mathematical induction, that the statement is true for all natural numbers. ∎

EXAMPLE 2

Prove that

$$1 \cdot 2 + 2 \cdot 3 + 3 \cdot 4 + \cdots + n(n+1) = \frac{n(n+1)(n+2)}{3} \qquad \text{for all } n \in N.$$

Proof

Part (a): we must verify the statement for n = 1 Although unnecessary, we shall also verify the statement for $n = 2$ and $n = 3$. When $n = 1$,

$$1 \cdot 2 = 2 = \frac{(1)(2)(3)}{3}.$$

When $n = 2$,

$$1 \cdot 2 + 2 \cdot 3 = 8 = \frac{(2)(3)(4)}{3}.$$

When $n = 3$,

$$1 \cdot 2 + 2 \cdot 3 + 3 \cdot 4 = 20 = \frac{(3)(4)(5)}{3}.$$

Hence the statement is true for $n = 1$, $n = 2$, and $n = 3$.

Part (b): we must prove that if the statement is true for n = k, then it is also true for n = k + 1 Our hypothesis is that the statement is true for $n = k$. In other words, we are given that

$$1 \cdot 2 + 2 \cdot 3 + 3 \cdot 4 + \cdots + k(k+1) = \frac{k(k+1)(k+2)}{3}.$$

Using this hypothesis we wish to conclude that

$$1 \cdot 2 + 2 \cdot 3 + 3 \cdot 4 + \cdots + k(k+1) + (k+1)(k+2) = \frac{(k+1)(k+2)(k+3)}{3}.$$

We do this as follows:

$$\begin{aligned}
1 \cdot 2 + 2 \cdot 3 + &\cdots + k(k+1) + (k+1)(k+2) \\
&= [1 \cdot 2 + 2 \cdot 3 + \cdots + k(k+1)] + (k+1)(k+2) \\
&= \left[\frac{k(k+1)(k+2)}{3}\right] + (k+1)(k+2) \\
&= (k+1)(k+2)\left[\frac{k}{3} + 1\right] = \frac{(k+1)(k+2)(k+3)}{3}.
\end{aligned}$$

Hence the statement is true for $n = k + 1$ when it is true for $n = k$.

  Conclusion. In part (a) we have shown that the statement is true for $n = 1$. In part (b) we have shown that the statement is true for $n = k + 1$ when it is true for $n = k$. Hence we conclude, by the axiom of mathematical induction, that the statement is true for all natural numbers.   ∎

Problems 10.4

1. Show that the expression $n^2 - n + 11$ represents a prime number when $n = 1, 2$, and 3. Does it represent a prime number when $n = 11$? (*Remark:* This problem shows that verification of a statement for a finite number of cases does not prove that the statement is true in general.)

2. Show that if $2 + 4 + 6 + \cdots + 2n = n(n + 1) + 5$ is true for $n = k$, then it is also true for $n = k + 1$. Is the statement true when $n = 1$? [*Remark:* This problem shows that part (b) alone does not constitute a proof by mathematical induction.]

In problems 3 – 17, use mathematical induction to prove the given statement for all natural numbers n.

3. $n^2 + n$ is divisible by 2.

4. $n(n + 1)(n + 2)$ is divisible by 3.

5. $5^n - 1$ is divisible by 4.

6. If $x \neq y$, $x^n - y^n$ is divisible by $x - y$.

7. $2n \leq 2^n$.

8. $1 + 2 + 3 + \cdots + n = \dfrac{n(n + 1)}{2}$

9. $1 + 3 + 5 + \cdots + (2n - 1) = n^2$

10. $1 + 4 + 7 + \cdots + (3n - 2) = \dfrac{n(3n - 1)}{2}$

11. $1^2 + 2^2 + 3^2 + \cdots + n^2 = \dfrac{n(n + 1)(2n + 1)}{6}$

12. $1^3 + 2^3 + 3^3 + \cdots + n^3 = \dfrac{n^2(n + 1)^2}{4}$

13. $1 \cdot 2 + 3 \cdot 4 + 5 \cdot 6 + \cdots + (2n - 1)(2n) = \dfrac{n(n + 1)(4n - 1)}{3}$

14. $\displaystyle\sum_{k=1}^{n} (k)(k + 2) = \dfrac{n(n + 1)(2n + 7)}{6}$

15. $\displaystyle\sum_{k=1}^{n} \dfrac{1}{k(k + 1)} = \dfrac{n}{n + 1}$

16. $\displaystyle\sum_{k=1}^{n} \dfrac{1}{(2k - 1)(2k + 1)} = \dfrac{n}{2n + 1}$

17. $\displaystyle\sum_{k=1}^{n} 2^{k-1} = 2^n - 1$

10.5 The Binomial Theorem

In this section, we shall often need to write the product of several consecutive natural numbers. To do this we use the notation $n!$ (read, "n factorial"), which is defined as

$$n! = 1 \cdot 2 \cdot 3 \cdot \ldots \cdot n,$$

where $n \in N$. Examples are

$$1! = 1, \qquad 3! = 1 \cdot 2 \cdot 3 = 6, \qquad 5! = 1 \cdot 2 \cdot 3 \cdot 4 \cdot 5 = 120,$$

and

$$(k+5)! = 1 \cdot 2 \cdot 3 \ldots (k+3)(k+4)(k+5).$$

For convenience, we define $0!$ by

$$0! = 1.$$

EXAMPLE 1

Express $4 \cdot 5 \cdot 6 \cdot 7$ in factorial notation.

Solution We have

$$4 \cdot 5 \cdot 6 \cdot 7 = \frac{1 \cdot 2 \cdot 3 \cdot 4 \cdot 5 \cdot 6 \cdot 7}{1 \cdot 2 \cdot 3} = \frac{7!}{3!}. \qquad \blacksquare$$

EXAMPLE 2

Simplify $(k+1)!/(k-1)!$.

Solution We have

$$\frac{(k+1)!}{(k-1)!} = \frac{1 \cdot 2 \cdot 3 \cdots (k-2)(k-1)(k)(k+1)}{1 \cdot 2 \cdot 3 \cdots (k-2)(k-1)} = k(k+1). \qquad \blacksquare$$

Using direct multiplication, we can verify each of the expansions

$$(a+b)^1 = a+b,$$
$$(a+b)^2 = a^2 + 2ab + b^2,$$
$$(a+b)^3 = a^3 + 3a^2b + 3ab^2 + b^3,$$
$$(a+b)^4 = a^4 + 4a^3b + 6a^2b^2 + 4ab^3 + b^4,$$

and

$$(a+b)^5 = a^5 + 5a^4b + 10a^3b^2 + 10a^2b^3 + 5ab^4 + b^5.$$

Using these expansions, we can observe the following patterns in the expansion of $(a+b)^n$, where $n = 1, 2, 3, 4,$ or 5.

1. The 1st term has the form a^n.
2. The 2nd term has the form $(n/1!)a^{n-1}b$.
3. The 3rd term has the form $[n(n-1)/2!]a^{n-2}b^2$.
4. The 4th term has the form $[n(n-1)(n-2)/3!]a^{n-3}b^3$.
5. The $(n+1)$th term has the form b^n.

The previous facts suggest the following theorem, which is known as the binomial theorem.

Theorem 10.1 If $n \in N$, then

$$(a+b)^n = a^n + \frac{n}{1!}\,a^{n-1}b + \frac{n(n-1)}{2!}\,a^{n-2}b^2 + \frac{n(n-1)(n-2)}{3!}\,a^{n-3}b^3 + \cdots + b^n.$$

Proof

Part (a): When $n = 1$, $(a+b)^1 = a+b$.

Part (b): Given that

$$(a+b)^k = a^k + \frac{k}{1!}\,a^{k-1}b + \cdots$$

$$+ \frac{k(k-1)\cdots(k-r+2)}{(r-1)!}\,a^{k-r+1}b^{r-1} + \cdots + b^k, \quad (10-8)$$

where

$$\frac{k(k-1)\cdots(k-r+2)}{(r-1)!}\,a^{k-r+1}b^{r-1}$$

is the rth term in the expansion of $(a+b)^k$, we must show that

$$(a+b)^{k+1} = a^{k+1} + \frac{k+1}{1!}\,a^k b + \cdots$$

$$+ \frac{(k+1)(k)\cdots(k-r+3)}{(r-1)!}\,a^{k-r+2}b^{r-1}$$

$$+ \cdots + b^{k+1}. \quad (10-9)$$

We do this as follows. Multiplying both sides of Eq. (10-8) by $(a+b)$, we get

$$(a+b)^{k+1} = \left(a^{k+1} + \cdots + \frac{k(k-1)\cdots(k-r+2)}{(r-1)!}\,a^{k-r+2}b^{r-1} + \cdots + ab^k\right)$$

$$+ \left(a^k b + \cdots + \frac{k(k-1)\cdots(k-r+2)}{(r-1)!}\,a^{k-r+1}b^r + \cdots + b^{k+1}\right).$$

The coefficient of $a^{k-r+2}b^{r-1}$ in the previous equation is

$$\frac{k(k-1)\cdots(k-r+2)}{(r-1)!}+\frac{k(k-1)\cdots(k-r+3)}{(r-2)!}$$
$$=\frac{k(k-1)\cdots(k-r+2)}{(r-1)!}+\frac{k(k-1)\cdots(k-r+3)(r-1)}{(r-1)!}$$
$$=\frac{k(k-1)\cdots(k-r+3)}{(r-1)!}\left[(k-r+2)+(r-1)\right]=\frac{(k-1)(k)\cdots(k-r+3)}{(r-1)!},$$

which is the correct coefficient of $a^{k-r+2}b^{r-1}$ in Eq. (10–9). Therefore, the theorem is true for all $n \in N$ according to the axiom of mathematical induction. ∎

Using the binomial theorem we can quickly expand powers of binomials, which would take a long time by direct multiplication.

EXAMPLE 3

Expand $(2x-3y)^4$ using the binomial theorem.

Solution Using the binomial theorem with $a = 2x$, $b = -3y$, and $n = 4$, it follows that

$$(2x-3y)^4=(2x)^4+\frac{4}{1!}(2x)^3(-3y)+\frac{4\cdot3}{2!}(2x)^2(-3y)^2+\frac{4\cdot3\cdot2}{3!}(2x)(-3y)^3$$
$$+\frac{4\cdot3\cdot2\cdot1}{4!}(-3y)^4$$
$$=16x^4-96x^3y+216x^2y^2-216xy^3+81y^4.$$ ∎

EXAMPLE 4

Write the 8th term in the expansion of $(2x-y)^{10}$.

Solution In the proof of the binomial theorem, we stated that the rth term in the expansion of $(a+b)^k$ is given by

$$\frac{k(k-1)\cdots(k-r+2)}{(r-1)!}a^{k-r+1}b^{r-1}.$$

In this problem, $a = 2x$, $b = -y$, and $k = 10$. Thus the 8th term ($r = 8$) is

$$\frac{10\cdot9\cdot8\cdot7\cdot6\cdot5\cdot4}{7!}(2x)^3(-y)^7=-960x^3y^7.$$ ∎

Problems 10.5

In problems 1–12, remove the factorial notation and then simplify the resulting fraction.

1. $4!/0!$
2. $9!/6!$
3. $7!/5!$

4. $\dfrac{6!}{2! \cdot 4!}$
5. $\dfrac{4! - 3!}{2!}$
6. $\dfrac{8!}{5!(8-5)!}$

7. $\dfrac{(k+3)!}{(k+1)!}$
8. $\dfrac{(k+2)!}{(k-1)!}$
9. $\dfrac{k!}{(k+2)!}$

10. $\dfrac{(k-2)!}{(k+1)!}$
11. $\dfrac{(k)(k+1)!}{(k+2)!}$
12. $\dfrac{(2k-2)!}{(2k)!}$

In problems 13–18, write the given product in factorial notation.

13. $1 \cdot 2 \cdot 3 \cdot 4 \cdot 5$
14. $3 \cdot 4 \cdot 5 \cdot 6$
15. $7 \cdot 8$
16. $8 \cdot 9 \cdot 10 \cdot 11$
17. $6 \cdot 7 \cdot 8 \cdot 9 \cdot 10$
18. $16 \cdot 17 \cdot 18$

In problems 19–24, expand the given expression using the binomial theorem.

19. $(2x+y)^4$
20. $(5x-y)^3$
21. $(x^2-1)^5$

22. $(x-3y)^5$
23. $(x^2+y^3)^6$
24. $\left(3x+\dfrac{2}{x}\right)^4$

25. Write the first four terms in the binomial expansion of $(2x - y)^9$.

26. Write the first four terms in the binomial expansion of $(x^3 + 2y)^8$.

27. Write the first four terms in the binomial expansion of $(x^2 + 3)^7$.

28. Write the 6th term in the binomial expansion of $(x^2 + y^3)^8$.

29. Write the 7th term in the binomial expansion of $(x^2 - 2)^{10}$.

30. Write the 8th term in the binomial expansion of $(x^3 - 3)^{12}$.

In problems 31–36, given that the binomial theorem holds when n is any rational number, write the first four terms in the binomial expansion of the given expression.

31. $(1+x)^{-1}$
32. $(1+x)^{1/2}$
33. $(1-x)^{-2}$
34. $(1-x)^{-3}$
35. $(1-x^2)^{-1}$
36. $(1-x^2)^{-1/2}$

Answers 10.5

1. 24
2. 504
4. 15
5. 9

7. $(k+2)(k+3)$
8. $k(k+1)(k+2)$
10. $1/(k-1)k(k+1)$
11. $k/(k+2)$

13. $5!$
14. $6!/2!$
16. $11!/7!$
17. $10!/5!$

19. $16x^4 + 32x^3y + 24x^2y^2 + 8xy^3 + y^4$
20. $125x^3 - 75x^2y + 15xy^2 - y^3$

22. $x^5 - 15x^4y + 90x^3y^2 - 270x^2y^3 + 405xy^4 - 243y^5$

23. $x^{12} + 6x^{10}y^3 + 15x^8y^6 + 30x^6y^9 + 15x^4y^{12} + 6x^2y^{15} + y^{18}$

25. $512x^9 - 2294x^8y + 4608x^7y^2 - 5376x^6y^3 + \cdots$

26. $x^{24} + 16x^{21}y + 112x^{18}y^2 + 448x^{15}y^3 + \cdots$

28. $56x^6y^{15}$
29. $13{,}440x^8$

31. $1 - x + x^2 - x^3 + \cdots$
32. $1 + \frac{1}{2}x - \frac{1}{8}x^2 + \frac{1}{16}x^3 + \cdots$

34. $1 + 3x + 6x^2 + 10x^3 + \cdots$
35. $1 + x^2 + x^4 + x^6 + \cdots$

chapter 10 review problems

1. Write the first four terms of the sequence determined by the given conditions.

   (a) $a_n = \dfrac{n}{n+2}$ (b) $a_1 = -3$, $a_{n+1} = a_n + 5$

2. Determine a formula for the nth term of a sequence beginning with the given terms.

   (a) 6, 12, 24, 48, . . .   (b) 2, $\frac{3}{4}$, $\frac{4}{9}$, $\frac{5}{16}$, . . .

3. Express the given series in sigma notation.

   (a) $2 + 4 + 6 + 8 + \cdots$ (b) $1 - 4 + 9 - 16 + 25$

4. Write the given series without sigma notation.

   (a) $\displaystyle\sum_{k=1}^{4} (2k - 5)$ (b) $\displaystyle\sum_{k=1}^{n} (3x)^k$

5. Determine the next two terms of the arithmetic sequence $-\frac{1}{3}$, 2, ... Also calculate a_{20} and S_{20}.

6. Given three of the five quantities a_1, d, n, a_n, and S_n of an arithmetic progression, determine the two remaining quantities.

   (a) $a_1 = 3$, $d = -2$, $n = 6$ (b) $a_1 = 8$, $n = 8$, $S_n = -20$

7. Insert three arithmetic means between a and b.

8. Find the sum of the numbers between 30 and 100 that are exactly divisible by 7.

9. Determine the next two terms of the geometric sequence $-\frac{1}{3}$, 2, ...

10. Given three of the five quantities a_1, r, n, a_n, and S_n of a geometric progression, determine the two missing quantities.

    (a) $a_1 = 6$, $r = \frac{1}{2}$, $n = 4$ (b) $a_1 = 8$, $n = 4$, $S_4 = 5$

11. Determine x so that $10 - x$, 10, $6x + 2$, . . . is a geometric progression.

12. Find the sum of the first six terms of a geometric progression in which $a_3 = 10$ and $a_5 = 40$.

13. Evaluate the following sums.

    (a) $\displaystyle\sum_{k=1}^{12} (1 - 3k)$ (b) $\displaystyle\sum_{k=1}^{8} (2)^k$

14. Use mathematical induction to prove each of the following statements.

    (a) When $n \in N$, $n^3 + 6n^2 + 2n$ is divisible by 3.

    (b) When $n \in N$, $\displaystyle\sum_{k=1}^{n} 3^k = \frac{3}{2}[3^n - 1]$.

15. Remove the factorial notation and simplify.

    (a) $7!/4!$ (b) $6!/(4! \cdot 2!)$ (c) $(k + 1)!/(k - 1)!$

16. Write the first four terms in the binomial expansion of the given expression.

    (a) $(x - 2y)^7$ (b) $(1 - x)^{-2}$

answers

1. (a) $\frac{1}{3}$, $\frac{2}{4}$, $\frac{3}{5}$, $\frac{4}{6}$, . . .   (b) -3, 2, 7, 12, . . .

2. (a) $a_n = 6(2)^{n-1}$ (b) $a_n = (n + 1)/n^2$

3. (a) $\displaystyle\sum_{k=1}^{\infty} 2k$ (b) $\displaystyle\sum_{k=1}^{5} (-1)^{k+1} k^2$

4. (a) $-3-1+1+3$ (b) $3x+9x^2+27x^3+\cdots+(3x)^k+\cdots$

5. $\frac{13}{3}$, $\frac{20}{3}$; 44; $\frac{1310}{3}$

6. (a) $a_6=-7$, $S_6=-12$ (b) $d=-3$, $a_8=-13$

7. $(3a+b)/4$, $(a+b)/2$, $(a+3b)/4$

8. 665   **9.** -12, 72

10. (a) $a_n=\frac{3}{4}$, $S_n=\frac{45}{4}$ (b) $a_4=-1$, $r=-\frac{1}{2}$

11. 8 or $\frac{5}{3}$ **12.** $\frac{315}{2}$

13. (a) -222 (b) 510

15. (a) 210   (b) 15   (c) k^2+k

16. (a) $x^7-14x^6y+84x^5y^2-280x^4y^3+\cdots$ (b) $1+2x+3x^2+4x^3+\cdots$

11

probability

11.1 The Fundamental Counting Axiom

In how many ways can a committee of 3 people be chosen from a group of 10 people? How many different bridge hands can be dealt from an ordinary deck of 52 cards? Questions of this kind will be considered in this and the next two sections. In these sections we shall develop systematic methods for counting the number of ways that certain events can occur.

The following axiom is fundamental in counting the number of different ways certain events can occur.

The Fundamental Counting Axiom If one event can occur in a different ways, and if after the occurrence of the first event, a second event can occur in b different ways, then both events can occur in the stated order in ab different ways.

EXAMPLE 1

How many different two-digit numbers can be formed by using only the digits 1, 2, 3, and 4?

Solution The tens digit can be chosen in any one of 4 different ways. After choosing the tens digit, the units digit can be chosen in any one of 4 different ways. Consequently, according to the fundamental counting axiom, the desired two-digit number can be formed in $4 \cdot 4 = 16$ different ways. ∎

EXAMPLE 2

How many different two-digit numbers can be formed from the digits 1, 2, 3, and 4 given that the digits cannot be repeated?

Solution   The tens digit can still be chosen in any one of 4 different ways. However, after choosing the tens digits, the units digit can now only be chosen in 3 different ways, since we are not allowed to repeat the digit that we choose for the tens digit. Thus, according to the fundamental counting axiom, the desired two-digit number can be formed in $4 \cdot 3 = 12$ different ways.

The fundamental counting axiom can be extended to any finite number of events provided that the outcomes of each successive event is independent of the outcomes of the previous events.   ∎

EXAMPLE 3

If 11 horses are entered in the Belmont Stakes, in how many ways can they win, place, and show?

Solution   Any one of the 11 horses can win the race. After one horse has won, any one of the remaining 10 horses can come in second (in racing jargon, place). After first and second have been decided, any one of the remaining 9 horses can come in third (in racing jargon, show). According to the fundamental counting axiom, the horses can win, place, and show in $11 \cdot 10 \cdot 9 = 990$ different ways.   ∎

EXAMPLE 4

In how many ways can a 5-question multiple-choice exam be answered if the first three questions have 4 possible answers each and the last two questions have 5 possible answers each?

Solution   Each of the first 3 questions can be answered independently in 4 different ways, and each of the last 2 questions can be answered independently in 5 different ways. According to the fundamental counting axiom, the exam can be answered in $4 \cdot 4 \cdot 4 \cdot 5 \cdot 5$ different ways.   ∎

EXAMPLE 5

How many integers less than 600, each containing 3 different digits, can be formed by using the digits 1, 3, 5, 7, and 9?

Solution   There are 3 possible choices (namely, 1, 3, and 5) for the hundreds digit of the required 3-digit number. After the hundreds digit has been selected, any one of the remaining 4 digits can be selected for the tens digit. Finally, any one of the remaining 3 digits can be selected for the units digit.

Then, according to the fundamental counting axiom, there are $3 \cdot 4 \cdot 3$ different ways of forming the required number from the given digits. ∎

Problems 11.1

1. If 2 dice are thrown, in how many ways can they fall?
2. If 5 coins are tossed, in how many ways can they fall?
3. In how many ways can a 10-question true–false exam be answered?
4. A cafeteria offers a choice of 3 meats, 7 vegetables, 5 salads, and 4 desserts. If a meal consists of 1 meat, 2 vegetables, 1 salad, and 1 dessert, how many different meals are possible?
5. A baseball stadium has 6 entrance gates and 10 exit gates. In how many ways can two spectators enter by the same gate and leave by different gates?
6. In a certain election, there are 3 candidates for president, 2 for vice-president, 2 for secretary, and 5 for treasurer. How many different outcomes are possible for the election?
7. A license plate consists of 2 letters followed by 3 digits. (a) How many such plates are possible? (b) How many such plates are possible if the letters can not be repeated and the first digit must be different from zero?
8. Three people get on a bus that has 6 vacant seats on each side. (a) In how many ways can they be seated? (b) In how many ways can they be seated if one person insists on sitting on the right side?
9. The Greek alphabet consists of 24 letters. How many names of fraternities can be formed (a) by using 3 different Greek letters? (b) by using 2 or 3 Greek letters?
10. Five boys and 4 girls enter a restaurant that has 9 seats (all empty) at the counter. In how many ways can the children sit at the counter (a) if they sit anywhere? (b) if the boys and girls must alternate?
11. In how many ways can 4 boys and 3 girls be arranged in a row for a picture if no 2 girls are to stand next to each other?
12. A bridge club consists of 10 women and 6 men. (a) In how many ways can a team consisting of 1 man and 1 woman be selected from the membership? (b) In how many ways can a bridge game consisting of two such teams be arranged?
13. How many integers less than 7000, each containing 4 different digits, can be formed by using the digits 1, 5, 6, 8, and 9?
14. How many integers greater than 7000, each containing all different digits, can be formed by using the digits 1, 5, 6, 8, and 9?
15. How many odd integers, each containing exactly 3 digits (all different), can be formed by using the digits 1, 5, 6, 8, and 9?
16. How many odd integers greater than 500, each containing exactly 3 digits (all different), can be formed by using the digits 1, 5, 6, 8, and 9?
17. How many even integers less than 7000, each containing 4 different digits, can be formed by using the digits 1, 5, 6, 8, and 9?
18. How many even integers less than 7000 can be formed by using the digits 1, 5, 6, 8, and 9?

11.2 Permutations

Suppose that we have a collection of n distinct objects. If we select $r(r \leq n)$ of the objects from this collection and arrange them in the order in which they were selected, the resulting arrangement is called a **permutation of n objects taken r at a time.** For example, the permutations of the three letters a, b, and c taken two at a time are ab, ac, ba, bc, ca, and cb.

The number of permutations of n objects taken r at a time is written symbolically as $P(n, r)$ or $_nP_r$. We shall use $P(n, r)$ in this book. In the following theorem, we derive a formula for $P(n, r)$.

Theorem 11.1   The number of permutations of n distinguishable objects taken r at a time is

$$P(n, r)=\frac{n!}{(n-r)!}.$$ (11-1)

Proof   We must determine how many ways we can select and order r objects from n objects. Since there are n objects to select from, we can select the 1st object in n ways. From the remaining $(n-1)$ objects, we can select the 2nd object in $(n-1)$ ways. Continuing this process, we can select the rth object in $[n-(r-1)]$ ways. Then, according to the fundamental counting axiom,

$$P(n, r)=n(n-1)\cdots(n-r+1).$$

Multiplying and dividing the right side of the previous equation by $(n-r)!$, we have

$$P(n, r)=\frac{n(n-1)\cdots(n-r+1)(n-r)!}{(n-r)!}=\frac{n!}{(n-r)!}.$$ ∎

EXAMPLE 1

In how many ways can a club having 20 members elect a president, a vice-president, a secretary, and a treasurer?

Solution From 20 objects (the 20 people in the club), we wish to select and order 4 objects (the officers to be elected). Thus we want to find the number of permutations of 20 objects taken 4 at a time. Using Eq. (11 – 1), we find that the number of possible ways of doing this is

$$P(20, 4) = \frac{20!}{(20-4)!} = \frac{20!}{16!} = 20 \cdot 19 \cdot 18 \cdot 17 = 116,280. \qquad \blacksquare$$

EXAMPLE 2

In how many ways can 6 people be seated in a row of 6 chairs?

Solution From 6 objects (the 6 people), we wish to select and order the 6 people by placing each of them in a particular chair. Thus we want to find the number of permutations of 6 objects taken 6 at a time. Using Eq. (11 – 1), we find that the number of possible ways of doing this is

$$P(6, 6) = \frac{6!}{(6-6)!} = \frac{6!}{0!} = 6! = 720. \qquad \blacksquare$$

EXAMPLE 3

In how many ways can 6 people be seated, relative to one another, around a circular table?

Solution Since we are only interested in the positions of the people relative to one another, we begin by placing one of the people in a fixed position. Then we seat everyone else relative to this person. Consequently, after seating one (any one) of the 6 people in a particular chair (any chair), the remaining 5 people can be seated in the remaining 5 chairs in

$$P(5, 5) = \frac{5!}{(5-5!)} = 5! = 120$$

ways. Thus the 6 people can be seated relative to one another in 120 different ways. $\blacksquare$

Next, we consider the problem of finding the number of distinguishable permutations of n objects taken r at a time when the n objects are *not all distinguishable*.

EXAMPLE 4

In how many ways can the letters of the word "VIRGINIA" be arranged?

Solution If we consider the I's as different, there would be $P(8, 8) = 8!$

ways of arranging the eight letters of "VIRGINIA." However, the I's are not different. That is, they are not distinguishable from one another. Since the I's themselves can be rearranged in 3! ways for each distinguishable arrangement of the other letters, it follows that the actual number of different arrangements is 8!/3!. ∎

The following theorem can be proved by using an argument similar to that given in the previous example.

Theorem 11.2   If n objects consist of n_1 of one kind, n_2 of a second kind, and so on, then the number of distinguishable permutations P of the n objects taken *all* at a time is

$$P = \frac{n!}{n_1! \cdot n_2! \cdot \ldots}. \tag{11-2}$$

EXAMPLE 5

In how many ways can the letters of the word "ARKANSAS" be arranged?

Solution   In this case, there are 3 A's, 2 S's, and 1 of each of the letters R, K, and N. Using Eq. (11–2), it follows that the number of distinguishable permutations of the 8 letters taken 8 at a time is

$$\frac{8!}{3! \cdot 2! \cdot 1! \cdot 1! \cdot 1!} = 3360. \qquad \blacksquare$$

Problems 11.2

1. How many permutations of 2 letters can be formed from the letters A, B, C, and D? List these permutations.
2. How many permutations of 3 letters can be formed from the letters A, B, C, and D? List these permutations.
3. In how many different orders can the 9 teams of the Southwest Football Conference finish the season (disregard ties)?
4. In how many different orders can the 12 teams of the National Baseball League (6 teams in each of 2 divisions) finish the season (disregard ties)?
5. In how many ways can an ordinary deck of 52 cards be arranged within the deck?
6. In how many ways can an ordinary deck of 52 cards be arranged if all the red cards are to be kept together?
7. In how many ways can a fraternity of 40 active members elect a president, a vice-president, and a pledge-trainer if no person is to hold more than one office?
8. In how many ways can 3 chemistry and 5 physics books be arranged on a shelf?
9. In how many ways can 3 chemistry and 5 physics books be arranged on a shelf if all the books of each subject must be kept together?

10. In how many ways can 3 chemistry and 5 physics books be arranged on a shelf if the chemistry books are kept together?

11. If 5 people enter a bus that has 5 vacant seats on each side of the aisle, in how many ways can the 5 people be seated if 2 of them insist upon sitting on the right side of the bus?

12. In how many ways can the letters of the word "ORANGE" be arranged if the letter N must occupy either the first or last place?

13. In how many ways can the letters of the word "ILLINOIS" be arranged?

14. In how many ways can the letters of the word "TENNESSEE" be arranged?

15. In how many ways can the letters of the word "MISSISSIPPI" be arranged?

16. A bag contains 5 red, 3 white, and 2 blue marbles. How many different color arrangements are possible if the marbles are drawn from the bag one at a time and arranged in a row?

17. How many 6-digit numbers can be formed by using 2 fives and 4 nines?

18. A bowl contains 3 apples, 2 oranges, and 4 bananas. In how many ways can the fruit be distributed to 9 children if each child is to get one piece of fruit?

19. In how many ways can 8 people be seated, relative to one another, around a circular table?

20. In how many ways can 8 people be seated, relative to one another, around a circular table if 2 of the people insist on sitting next to each other?

21. In how many ways can 8 people be seated, relative to one another, around a circular table if 2 of the people refuse to sit next to each other?

22. In how many ways can 4 men and 4 women be seated, relative to one another, around a circular table if no 2 men are to sit next to each other?

23. In how many ways can 4 men and 4 women be seated, relative to one another, around a circular table if all the women insist on sitting next to each other?

24. In how many ways can 4 men and 4 women be seated, relative to one another, around a circular table if a certain man and a certain woman insist on sitting next to each other?

25. Show that $P(n+1, r) = (n+1)P(n, r-1)$.

Answers 11.2

1. 12	**2.** 24	**4.** $(6!)^2$	**5.** 52!
7. 59,280	**8.** 40,320	**10.** 4320	**11.** 6720
13. 3360	**14.** 3780	**16.** 2520	**17.** 15
19. 5040	**20.** 1440	**22.** 144	**23.** 576

11.3 Combinations

Any r objects chosen from a collection of n objects *without regard to order* is called a **combination of n objects taken r at a time.** For example, the combinations of the 3 letters a, b, and c taken two at a time are ab, ac, and bc. Note that ab and ba are *different* permutations, but they are the *same* combination.

The number of combinations of n objects taken r at a time is denoted by $C(n, r)$, $_nC_r$, or $\binom{n}{r}$. We shall use $C(n, r)$ in this book. As we can see from the following theorem, the counting of combinations is closely related to the counting of permutations.

Theorem 11.3   The number of combinations of n objects taken r at a time is

$$C(n, r) = \frac{n!}{r!(n-r)!}. \tag{11-3}$$

Proof   We must determine how many ways we can select (but not order) r objects from n objects. According to Theorem 11.1, we can select and order r objects from n objects in $P(n, r)$ ways. Since each combination of r objects can be ordered in $r!$ ways, it follows that $P(n, r) = r!C(n, r)$. Therefore,

$$C(n, r) = \frac{P(n, r)}{r!} = \frac{n!}{r!(n-r)!}. \qquad\blacksquare$$

EXAMPLE 1

From 8 seniors and 6 juniors, how many different committees of 5 people can be formed if each committee is to consist of 3 seniors and 2 juniors?

Solution   We can select (but not order) 3 seniors from 8 seniors in $C(8, 3)$ ways, and we can select (but not order) 2 juniors from 6 juniors in $C(6, 2)$ ways. Then according to the fundamental counting axiom, there are

$$C(8, 3) \cdot C(6, 2) = \frac{8!}{3!\,5!} \cdot \frac{6!}{2!\,4!} = 840$$

ways of selecting a committee consisting of 3 seniors and 2 juniors. $\blacksquare$

EXAMPLE 2

A poker hand consists of 5 cards drawn from an ordinary deck of 52 cards. How many poker hands (a) contain all 4 aces? (b) contain at least 4 spades?

Solution   (a) The required hand must consist of 4 aces and 1 card that is not an ace. We can select 4 aces from 4 aces in $C(4, 4)$ ways, and we can select the 1 card that is not an ace from 48 cards in $C(48, 1)$ ways. Then according to the fundamental counting axiom, there are

$$C(4, 4) \cdot C(48, 1) = \frac{4!}{4! \ 0!} \cdot \frac{48!}{1! \ 47!} = 48$$

ways for a poker hand to contain 4 aces.

(b) The required hand must contain 4 spades and one card that is not a spade, or it must contain 5 spades. In an ordinary deck of 52 cards, there are 13 cards that are spades and 39 cards that are not spades. We can select 4 spades from 13 spades in $C(13, 4)$ ways, and we can select the 1 card that is not a spade in $C(39, 1)$ ways. Then according to the fundamental counting axiom, there are

$$C(13, 4) \cdot C(39, 1) = \frac{13!}{4! \ 9!} \cdot \frac{39!}{1! \ 38!} = 27{,}885$$

ways for a poker hand to contain 4 spades and 1 card that is not a spade. Using the same procedure, we find there are

$$C(13, 5) = \frac{13!}{5! \ 8!} = 1287$$

ways for a poker hand to contain 5 spades. Hence the number of ways of drawing a poker hand that contains *at least* 4 spades is

$$\begin{pmatrix} \text{number of hands} \\ \text{consisting of 4 spades and} \\ \text{1 card that is not a spade} \end{pmatrix} + \begin{pmatrix} \text{number of hands} \\ \text{consisting of 5 spades} \end{pmatrix}$$
$$= 27{,}885 + 1287 = 29{,}172. \qquad \blacksquare$$

Problems 11.3

1. How many combinations of 2 letters can be formed from the letters A, B, C, and D? List the combinations.
2. How many combinations of 3 letters can be formed from the letters A, B, C, and D? List the combinations.
3. In how many ways can a fraternity of 30 active members select 3 delegates to their national convention?
4. From 10 men and 6 women, how many committees of 5 people can be chosen if each committee is to have exactly 3 men?
5. From 10 men and 6 women, how many committees of 5 people can be chosen if each committee is to have at least 3 men?
6. From 10 men and 6 women, how many committees of 3 men and 2 women can be chosen if 2 of the men refuse to serve on the same committee?

7. How many sums of money can be made from a penny, a nickel, a dime, and a quarter?

8. How many sums of money can be made from a penny, a nickel, a dime, a quarter, and a half-dollar if no more than 3 coins are used?

9. In a certain conference of 9 schools, how many intraconference football games are played each season if each team plays every other team exactly once?

10. A bridge hand consists of 13 cards chosen from an ordinary deck of 52 cards. (a) How many different bridge hands are possible? (b) How many bridge hands will contain all cards of the same color? (c) How many bridge hands will contain exactly 11 red cards?

11. See problem 10. How many bridge hands (a) consist of at least 11 red cards? (b) consist entirely of aces or face cards? (c) consist of 2 aces, 5 face cards, 3 tens, and 3 cards each less than ten?

12. See problem 10. How many bridge hands (a) consist of 10 spades and 3 red cards? (b) consist of at least 11 spades? (c) consist of exactly 2 hearts and at least 9 clubs?

13. See problem 10. How many bridge hands (a) consist of 10 black cards and not more than 2 diamonds? (b) consist of 4 spades, 4 hearts, 3 diamonds, and 2 clubs? (c) have suits consisting of 4, 4, 3, and 2 cards?

14. Three marbles are chosen at random from a bag containing 3 red, 4 white, and 5 blue marbles. In how many ways can the marbles chosen (a) consist of 1 red, 1 white, and 1 blue marble? (b) include no blue marbles? (c) contain at least 2 white marbles?

15. Three marbles are chosen at random from a bag containing 3 red, 4 white, and 5 blue marbles. In how many ways can the marbles chosen (a) contain at least 1 white and 1 blue marble? (b) contain no more than 2 red marbles? (c) contain no white and at least 1 blue marble?

16. Show that $C(n, r) = C(n, n - r)$.

17. Show that $C(n, r) + C(n, r - 1) = C(n + 1, r)$.

Answers 11.3

1. 6   2. 4   4. 1800   5. 3312
7. 15   8. 25   10. (a) $C(52, 13)$ (b) $2C(26, 13)$
11. (a) $C(26, 11) \cdot C(26, 2) + 26 \cdot C(26, 12) + C(26, 13)$ (b) $C(16, 13)$
13. (a) $C(26, 10)[26 \cdot C(13, 2) + C(13, 3)]$
     (b) $[C(13, 4) \cdot C(13, 4) \cdot C(13, 3) \cdot C(13, 2)](4!/2)$
14. (a) 60   (b) 35   (c) 52

11.4 Probability

We begin by defining some preliminary terms. When we perform an experiment, the set of possible results associated with this experiment is called the **sample space** for the experiment. In this book, each sample space will contain a finite number of possible results. Each element of the sample space is called an **outcome** of the experiment.

EXAMPLE 1

Suppose that we perform the experiment of flipping a coin. When we flip the coin, the coin will come to rest with either a head or a tail on its upper face. If we denote the possible results as H for heads and T for tails, the sample space of this experiment is {H, T}. The elements H and T of the sample space are the possible outcomes of the experiment.

EXAMPLE 2

Suppose that we perform the experiment of flipping two coins one after the other. Since each coin can have a head or a tail on its upper face, the sample space is {(H, H), (H, T), (T, H), (T, T)}, where the first and second components of each ordered pair in the sample space represent the outcomes obtained when we flip the first and second coins, respectively. Note that (H, T) and (T, H) are two different outcomes.

EXAMPLE 3

Suppose that we perform the experiment of rolling a die. When we roll the die, the die will come to rest with 1, 2, 3, 4, 5, or 6 spots on its upper face. Thus the sample space is {1, 2, 3, 4, 5, 6} and the possible outcomes are 1, 2, 3, 4, 5, and 6.

EXERCISE 1

What is the sample space for the roll of two dice?

Answer

$$\begin{Bmatrix} (1,\ 1),\ (1,\ 2),\ (1,\ 3),\ (1,\ 4),\ (1,\ 5),\ (1,\ 6), \\ (2,\ 1),\ (2,\ 2),\ (2,\ 3),\ (2,\ 4),\ (2,\ 5),\ (2,\ 6), \\ (3,\ 1),\ (3,\ 2),\ (3,\ 3),\ (3,\ 4),\ (3,\ 5),\ (3,\ 6), \\ (4,\ 1),\ (4,\ 2),\ (4,\ 3),\ (4,\ 4),\ (4,\ 5),\ (4,\ 6), \\ (5,\ 1),\ (5,\ 2),\ (5,\ 3),\ (5,\ 4),\ (5,\ 5),\ (5,\ 6), \\ (6,\ 1),\ (6,\ 2),\ (6,\ 3),\ (6,\ 4),\ (6,\ 5),\ (6,\ 6) \end{Bmatrix}$$

Any subset of a sample space S is called an **event in S.** Events are commonly denoted by the letter E.

EXAMPLE 4

Returning to the experiment in which a die was rolled, we have the following as examples of events:

the event E_1 that the outcome is even is $\{2, 4, 6\}$,
the event E_2 that the outcome is not even is $\{1, 3, 5\}$,
the event E_3 that the outcome is less than 3 is $\{1, 2\}$,
the event E_4 that the outcome is less than 8 is $\{1, 2, 3, 4, 5, 6\}$,
the event E_5 that the outcome is 8 is $\varnothing$.

EXERCISE 2

Referring to Exercise 1, write the following events in set notation.
(a) E_1: the sum of the numbers rolled is 7.
(b) E_2: the sum of the numbers rolled is greater than 10.

Answer (a) $E_1 = \{(1, 6), (2, 5), (3, 4), (4, 3), (5, 2), (6, 1)\}$ (b) $E_2 = \{(5, 6), (6, 5), (6, 6)\}$

In this book we shall consider only experiments in which each possible outcome is equally likely to occur. Under these conditions we are now prepared to introduce the concept of probability.

Definition 11.1 If S is a sample space whose outcomes are equally likely to occur and E is an event in S, then the probability that E will occur, denoted by $P(E)$, is defined as

$$P(E) = \frac{n(E)}{n(S)},\tag{11-4}$$

where $n(E)$ is the number of elements (outcomes) in E and $n(S)$ is the number of elements (outcomes) in S.

EXAMPLE 5

If an ordinary die is rolled, what is the probability of an even number appearing on the upper face of the die when it comes to rest? What is the probability that a seven will appear on the upper face?

Solution Let

$$S = \text{sample space of the experiment,}$$
$$E_1 = \text{event that the outcome is even,}$$

and

$$E_2 = \text{event that the outcome is 7.}$$

Then,

$$S = \{1, 2, 3, 4, 5, 6\}, \quad E_1 = \{2, 4, 6\}, \quad \text{and} \quad E_2 = \emptyset.$$

Hence

$$n(S) = 6, \quad n(E_1) = 3, \quad \text{and} \quad n(E_2) = 0.$$

Thus

$$P(E_1) = P(\text{outcome is even}) = \frac{n(E_1)}{n(S)} = \frac{3}{6} = \frac{1}{2}$$

and

$$P(E_2) = P(\text{outcome is 7}) = \frac{n(E_2)}{n(S)} = \frac{0}{6} = 0. \qquad \blacksquare$$

EXERCISE 3

If an ordinary die is rolled, what is the probability of obtaining
(a) a number greater than 2?   (b) a number less than 7?

Answer (a) $\frac{2}{3}$ (b) 1

EXAMPLE 6

Two marbles are drawn at random (i.e., it is equally likely that any particular pair of marbles is drawn) from a bag containing 3 crimson marbles and 5 gold marbles. What is the probability that both marbles are gold?

Solution Let

$$S = \text{sample space of the experiment,}$$

and

$$E = \text{event that both marbles drawn are gold.}$$

We need to calculate $n(S)$ and $n(E)$. The number of elements in the sample space S is the number of combinations of all 8 marbles taken 2 at a time. Thus

$$n(S) = C(8, 2) = \frac{8!}{2! \, 6!} = 28.$$

Similarly, the number of elements in the event E is the number of combinations of 5 gold marbles taken 2 at a time. Thus

$$n(E) = C(5, 2) = \frac{5!}{2! \, 3!} = 10.$$

Hence

$$P(E) = P(\text{both marbles are gold}) = \frac{n(E)}{n(S)} = \frac{10}{28} = \frac{5}{14}. \qquad \blacksquare$$

Problems 11.4

In problems 1–6, write the sample space for the given experiment.

1. A coin is tossed and then a die is rolled.
2. Three coins are tossed one after the other.
3. A two-headed coin is tossed and then an ordinary coin is tossed.
4. Two balls are drawn at random from a bag that contains a red ball, a blue ball, a white ball, and a green ball.
5. A bag contains a red marble, a blue marble, and a white marble. A marble is drawn from the bag, and then a second marble is drawn from the bag after the first marble has been returned to the bag.
6. A deck of cards consists of the jack, the queen, the king, and the ace of spades. Two cards are drawn at random from the deck.
7. When a die is rolled, what is the probability of rolling a three?
8. When a die is rolled, what is the probability of rolling a number greater than one?
9. When a die is rolled, what is the probability of rolling a number less than ten?
10. When a pair of dice are rolled, what is the probability that the sum of the numbers on the dice is (a) eight? (b) less than five?
11. When a pair of dice are rolled, what is the probability that the sum of the numbers on the dice is (a) not seven? (b) exactly divisible by 5?
12. When a pair of dice are rolled, what is the probability that (a) both numbers on the dice are the same? (b) exactly one five appears on the dice?
13. If 2 coins are tossed one after another, what is the probability of getting (a) 2 heads? (b) 1 head and 1 tail?
14. If 3 coins are tossed one after another, what is the probability of getting (a) exactly 2 heads? (b) at least 2 heads?
15. If 4 coins are tossed one after another, what is the probability of getting (a) no tails? (b) at least 1 head?
16. If 3 cards are drawn from an ordinary deck of cards, what is the probability of getting (a) all red cards? (b) no spades? (c) only face cards and aces?
17. If 3 cards are drawn from an ordinary deck of cards, what is the probability of getting (a) no cards lower than a seven? (b) 1 spade and 2 red cards? (c) at least 2 red cards?
18. If 3 cards are drawn from an ordinary deck of cards, what is the probability of getting (a) all kings? (b) a pair of aces and one other card that is not an ace? (c) 3 cards of the same suit?
19. Three marbles are drawn at random from a bag containing 3 crimson marbles and 5 gold marbles. What is the probability that (a) the marbles drawn are all gold? (b) none of the marbles drawn are gold?
20. John and 5 of his friends have managed to get 2 tickets to the Superbowl. Since they only have 2 tickets, they draw to see which 2 will see the game. What is the probability that John will draw one of the tickets?
21. If the 6 digits 1, 5, 7, 7, 2, and 7 are selected one at a time at random, what is the probability that each successive digit will be equal to or greater than all the previously selected digits?

22. An urn contains 3 crimson marbles, 5 gold marbles, and 4 white marbles. If 3 marbles are drawn from the urn at random, what is the probability that 1 marble of each color is drawn?

23. In the experiment of problem 22, what is the probability that at least 2 of the marbles drawn are gold or crimson?

24. In the experiment of problem 22, what is the probability that no more than 2 of the marbles drawn are white?

25. If 5 cards are dealt at random from an ordinary deck of 52 cards, determine the probability of getting each of the following poker hands.
    (a) royal flush (10, J, Q, K, and A in the same suit)
    (b) straight flush (5 cards in a sequence in the same suit, but not a royal flush).
    (c) four of a kind
    (d) full house (3 of a kind and 2 of another kind)
    (e) flush (5 cards in the same suit, but not a straight flush or a royal flush)
    (f) straight (5 cards in a sequence, but not a straight flush or a royal flush)
    (g) three of a kind   (h) two pairs
    (i) one pair   (j) a pair or better
    (k) a pair of jacks or better

Answers 11.4

1. {(H, 1), (H, 2), (H, 3), (H, 4), (H, 5), (H, 6), (T, 1), (T, 2), (T, 3), (T, 4), (T, 5), (T, 6)}

2. {(H, H, H), (H, H, T), (H, T, H), (H, T, T), (T, H, H), (T, H, T), (T, T, H), (T, T, T)}

4. {RB, RW, RG, BW, BG, WG}

5. {(R, B), (R, W), (R, R), (B, R), (B, W), (B, B), (W, R), (W, B), (W, W)}

7. $\frac{1}{6}$ 8. $\frac{5}{6}$ 10. (a) $\frac{5}{36}$ (b) $\frac{6}{36}$

11. (a) $\frac{30}{36}$ (b) $\frac{7}{36}$ 13. (a) $\frac{1}{4}$ (b) $\frac{2}{4}$ 14. (a) $\frac{3}{8}$ (b) $\frac{4}{8}$

16. (a) $2600/C(52, 3)$ (b) $9139/C(52, 3)$ (c) $220/C(52, 3)$

17. (a) $4960/C(52, 3)$ (b) $4225/C(52, 3)$ (c) $11,050/C(52, 3)$

19. (a) $10/C(8, 3)$ (b) $1/C(8, 3)$ 20. $5/C(6, 2)$

22. $60/C(12, 3)$ 23. $168/C(12, 3)$

25. (a) $4/C(52, 5)$ (b) $36/C(52, 5)$ (c) $624/C(52, 5)$ (d) $3744/C(52, 5)$
    (e) $5108/C(52, 5)$ (f) $10,200/C(52, 5)$ (g) $54,912/C(52, 5)$
    (h) $123,552/C(52, 5)$ (i) $1,098,240/C(52, 5)$ (j) $1,296,420/C(52, 5)$
    (k) $536,100/C(52, 5)$

11.5 Basic Probability Properties

The set of outcomes in a sample space that are *not* favorable to an event E is called the **complementary event** of E. We denote the complementary event of E as E'. For example, in the experiment of rolling a die, if E is the event "we roll an even number," then E' is the event "we do not roll an even number." That is, E' is the event "we roll an odd number."

Theorem 11.4 If S is a sample space and E is an event in S, then

$$P(E) + P(E') = 1 \qquad\qquad (11-5)$$

Proof Since we are considering only finite sample spaces, the sample space contains a finite number, say k, of possible outcomes. If n of these outcomes are favorable to the event E, then the remaining $k - n$ outcomes are not favorable to E. Consequently, these $k - n$ outcomes are favorable to the complementary event E'. Thus

$$n(S) = k, \quad n(E) = n, \quad \text{and} \quad n(E') = k - n.$$

Hence

$$n(E) + n(E') = n + (k - n) = k = n(S).$$

Dividing by $n(S)$, we have

$$\frac{n(E)}{n(S)} + \frac{n(E')}{n(S)} = \frac{n(S)}{n(S)},$$

and hence

$$P(E) + P(E') = 1. \qquad\qquad \blacksquare$$

Theorem 11.4 is useful for calculating the probability of an event E when it is easier to count the possible outcomes in the complementary event E' rather than to count the possible outcomes in the event E itself.

EXAMPLE 1

If a pair of dice are rolled, determine the probability that the sum of the numbers is greater than three.

Solution Let

$$S = \text{sample space of the experiment,}$$

and

$$E = \text{event that the sum of the numbers is greater than three.}$$

Then

$$E' = \text{event that the sum of the numbers is three or less.}$$

Recall from Exercise 1 in the previous section that there are $6 \cdot 6 = 36$ possible outcomes for the given experiment. That is, $n(S) = 36$. Listing and counting the outcomes that belong to E' (which is easier than listing and counting the outcomes which belong to E), we have

$$E' = \{(1, 1), (1, 2), (2, 1)\}$$

and

$$n(E') = 3.$$

Consequently, it follows from Eq. (11–5) that

$$P(E) = P(\text{sum of the numbers is greater than 3})$$
$$= 1 - P(E') = 1 - \frac{n(E')}{n(S)}$$
$$= 1 - \frac{3}{36} = \frac{33}{36} = \frac{11}{12}. \qquad ∎$$

Another useful probability property is given in the following theorem.

Theorem 11.5   If S is a sample space and E_1 and E_2 are events in S, then

$$P(E_1 \text{ or } E_2) = P(E_1 \cup E_2) = P(E_1) + P(E_2) - P(E_1 \cap E_2). \qquad (11-6)$$

Proof   Recall that the union, $E_1 \cup E_2$, of the two sets E_1 and E_2 is the set consisting of all elements that belong to E_1 or to E_2. Also recall that the intersection, $E_1 \cap E_2$, of the two sets E_1 and E_2 is the set consisting of all elements that belong to both E_1 and E_2. Using these two facts, it follows that

$$n(E_1 \cup E_2) = n(E_1) + n(E_2) - n(E_1 \cap E_2).$$

Dividing by $n(S)$, we have

$$\frac{n(E_1 \cup E_2)}{n(S)} = \frac{n(E_1)}{n(S)} + \frac{n(E_2)}{n(S)} - \frac{n(E_1 \cap E_2)}{n(S)},$$

and hence

$$P(E_1 \text{ or } E_2) = P(E_1) + P(E_2) - P(E_1 \cap E_2). \qquad ∎$$

Theorem 11.5 is useful when we want to calculate the probability that at least one of two events will occur.

EXAMPLE 2

If a die is rolled, determine the probability of getting an odd number or a number less than four.

Solution   Since the sample space is $S = \{1, 2, 3, 4, 5, 6\}$, we have $n(S) = 6$. With

$$E_1 = \text{event that we get an odd number}$$

and

$$E_2 = \text{event that we get a number less than four,}$$

we have

$$E_1 = \{1, 3, 5\}, \quad E_2 = \{1, 2, 3\}, \quad \text{and} \quad E_1 \cap E_2 = \{1, 3\}.$$

Thus

$$n(E_1) = 3, \quad n(E_2) = 3, \quad \text{and} \quad n(E_1 \cap E_2) = 2.$$

Consequently, it follows from Eq. (11–6) that

$$
\begin{aligned}
P(E_1 \text{ or } E_2) &= P(\text{we get an odd number or a number less than four}) \\
&= P(E_1) + P(E_2) - P(E_1 \cap E_2) \\
&= \frac{n(E_1)}{n(S)} + \frac{n(E_2)}{n(S)} - \frac{n(E_1 \cap E_2)}{n(S)} \\
&= \tfrac{3}{6} + \tfrac{3}{6} - \tfrac{2}{6} = \tfrac{4}{6} = \tfrac{2}{3}.
\end{aligned}
$$
∎

Two events E_1 and E_2 in a sample space S are called **mutually exclusive events** if $E_1 \cap E_2 = \varnothing$. That is, the events E_1 and E_2 are mutually exclusive if they have no outcomes in common.

Theorem 11.6   If S is a sample space and E_1 and E_2 are mutually exclusive events in S, then

$$P(E_1 \text{ or } E_2) = P(E_1 \cup E_2) = P(E_1) + P(E_2). \qquad (11-7)$$

Proof   Since E_1 and E_2 are mutually exclusive,

$$P(E_1 \cap E_2) = P(\varnothing) = \frac{n(\varnothing)}{n(S)} = \frac{0}{n(S)} = 0.$$

Thus it follows from Theorem 11.5 that

$$P(E_1 \text{ or } E_2) = P(E_1) + P(E_2).$$
∎

EXAMPLE 3

A card is drawn from an ordinary deck of 52 cards, what is the probability of drawing a club or a diamond?

Solution The sample space S consists of the set of 52 cards. Thus $n(S) = 52$. With

$$E_1 = \text{event that we draw a club}$$

and

$$E_2 = \text{event that we draw a diamond,}$$

we have

$$E_1 = \{2_c, 3_c, 4_c, 5_c, 6_c, 7_c, 8_c, 9_c, 10_c, J_c, Q_c, K_c, A_c\}$$

and

$$E_2 = \{2_d, 3_d, 4_d, 5_d, 6_d, 7_d, 8_d, 9_d, 10_d, J_d, Q_d, K_d, A_d\}.$$

Thus

$$n(E_1) = 13 \quad \text{and} \quad n(E_2) = 13. \qquad \blacksquare$$

Since E_1 and E_2 are mutually exclusive, it follows by Theorem 11.6 that

$$
\begin{aligned}
P(E_1 \text{ or } E_2) &= P(\text{we draw a club or a diamond}) \\
&= P(E_1) + P(E_2) \\
&= \frac{n(E_1)}{n(S)} + \frac{n(E_2)}{n(S)} \\
&= \tfrac{13}{52} + \tfrac{13}{52} = \tfrac{26}{52} = \tfrac{1}{2}.
\end{aligned}
$$

Problems 11.5

In problems 1–6, use Theorem 11.4 to calculate the required probability.

1. If 5 cards are drawn at random from an ordinary deck of 52 cards, what is the probability of getting at least 1 ace?
2. Four coins are tossed one after another. What is the probability of getting at least 1 head?
3. A man has 6 dimes and 4 nickels in his pocket. If he draws 3 coins from his pocket at random, what is the probability that the sum of the coins drawn is greater than 15 cents?

4. A bag contains 6 red, 5 white, and 4 blue marbles. If 4 marbles are drawn from the bag at random, what is the probability that at least 1 is white?

5. A bag contains 6 red, 2 white, and 2 blue marbles. If 3 marbles are drawn from the bag at random, what is the probability that they are not all the same color?

6. A bag contains 3 red and 3 white marbles. If the marbles are drawn from the bag one at a time and placed in a row from left to right as they are drawn, what is the probability that the white marbles are not all next to each other?

In problems 7–15, use Theorem 11.5 or Theorem 11.6 to calculate the required probability.

7. Four coins are tossed one after another. What is the probability of tossing either 2 heads or 3 heads?

8. A committee of 3 people is chosen from 4 boys and 5 girls. What is the probability that the committee will contain all boys or all girls?

9. A box contains 6 good transistors and 3 bad transistors, all of the same type. If two transistors are taken from the box at random, what is the probability that both are good or both are bad?

10. If a die is rolled, what is the probability that the number is odd or the number is prime?

11. If 2 dice are rolled, what is the probability that the sum is seven or at least one of the numbers is a six?

12. If 2 dice are rolled, what is the probability of a double or a sum greater than ten?

13. A card is drawn at random from an ordinary deck of 52 cards. What is the probability that it is black or it is a face card?

14. Three marbles are drawn at random from a bag which contains 3 red, 2 white, and 5 blue marbles. What is the probability of obtaining both white marbles or one marble of each color?

15. Two cards are drawn at random from an ordinary deck of 52 cards. What is the probability that both are hearts or both are aces?

In problems 16–24, determine the required probability by any appropriate method.

16. Half of the eggs in a dozen eggs are rotten. If 3 eggs are selected at random from the dozen eggs, what is the probability that at least one rotten egg was selected?

17. A committee of 3 people is chosen at random from 5 boys and 4 girls. What is the probability that at least 2 boys are on the committee?

18. Four coins are tossed one after another. What is the probability of getting an odd number of heads?

19. Two cards are drawn at random from an ordinary deck of 52 cards. What is the probability that one is red and the other is a black face card?

20. Two cards are drawn at random from an ordinary deck of 52 cards. What is the probability that both are black or one is a queen and the other is a king?

21. A special deck of 8 cards consists of the queens and the kings removed from an ordinary deck of cards. If 2 cards are drawn at random from the special deck, what is the probability that both are black or both are kings?

22. A bag contains 5 crimson and 7 gold marbles. If 3 marbles are drawn at random from the bag, what is the probability that all are gold or none are gold?

23. A bag contains 5 red, 3 white, and 2 blue marbles. If 2 marbles are drawn at random from the bag, what is the probability that neither is blue or both are red?

24. A bag contains 5 marbles that are marked 1, 2, 3, 4 and 5, respectively. If two marbles are drawn at random from the bag, what is the probability that the sum of the numbers on the marbles is 5 or 6?

25. If E_1, E_2, . . ., E_n are mutually exclusive events in a sample space S, prove that

$$P(E_1 \text{ or } E_2 \text{ or } \cdots \text{ or } E_n) = P(E_1) + P(E_2) + \cdots + P(E_n)$$

by using mathematical induction.

In problems 26–29, use the result in problem 25 to calculate the required probability.

26. If 2 dice are tossed, what is the probability that the sum of the dice will be 5, 6, or 7?

27. If a card is drawn at random from an ordinary deck of cards, what is the probability that the card is black, a heart, or the three of diamonds?

28. If 4 coins are tossed one after another, what is the probability of getting an even number of heads?

29. An exam consists of 10 true–false questions. If a student guesses all the answers to the exam, what is the probability that the student's grade will be 70 or better?

Answers 11.5

1. $1 - C(48, 5)/C(52, 5)$ 2. $\frac{15}{16}$
4. $1 - C(10, 4)/C(15, 4)$ 5. $1 - C(6, 3)/C(10, 3)$
7. $\frac{5}{8}$ 8. $14/C(9, 3)$ 10. $\frac{2}{3}$ 11. $\frac{5}{12}$
13. $\frac{8}{13}$ 14. $38/C(10, 3)$ 16. $1 - C(6, 3)/C(12, 3)$
17. $50/C(9, 3)$ 19. $156/C(52, 2)$ 20. $337/C(52, 2)$ 22. $45/C(12, 3)$
23. $28/C(10, 2)$ 26. $\frac{5}{12}$ 28. $\frac{1}{2}$ 29. $176/1024$

chapter 11 review problems

1. How many integers less than 6000, each containing 4 different digits, can be formed by using the digits 1, 2, 4, 7, and 8?

2. How many even integers less than 6000, each containing 4 different digits, can be formed by using the digits 1, 2, 4, 7, and 8?

3. A bag contains 5 crimson and 3 gold marbles. How many different color arrangements are possible if the marbles are drawn from the bag one at a time and arranged in a row in the order in which they are drawn?

4. In how many ways can 7 people be seated, relative to one another, around a circular table if 3 of the people insist on sitting next to each other?

5. From 10 men and 6 women, a committee of 5 people is chosen at random. What is the probability that the committee will consist of all men or all women?

6. When a pair of dice are rolled, what is the probability of rolling an odd number?

7. Two marbles are drawn at random from a bag containing 7 crimson and 4 gold marbles. What is the probability that one marble of each color is drawn?

8. Four marbles are drawn at random from a bag containing 7 crimson, 4 gold, and 4 white marbles. What is the probability of drawing no gold marbles?

9. If two cards are drawn at random from an ordinary deck of cards, what is the probability that both are face cards?

10. If 3 cards are drawn at random from an ordinary deck of cards, what is the probability that at least one is a spade?

11. A bridge hand consists of 13 cards dealt at random from an ordinary deck of 52 cards. What is the probability that a bridge hand will consist of at least 11 spades?

12. If 2 dice are rolled, what is the probability of rolling a double or a sum of eight?

13. A card is drawn at random from an ordinary deck of cards. What is the probability that it is a spade or a face card?

14. Two cards are drawn at random from an ordinary deck of cards. What is the probability that both are spades or both are face cards?

answers

1. 72   2. 42   3. 56   4. 144
5. $258/C(16, 5)$ 6. $\frac{1}{2}$ 7. $28/C(11, 2)$ 8. $330/C(15, 4)$
9. $C(12,2)/C(52, 2)$ 10. $1 - C(39, 3)/C(52, 3)$ 11. $58,306/C(52, 13)$
12. $\frac{5}{18}$ 13. $\frac{11}{26}$ 14. $141/C(52, 2)$

Table A Common Logarithms of Numbers

x	0	1	2	3	4	5	6	7	8	9
1.0	.0000	.0043	.0086	.0128	.0170	.0212	.0253	.0294	.0334	.0374
1.1	.0414	.0453	.0492	.0531	.0569	.0607	.0645	.0682	.0719	.0755
1.2	.0792	.0828	.0864	.0899	.0934	.0969	.1004	.1038	.1072	.1106
1.3	.1139	.1173	.1206	.1239	.1271	.1303	.1335	.1367	.1399	.1430
1.4	.1461	.1492	.1523	.1553	.1584	.1614	.1644	.1673	.1703	.1732
1.5	.1761	.1790	.1818	.1847	.1875	.1903	.1931	.1959	.1987	.2014
1.6	.2041	.2068	.2095	.2122	.2148	.2175	.2201	.2227	.2253	.2279
1.7	.2304	.2330	.2355	.2380	.2405	.2430	.2455	.2480	.2504	.2529
1.8	.2553	.2577	.2601	.2625	.2648	.2672	.2695	.2718	.2742	.2765
1.9	.2788	.2810	.2833	.2856	.2878	.2900	.2923	.2945	.2967	.2989
2.0	.3010	.3032	.3054	.3075	.3096	.3118	.3139	.3160	.3181	.3201
2.1	.3222	.3243	.3263	.3284	.3304	.3324	.3345	.3365	.3385	.3404
2.2	.3424	.3444	.3464	.3483	.3502	.3522	.3541	.3560	.3579	.3598
2.3	.3617	.3636	.3655	.3674	.3692	.3711	.3729	.3747	.3766	.3784
2.4	.3802	.3820	.3838	.3856	.3874	.3892	.3909	.3927	.3945	.3962
2.5	.3979	.3997	.4014	.4031	.4048	.4065	.4082	.4099	.4116	.4133
2.6	.4150	.4166	.4183	.4200	.4216	.4232	.4249	.4265	.4281	.4298
2.7	.4314	.4330	.4346	.4362	.4378	.4393	.4409	.4425	.4440	.4456
2.8	.4472	.4487	.4502	.4518	.4533	.4548	.4564	.4579	.4594	.4609
2.9	.4624	.4639	.4654	.4669	.4683	.4698	.4713	.4728	.4742	.4757
3.0	.4771	.4786	.4800	.4814	.4829	.4843	.4857	.4871	.4886	.4900
3.1	.4914	.4928	.4942	.4955	.4969	.4983	.4997	.5011	.5024	.5038
3.2	.5051	.5065	.5079	.5092	.5105	.5119	.5132	.5145	.5159	.5172
3.3	.5185	.5198	.5211	.5224	.5237	.5250	.5263	.5276	.5289	.5302
3.4	.5315	.5328	.5340	.5353	.5366	.5378	.5391	.5403	.5416	.5428
3.5	.5441	.5453	.5465	.5478	.5490	.5502	.5514	.5527	.5539	.5551
3.6	.5563	.5575	.5587	.5599	.5611	.5623	.5635	.5647	.5658	.5670
3.7	.5682	.5694	.5705	.5717	.5729	.5740	.5752	.5763	.5775	.5786
3.8	.5798	.5809	.5821	.5832	.5843	.5855	.5866	.5877	.5888	.5899
3.9	.5911	.5922	.5933	.5944	.5955	.5966	.5977	.5988	.5999	.6010
4.0	.6021	.6031	.6042	.6053	.6064	.6075	.6085	.6096	.6107	.6117
4.1	.6128	.6138	.6149	.6160	.6170	.6180	.6191	.6201	.6212	.6222
4.2	.6232	.6243	.6253	.6263	.6274	.6284	.6294	.6304	.6314	.6325
4.3	.6335	.6345	.6355	.6365	.6375	.6385	.6395	.6405	.6415	.6425
4.4	.6435	.6444	.6454	.6464	.6474	.6484	.6493	.6503	.6513	.6522
4.5	.6532	.6542	.6551	.6561	.6571	.6580	.6590	.6599	.6609	.6618
4.6	.6628	.6637	.6646	.6656	.6665	.6675	.6684	.6693	.6702	.6712
4.7	.6721	.6730	.6739	.6749	.6758	.6767	.6776	.6785	.6794	.6803
4.8	.6812	.6821	.6830	.6839	.6848	.6857	.6866	.6875	.6884	.6893
4.9	.6902	.6911	.6920	.6928	.6937	.6946	.6955	.6964	.6972	.6981
5.0	.6990	.6998	.7007	.7016	.7024	.7033	.7042	.7050	.7059	.7067
5.1	.7076	.7084	.7093	.7101	.7110	.7118	.7126	.7135	.7143	.7152
5.2	.7160	.7168	.7177	.7185	.7193	.7202	.7210	.7218	.7226	.7235
5.3	.7243	.7251	.7259	.7267	.7275	.7284	.7292	.7300	.7308	.7316
5.4	.7324	.7332	.7340	.7348	.7356	.7364	.7372	.7380	.7388	.7396
x	0	1	2	3	4	5	6	7	8	9

x	0	1	2	3	4	5	6	7	8	9
5.5	.7404	.7412	.7419	.7427	.7435	.7443	.7451	.7459	.7466	.7474
5.6	.7482	.7490	.7497	.7505	.7513	.7520	.7528	.7536	.7543	.7551
5.7	.7559	.7566	.7574	.7582	.7589	.7597	.7604	.7612	.7619	.7627
5.8	.7634	.7642	.7649	.7657	.7664	.7672	.7679	.7686	.7694	.7701
5.9	.7709	.7716	.7723	.7731	.7738	.7745	.7752	.7760	.7767	.7774
6.0	.7782	.7789	.7796	.7803	.7810	.7818	.7825	.7832	.7839	.7846
6.1	.7853	.7860	.7868	.7875	.7882	.7889	.7896	.7903	.7910	.7917
6.2	.7924	.7931	.7938	.7945	.7952	.7959	.7966	.7973	.7980	.7987
6.3	.7993	.8000	.8007	.8014	.8021	.8028	.8035	.8041	.8048	.8055
6.4	.8062	.8069	.8075	.8082	.8089	.8096	.8102	.8109	.8116	.8122
6.5	.8129	.8136	.8142	.8149	.8156	.8162	.8169	.8176	.8182	.8189
6.6	.8195	.8202	.8209	.8215	.8222	.8228	.8235	.8241	.8248	.8254
6.7	.8261	.8267	.8274	.8280	.8287	.8293	.8299	.8306	.8312	.8319
6.8	.8325	.8331	.8338	.8344	.8351	.8357	.8363	.8370	.8376	.8382
6.9	.8388	.8395	.8401	.8407	.8414	.8420	.8426	.8432	.8439	.8445
7.0	.8451	.8457	.8463	.8470	.8476	.8482	.8488	.8494	.8500	.8506
7.1	.8513	.8519	.8525	.8531	.8537	.8543	.8549	.8555	.8561	.8567
7.2	.8573	.8579	.8585	.8591	.8597	.8603	.8609	.8615	.8621	.8627
7.3	.8633	.8639	.8645	.8651	.8657	.8663	.8669	.8675	.8681	.8686
7.4	.8692	.8698	.8704	.8710	.8716	.8722	.8727	.8733	.8739	.8745
7.5	.8751	.8756	.8762	.8768	.8774	.8779	.8785	.8791	.8797	.8802
7.6	.8808	.8814	.8820	.8825	.8831	.8837	.8842	.8848	.8854	.8859
7.7	.8865	.8871	.8876	.8882	.8887	.8893	.8899	.8904	.8910	.8915
7.8	.8921	.8927	.8932	.8938	.8943	.8949	.8954	.8960	.8965	.8971
7.9	.8976	.8982	.8987	.8993	.8998	.9004	.9009	.9015	.9020	.9025
8.0	.9031	.9036	.9042	.9047	.9053	.9058	.9063	.9069	.9074	.9079
8.1	.9085	.9090	.9096	.9101	.9106	.9112	.9117	.9122	.9128	.9133
8.2	.9138	.9143	.9149	.9154	.9159	.9165	.9170	.9175	.9180	.9186
8.3	.9191	.9196	.9201	.9206	.9212	.9217	.9222	.9227	.9232	.9238
8.4	.9243	.9248	.9253	.9258	.9263	.9269	.9274	.9279	.9284	.9289
8.5	.9294	.9299	.9304	.9309	.9315	.9320	.9325	.9330	.9335	.9340
8.6	.9345	.9350	.9355	.9360	.9365	.9370	.9375	.9380	.9385	.9390
8.7	.9395	.9400	.9405	.9410	.9415	.9420	.9425	.9430	.9435	.9440
8.8	.9445	.9450	.9455	.9460	.9465	.9469	.9474	.9479	.9484	.9489
8.9	.9494	.9499	.9504	.9509	.9513	.9518	.9523	.9528	.9533	.9538
9.0	.9542	.9547	.9552	.9557	.9562	.9566	.9571	.9576	.9581	.9586
9.1	.9590	.9595	.9600	.9605	.9609	.9614	.9619	.9624	.9628	.9633
9.2	.9638	.9643	.9647	.9652	.9657	.9661	.9666	.9671	.9675	.9680
9.3	.9685	.9689	.9694	.9699	.9703	.9708	.9713	.9717	.9722	.9727
9.4	.9731	.9736	.9741	.9745	.9750	.9754	.9759	.9763	.9768	.9773
9.5	.9777	.9782	.9786	.9791	.9795	.9800	.9805	.9809	.9814	.9818
9.6	.9823	.9827	.9832	.9836	.9841	.9845	.9850	.9854	.9859	.9863
9.7	.9868	.9872	.9877	.9881	.9886	.9890	.9894	.9899	.9903	.9908
9.8	.9912	.9917	.9921	.9926	.9930	.9934	.9939	.9943	.9948	.9952
9.9	.9956	.9961	.9965	.9969	.9974	.9978	.9983	.9987	.9991	.9996
x	0	1	2	3	4	5	6	7	8	9

Table B Powers and Roots

x	x^2	$\sqrt{x}$	x^3	$\sqrt[3]{x}$	x	x^2	$\sqrt{x}$	x^3	$\sqrt[3]{x}$
1	1	1.000	1	1.000	51	2,601	7.141	132,651	3.708
2	4	1.414	8	1.260	52	2,704	7.211	140,608	3.732
3	9	1.732	27	1.442	53	2,809	7.280	148,877	3.756
4	16	2.000	64	1.587	54	2,916	7.348	157,464	3.780
5	25	2.236	125	1.710	55	3,025	7.416	166,375	3.803
6	36	2.449	216	1.817	56	3,136	7.483	175,616	3.826
7	49	2.646	343	1.913	57	3,249	7.550	185,193	3.848
8	64	2.828	512	2.000	58	3,364	7.616	195,112	3.871
9	81	3.000	729	2.080	59	3,481	7.681	205,379	3.893
10	100	3.162	1,000	2.154	60	3,600	7.746	216,000	3.915
11	121	3.317	1,331	2.224	61	3,721	7.810	226,981	3.936
12	144	3.464	1,728	3.289	62	3,844	7.874	238,328	3.958
13	169	3.606	2,197	2.351	63	3,969	7.937	250,047	3.979
14	196	3.742	2,744	2.410	64	4,096	8.000	262,144	4.000
15	225	3.873	3,375	2.466	65	4,225	8.062	274,625	4.021
16	256	4.000	4,096	2.520	66	4,356	8.124	287,496	4.041
17	289	4.123	4,913	2.571	67	4,489	8.185	300,763	4.062
18	324	4.243	5,832	2.621	68	4,624	8.246	314,432	4.082
19	361	4.359	6,859	2.668	69	4,761	8.307	328,509	4.102
20	400	4.472	8,000	2.714	70	4,900	8.367	343,000	4.121
21	441	4.583	9,261	2.759	71	5,041	8.426	357,911	4.141
22	484	4.690	10,648	2.802	72	5,184	8.485	373,248	4.160
23	529	4.796	12,167	2.844	73	5,329	8.544	389,017	4.179
24	576	4.899	13,824	2.884	74	5,476	8.602	405,224	4.198
25	625	5.000	15,625	2.924	75	5,625	8.660	421,875	4.217
26	676	5.099	17,576	2.962	76	5,776	8.718	438,976	4.236
27	729	5.196	19,683	3.000	77	5,929	8.775	456,533	4.254
28	784	5.291	21,952	3.037	78	6,084	8.832	474,552	4.273
29	841	5.385	24,389	3.072	79	6,241	8.888	493,039	4.291
30	900	5.477	27,000	3.107	80	6,400	8.944	512,000	4.309
31	961	5.568	29,791	3.141	81	6,561	9.000	531,441	4.327
32	1,024	5.657	32,768	3.175	82	6,724	9.055	551,368	4.344
33	1,089	5.745	35,937	3.208	83	6,889	9.110	571,787	4.362
34	1,156	5.831	39,304	3.240	84	7,056	9.165	592,704	4.380
35	1,225	5.916	42,875	3.271	85	7,225	9.220	614,125	4.397
36	1,296	6.000	46,656	3.302	86	7,396	9.274	636,056	4.414
37	1,369	6.083	50,653	3.332	87	7,569	9.327	658,503	4.431
38	1,444	6.164	54,872	3.362	88	7,744	9.381	681,472	4.448
39	1,521	6.245	59,319	3.391	89	7,921	9.434	704,969	4.465
40	1,600	6.325	64,000	3.420	90	8,100	9.487	729,000	4.481
41	1,681	6.403	68,921	3.448	91	8,281	9.539	753,571	4.498
42	1,764	6.481	74,088	3.476	92	8,464	9.592	778,688	4.514
43	1,849	6.557	79,507	3.503	93	8,649	9.643	804,357	4.531
44	1,936	6.633	85,184	3.530	94	8,836	9.695	830,584	4.547
45	2,025	6.708	91,125	3.557	95	9,025	9.747	857,375	4.563
46	2,116	6.782	97,336	3.583	96	9,216	9.798	884,736	4.579
47	2,209	6.856	103,823	3.609	97	9,409	9.849	912,673	4.595
48	2,304	6.928	110,592	3.634	98	9,604	9.899	941,192	4.610
49	2,401	7.000	117,649	3.659	99	9,801	9.950	970,299	4.626
50	2,500	7.071	125,000	3.684	100	10,000	10.000	1,000,000	4.642

Index

Properties of Real Numbers:

$(a+b)+c = a+(b+c)$

$(ab)c = a(bc)$

$a+b = b+a$

$ab = ba$

$a(b+c) = ab+ac$

$a+0 = 0+a = a$

$a \cdot 1 = 1 \cdot a = a$

$a+(-a) = (-a)+a = 0$

$a \cdot (1/a) = (1/a) \cdot a = 1 \ (a \neq 0)$

$a = b$ iff $a+c = b+c$

$a = b$ iff $ac = bc \ (c \neq 0)$

$a \cdot 0 = 0$

$ab = 0$ iff $(a=0$ or $b=0)$

$-(-a) = a$

$(-a)b = -(ab)$

$(-a)(-b) = ab$

$-(a+b) = (-a)+(-b)$

$\dfrac{a}{b} = \dfrac{c}{d}$ iff $ad = bc \ (b, d \neq 0)$

$\dfrac{a}{b} = \dfrac{ac}{bc} \ (b, c \neq 0)$

$\dfrac{a}{d} + \dfrac{c}{d} = \dfrac{a+c}{d} \ (d \neq 0)$

$\dfrac{a}{d} - \dfrac{c}{d} = \dfrac{a-c}{d} \ (d \neq 0)$

$\dfrac{a}{b} \cdot \dfrac{c}{d} = \dfrac{ac}{bd} \ (b, d \neq 0)$

$\dfrac{a/b}{c/d} = \dfrac{ad}{bc} \ (b, c, d \neq 0)$

$\dfrac{-a}{-b} = \dfrac{a}{b} \ (b \neq 0)$

$\dfrac{-a}{b} = \dfrac{a}{-b} = -\left(\dfrac{a}{b}\right) \ (b \neq 0)$

If $a > b$ and $b > c$, then $a > c$

$a > b$ iff $a+c > b+c$

When $c > 0$, $a > b$ iff $ac > bc$

When $c < 0$, $a > b$ iff $ac < bc$

$ab > 0$ iff $(a > 0$ and $b > 0)$ or $(a < 0$ and $b <$

$ab < 0$ iff $(a > 0$ and $b < 0)$ or $(a < 0$ and $b >$

Properties of Exponents:

$a^0 = 1 \ (a \neq 0)$

$a^{-m} = \dfrac{1}{a^m} \ (a \neq 0)$

$a^m a^n = a^{m+n}$

$(a^m)^n = a^{mn}$

$(ab)^m = a^m b^m$

$\dfrac{a^m}{a^n} = a^{m-n}$

$\left(\dfrac{a}{b}\right)^m = \dfrac{a^m}{b^m}$